THE NINTH WORLD BESTIARY

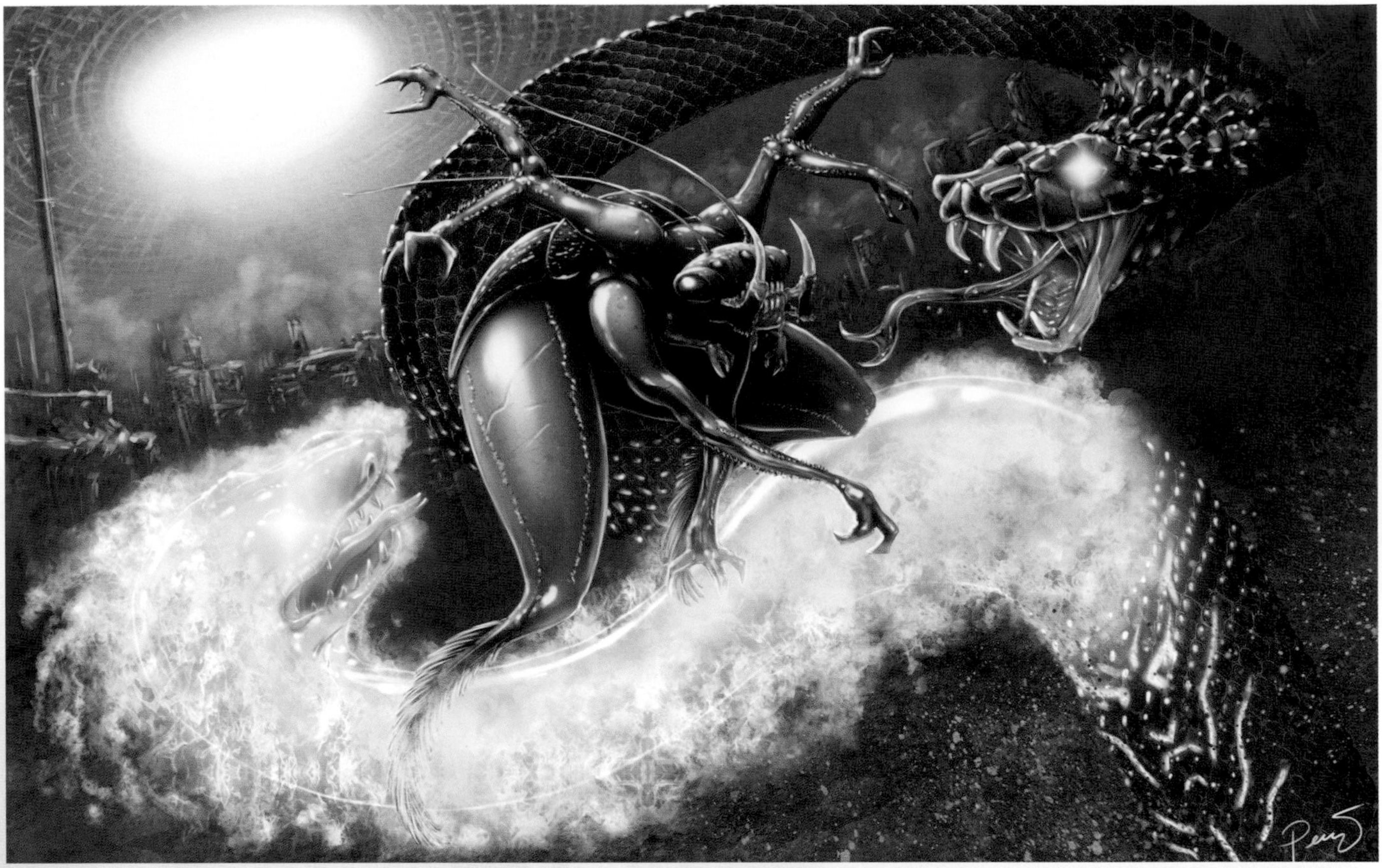

CREDITS

Writers/Designers Monte Cook and Bruce Cordell
Additional Writing Shanna Germain
Lead Editor Shanna Germain
Editor and Proofreader Ray Vallese
Lead Artist Kieran Yanner
Graphic Designer Sarah Robinson

Artists
Chrom, Dreamstime.com, Jason Engle, Guido Kuip, Eric Lofgren, Patrick McEvoy, Jeremy McHugh, Brynn Metheny, Michael Perry, Roberto Pitturru, Scott Purdy, Lee Smith, Matt Stawicki, Keith Thompson, Cory Trego-Erdner, Shane Tyree, Kieran Yanner

Kickstarter Creature Contributors Chris Avellone, Leslie Balazs, Clint Barkely, Henk Birkholz, Cameron Corniuk, Steven Dengler, Daniel Knoop, Mike Loftus

TABLE OF CONTENTS

INTRODUCTION: CREATURE FEATURE

When I was a kid, there was a show on the local TV channel on Saturday afternoons called "Creature Double Feature." It played old black-and-white science fiction and horror movies. That might have been the beginning of my fascination with monsters. Or you know, maybe it was that red-haired thing that wore white sneakers and chased Bugs Bunny around. (Its name was Gossamer, by the way.) Or the monsters on Sesame Street.

Regardless, I've been a fan of monsters and creatures for as long as I can remember. Which means that, of all the kinds of RPG books out there, the ones filled with creatures are my favorites: bestiaries. And there are a lot of them. I've written a few, in fact.

That means, of course, that I spent a lot of time thinking about how this bestiary would be different. I thought of a lot of ideas, but they were all very gimmicky. Finally, I realized that it was a waste of brainpower. Why? Because Numenera takes care of it for me. Numenera is weird. Numenera creatures are one of the best ways—if not the best way—to characterize and personify that weirdness in one single thing.

I knew that *The Ninth World Bestiary* would be different and great if we just stayed true to that ideal. If we focused on the weird and took it even farther than we did in the corebook, we would have an amazing bestiary.

I'm proud and happy to say that I think we pulled it off.

In these pages you'll find the jurulisk, a creature from another reality where geometry works differently. You'll find the silver orphans, left over from an ancient aeon, their original reason to exist now long gone. You'll also find the Nibovian companion and Nibovian child, each more horrific and weird than the Nibovian wife. (Who *are* these Nibovians, anyway?) And of course, there's the latos, which is a creature, a location, and an entire adventure in one package. And that's just the beginning.

We referenced a lot of source material while creating this bestiary. A small sampling of these sources includes:

All Yesterdays, John Conway
Cabinet of Natural Curiosities, Albertus Seba
Codex Seraphinianus, Luigi Serafini
Frankenstein's Cat, Emily Anthes
Future Evolution, Peter Ward
The Future Is Wild, Dougal Dixon
Man After Man, Dougal Dixon
The New Dinosaurs, Dougal Dixon

DESIGNING NUMENERA CREATURES

Designing creatures for Numenera is intentionally very easy. At its most basic, a creature—like any NPC—is just a level. That tells you all you need, and then you just layer in the description. That's kind of the amazing thing. You can describe a terrible slavering beast with three clawed limbs, a mouth like a sphincter, and some kind of blue jelly covering its flesh, but "behind the screen" (so to speak) all you have is "level 5."

The key, as with everything in Numenera, is making it weird. A standard bear or wolf isn't really going to cut it in this setting. But a twisted thing with a bearlike head, a four-legged frame like a wolf (oh, make it six legs), a magnetic-resonating metal plate where its eyes should be, and an extraneous sac of poison to spray? Now you've got a Numenera creature.

The Numenera corebook gives a brief discussion on designing new creatures in Chapter 21 (page 339). Basically, all a Numenera GM really needs to know is that creatures can work however you want them to. But for those who would like more details, suggestions, guidelines, and food for thought, this chapter is for you.

Creatures, of course, don't follow the same rules as the player characters. They don't have stat Pools, don't use Effort, and aren't as strictly limited in what they can do in an action because their form, size, and nature can vary so wildly.

COREBOOK CALLOUTS

Throughout this supplement, you'll see page references to various items accompanied by this symbol. These are page references to the Numenera corebook, where you can find additional details about that item, place, creature or concept. It isn't necessary to look up the referenced items in the corebook; it's an optional way to learn more about the Ninth World and provide additional information to your players.

LEVEL

A creature's level is a measure of its power, defense, intelligence, speed, and ability to interact with the world around it. Generally, it is an indicator of toughness in combat, although it's certainly possible to have a lower-level creature be a tougher opponent than a slightly higher one, particularly in certain circumstances. Level isn't an abstract tool to match up NPCs to PCs for "appropriate" encounters. Instead, it's an overall rating of the creature to show how it fits into the context of the world. There is no rule that says a certain ability should be given only to a creature of

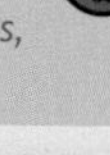
Designing creatures, page 339

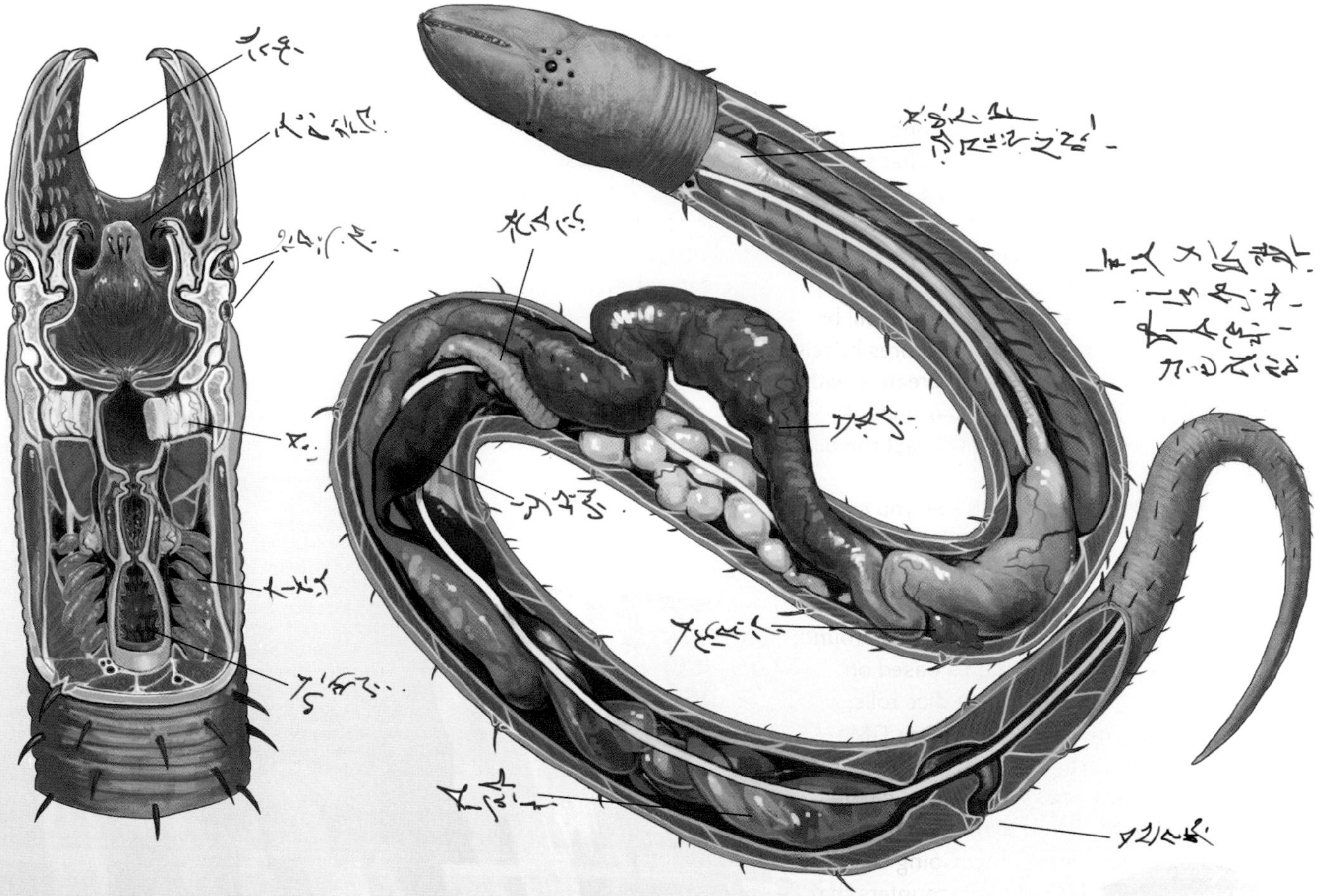

"The largest and most impressive specimen I was ever able to fully dissect was a cragworm. Obtaining that specimen was a task that gives me nightmares to this day."

~Jarash, well-known naturalist

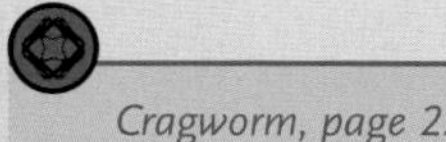

Cragworm, page 236

a certain level, and there is no rule dictating how many abilities a creature of a given level should have. But keep the spirit of the system in mind: lower-level creatures are less dangerous.

Obviously, a creature's level is its most important feature. For some creatures, it is the only feature. If you know only the level, you have everything you need. Level determines how hard it is to hit, how hard it is to dodge or resist, how much damage it does, and even its health (typically its level times three). It tells you how hard it is to interact with, fool, or intimidate, and how well it can run, climb, and so on. It even tells you how fast it acts in terms of initiative.

Of course, you're free to modify any of this as fits the creature, either for what you want it to do in an encounter or—even better—to try to ensure that it makes sense in terms of its place in the story and in the world. A really big creature should have more health but be easier to hit in combat, for example.

But in general, level becomes the default stat for the creature, with pretty much everything else being an exception. So when determining a level, figure out an appropriate rating (on a scale of 1 to 10) for the creature for most things. Don't base its level on the one thing it does best because you can portray that as a modification. Level is the baseline.

HEALTH

Since creatures don't have stat Pools, you have to determine how much damage they can take, and that's health. Health should make sense. Really big creatures should have lots of health, and tiny ones should have very little. You can also "cheat" a bit and give a creature that is really good in combat more health than its physicality might suggest to represent the fact that it is no pushover and not easily defeated.

Although there are many, many variables, it's safe to think—as a baseline—that a group of four low-tier PCs is likely to dish out about 10 points of damage in a round. This figure assumes a nano with Onslaught, a glaive and a jack with medium

weapons, and a glaive with a heavy weapon. The nano deals 4 points of damage, the first glaive 5 points (medium weapon and the pierce fighting move), the jack 4 points, and the second glaive 7 points (heavy weapon and pierce). That's a total of 20 points, and we can assume that they hit their target with a bit better than 50 percent accuracy if they are fighting a level 3 or 4 foe and using Effort. This very rough estimate tells you that a creature with a health of 11 or less will be wiped out in a single round (Armor figures hugely into this, however, so see below). A creature with a health of 12 to 22 will last for two rounds. A creature with a health of 23 to 33 will last three. And so on.

For PCs who are third or fourth tier, you can add about 6 points to the average damage figure, based on using Effort to increase damage. At fifth and sixth tiers, you can figure that the PCs will deal about 20 to 25 points of damage each round.

Again, these are rough estimates based on averages. They don't figure in high dice rolls, using lots of Effort, cyphers, artifacts, or GM intrusions. They're useful as a rule of thumb to determine how hard or easy you want the fight to be. A single-round fight is kind of a pushover. Two to four rounds is interesting. Going five or six rounds is a tough fight. Combat encounters that go on longer than that can start to drag unless the creature is really interesting or the encounter offers something unique (for example, it occurs on a precipice over a river of toxic sludge, and the PCs have to protect a sickly NPC while dealing with their foes).

In other words, creature health is the knob to adjust when determining how long you want a combat encounter to last.

DAMAGE

It's important to remember that damage is based on the creature's level, not other factors. So a level 6 creature that picks up a broadsword still inflicts 6 points of damage, not 4 points. You can adjust the damage to fit the creature's attack, but the level should always be the baseline. A massive, strong creature will deal more damage than its level might suggest, and a creature with particularly large claws or a powerful bite might do so as well. A particularly skillful combatant will deal more damage, too. Only very rarely should a creature deal less damage than its level.

Remember that more PCs have Armor than don't, so it's difficult (but not impossible) to make creatures that deal only 1 or 2 points of damage a challenge to the characters.

You can compare the determinations you made about the creature's health as a useful gauge to figure out how much damage a creature will deal to the PCs in an encounter. Again, if you figure 50 percent accuracy, the creature will deal its damage every other round. So if a creature has enough health to last three rounds, on average, it will deal its damage twice.

Creatures that make more than one attack on their turn potentially deal their damage with each attack, which can greatly affect damage output.

ARMOR

Armor doesn't depend on level. The default is no Armor.

Armor represents a suit of physical armor, thick skin, metal plating, scales, carapace, mental wards, or any other type of similar protection. Armor does not represent other things that might make a creature hard to damage, such as intangibility (that's represented in other ways).

Armor greatly influences how long a creature can last in a combat encounter. The Armor rating reduces the damage the creature suffers each round *per character*. So take our four characters mentioned above, who inflict 4, 5, 4, and 7 points of damage, respectively. Give their foe 3 points of Armor, and now they inflict 1, 2, 1, and 4 points. On an average round, they'll inflict a total of 4 points of damage, and that creature with 11 health will last three rounds, not one. (Of course, against such a foe, smart PCs will use Effort to increase their damage.)

Don't give every creature Armor, though. If everything has 2 points of Armor, then all attacks just deal 2 fewer points of damage, and that's not terribly interesting. Sometimes a creature with lots of health and no Armor can be an interesting encounter, too.

MOVEMENT

Other than Armor, the only thing that level doesn't tell you is how fast a creature moves. However, unless there's a really good reason to do otherwise, just assume that it has a move of short. This means that the creature moves like a PC—it moves a short distance as an action. Typically, flying creatures move a long distance in the air and a short distance (or less) on the ground.

Creatures with a long movement are usually large beings with a big stride. Small creatures can be very quick, but that doesn't mean they move a long distance in a single round.

While figuring out a creature's Armor is an issue involving game mechanics, it should also reflect the nature of the creature. Thus, a beast with a somewhat thick hide might have 1 or perhaps 2 points of armor. A mechanical creature, made mostly of metal, should have at least 3 points of Armor. Some creatures might have a natural carapace that gives them 4 or more points of Armor.

Generally, larger creatures have thicker hides or outer shells and so will have higher Armor. Creatures with some type of energy field or numenera-generated shields could have very high Armor. There is no maximum amount of Armor, but keep in mind that 6 is a very high Armor rating and 10 points of armor is going to make a creature almost invincible.

MODIFICATIONS

Health, damage, and almost everything else in the creature's entry provide a chance to mention exceptions to the default assumptions based on the creature's level. Modifications are a catch-all of other exceptions. Basically, these are all tasks that the creature performs at something other than its normal level.

A level 2 tree-dwelling beast might be level 4 when it comes to climbing. A level 3 creature with a heightened sense of smell and good hearing is probably level 4 or 5 when it comes to perception. Tiny, quiet creatures are usually a level or two higher than their creature level at stealth.

Not all modifications are positive. If you make a huge creature that is little more than a beast, you might want to make it a lower level for things like resisting trickery. A big, lumbering brute would likely be worse at stealth than its level would suggest. A stupid creature might be terrible at perception. Modifications that modify creatures down are just as interesting as those that modify up.

Don't bother considering modifications in too much detail. Only think about things that will come up at the table. Figuring out how good a creature is at basket weaving or how much it knows about tidal pools probably isn't worth the effort unless those elements play directly into your encounter.

For a complete explanation of the rules and a detailed description of terms like Effort, Armor, cypher and stat Pools, please see the Numenera corebook, Chapter 8: Rules of the Game (page 84).

"Differences in pack behavior, something I'm tempted to call cultural differences—have been reported among vapes, slurgen, slicer beetles, and many other creatures that most think of as mere animals. In my travels, I have learned to keep an open mind when it comes to what so-called simple creatures can accomplish and achieve. Sometimes, I wonder what they think of us." ~Jarash, well-known naturalist

COMBAT

Combat is simply where we note what the creature does in a fight, how it reacts to combat, and—most importantly—any special combat-related abilities it might have. There are no hard-and-fast rules here. In fact, it's very much the opposite. This is the place where you note how the creature makes its own rules. Multiple agtacks in a single action? Fine. Poison? Good. Mental powers? Interesting. If you're making a creature for your own use, just make simple notes for how you want a combat encounter to play out, so that it fits the role you want it to fit in the grander scheme. Use (or create) the mechanics to best replicate what you want the creature to do, not the other way around.

MOTIVE, ENVIRONMENT, INTERACTION, USE, LOOT

The bestiary provides these entries for creatures, but for a GM's home-brewed creature, they probably aren't necessary. After all, you created the creature, so you know how to use it and where it's found, and you probably have a good idea of how the PCs can interact with it.

OTHER CONSIDERATIONS

Those are all the main "headers" in the creature format, but there are other things to think about.

Creature Size: Consider creature size very carefully. For those that are quick and hard to hit, increase the difficulty to attack them by one step. Large, slow creatures should be easier to hit, so decrease the difficulty to attack them by one step.

Multiple Attacks: No matter how big and tough it is, it's difficult for a single creature to hold its own against a group of foes like the PCs. Giving a creature multiple attacks as a single action—so that it can attack some or all of the characters at once—goes a long way toward making it a suitable foe for a group of opponents.

However, creatures with multiple attacks that appear in groups can simply be annoying, as the combat encounter will take quite a while to resolve (with lots of defense rolls to be made).

Ignoring Armor: Attacks that ignore Armor are interesting because they really scare players. Such attacks might be from intense heat, out-of-phase tentacles, or something so sharp that it cuts right through whatever the PC is wearing.

Use your discretion, however. For example, if Armor comes from a force field, a fiery blast seems less likely to ignore it. And use this kind of thing sparingly because if everything ignores Armor, Armor loses its meaning.

Poison and Disease: A level 1 creature could be poisonous, but its venom should inflict a few points of damage at most. The venom of a level 6 creature, on the other hand, might knock a PC down a step on the damage track or put him into a coma if he fails a Might defense roll.

Other Special Abilities: A Numenera creature can have almost any kind of power or ability you want to dream up. Basically, it comes down to what kind of roll the player makes—an Intellect defense roll to ward off a weird mind attack, a Speed defense roll to dodge a barrage of spikes, a Might defense roll to resist a cellular disintegration, or perhaps something else. The difficulty of the roll and the damage dealt by the attack is based primarily on the level of the creature, although this can be modified if it seems appropriate.

Maybe there's no roll involved. The creature just walks through the wall, teleports, or melts the metal object it holds in its clutches. Although some of these abilities can give a creature a tactical advantage in a combat encounter, they're just as often there to make it more interesting.

This means that level is probably more important than any particular ability when it

comes to determining a creature's "toughness." And it also means that you don't have to save the cool abilities just for high-level creatures.

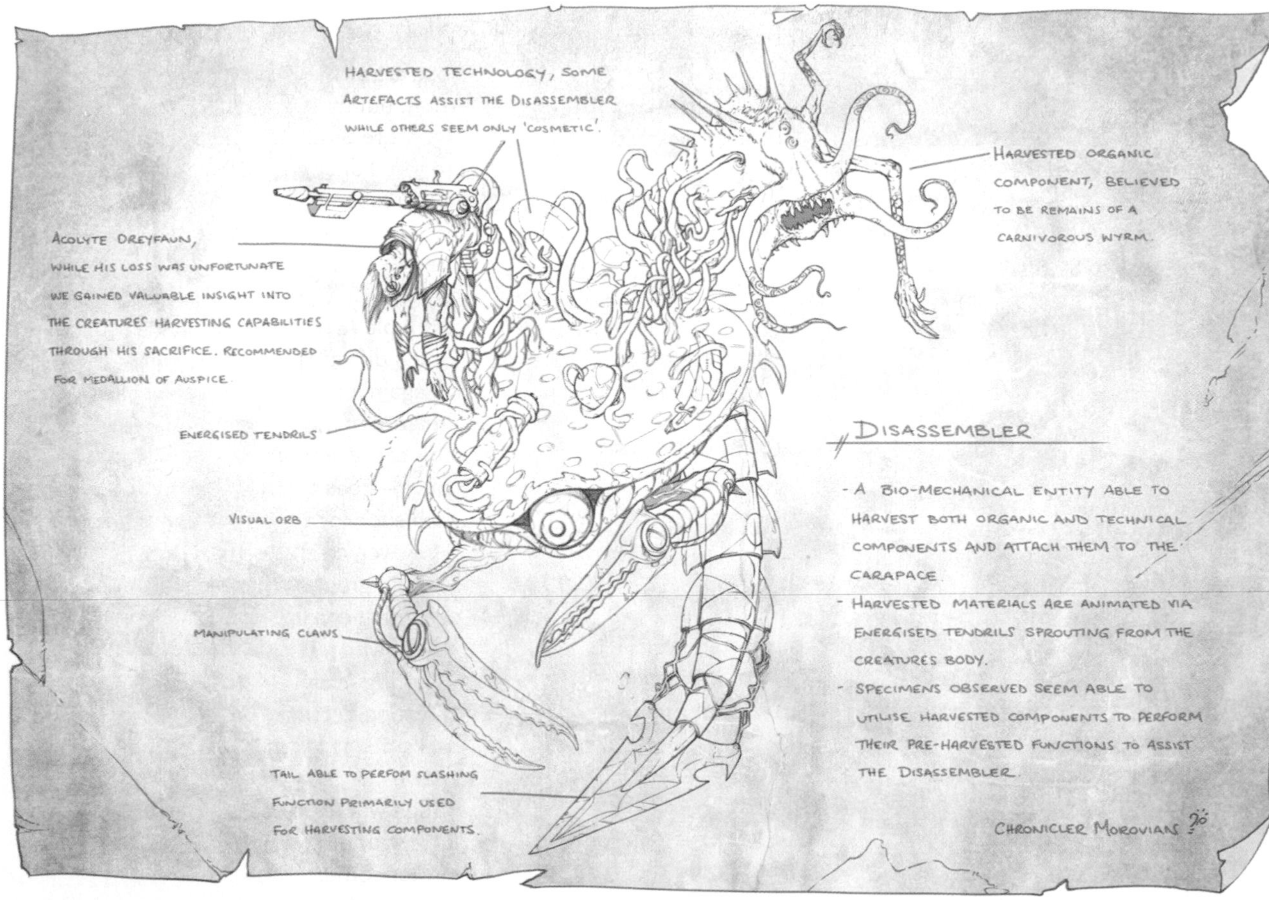

MAKING CREATURES REALLY DANGEROUS

Although a high-level creature is already pretty dangerous, there are a few things you can do to make any creature particularly threatening to the PCs (if that's something you want to do—not every encounter should threaten instant death for everyone in the group).

The Damage Track: First and foremost, moving PCs down the damage track rather than (or in addition to) dealing damage is a sure way to put fear into the heart of a player. It doesn't matter how many points you have in your Pools or what abilities you have—it's still just three steps to death on the damage track.

Attacks that Do More Than Damage: Attacks that do more than just deal damage make it clearer that a player should spend points from his Pool to avoid them. If an attack deals 3 points of damage, does it make sense to spend 3 points to use a level of Effort to avoid it? Maybe—losing Speed might be better in many situations than losing Might. But spending points to avoid moving a step down the damage track? That makes more sense. Spending Intellect points to avoid being mind-controlled? Again, very fitting.

Ignoring Armor: Bypassing the PCs' primary defense mechanism is scary.

Multiple Attacks: Creatures that can attack all the PCs at once, whether with multiple arms or a radius or aura effect, can be very challenging. Sometimes a group's tactics rely on one or two characters going toe to toe with the enemy while the others hang back. Those PCs in the back might not be prepared for an attack that affects them as well.

Longer Than Long-Range Attacks: Most PCs have limited options at long range, but what if the creature can attack them from a quarter mile away with mental blasts or homing missiles? Now they have an entirely different kind of encounter to deal with.

FITTING THE CREATURE INTO THE WORLD

The ideas behind a creature are just as important as its combat stats—or more important. How does it fit into the world? What role will it play

When designating creatures for weird habitats, GMs should feel free to push the edges of what lives there. Combine the elements of two distinct creatures to create one that is uniquely designed to thrive in that particular environment, change some characteristics of a creature, or even create wholly new, never-seen-before beasts that could live nowhere else in the world.

An elite group called the Pact of Jarash is affiliated with the Order of Truth. The organization gets its name from the infamous naturalist and creature expert, Jarash, who was also an Aeon Priest. Like Jarash, the pact members seek out new creatures that inhabit the world in order to catalog and understand them. Recently, the Pact of Jarash collated all the data they'd gathered and compiled a massive tome. They call it The Ninth World Bestiary.

The most interesting, most believable creatures have a purpose for their existence and place in the world, and it may or may not have anything to do with the humans who share the space. Nothing should exist in a vacuum; every creature or plant is connected to at least one other element in the environment in order to survive.

"The creatures inhabiting the world are amazing in their diversity. One might expect that over time, top-level predators would emerge and prune back the assortment of others that feed on less ferocious creatures. In limited environments, that's how it appears to work. But something about the Ninth World as a whole keeps things out of equilibrium. How can that be? What is the quality, or qualities, that continually disrupt predator-prey population dynamics?" ~Visixtru, varjellen philosopher

in your story? What's right and what's wrong for Numenera?

Don't give a detailed backstory to a creature originating in a prior world. We might know that something is ancient and might even suggest tales that it was designed in a prior world as a mining automaton, but we don't know that to be the case for certain. And Ninth Worlders know nothing of the previous worlds (they don't even know if there really were eight other worlds), so they (and their players) shouldn't know anything about the origins of creatures that didn't come to be within recorded or spoken history of the Ninth World. Most creatures don't need a detailed origin. Of course, hints or rumors are fine.

In addition, stuff from the prior worlds isn't weird to people in the Ninth World just because it's more advanced than they can understand—it's also utterly and incomprehensibly alien. So even if a bizarre creature from an ancient world *could* find a way to communicate with a PC, it probably couldn't do so in a way that the character would understand. And most of them can't or won't communicate with characters at all.

Another way to think about it: Ninth World creatures should be totally incomprehensible not just to the PCs but also to the players—and, in a way, even to you as well. Can't explain something? No problem. That's part of the weird.

Along those lines, while the GM might know a creature's backstory, it's important to resist the urge to provide that information to the players most of the time. You can write it down for yourself if it's important that you know it, but you need to portray the creature without presenting all that exposition. If you want your players to think, "Aha! These beings were created by a prior world to defend a spaceship," you can give them clues, but you should never come right out and say anything of the kind.

Less is more when it comes to Numenera creatures. Don't worry about where it came from—worry about how it fits into the world *now*. What's it doing now? That's what the PCs need to face, not how it evolved, what planet it came from, or what its original purpose was.

This is also true of the science behind creatures. While the GM might need to know that a creature or its actions are scientifically feasible and what that means in terms of how its abilities function, in most cases you don't need to worry about the science at all. Better to be weird and mysterious—with the implication that there's a strange, super-advanced science behind it—than to adhere to a scientific principle. And when you're describing the creature, be careful not to use the high-end science phrases of today, since people of the Ninth World wouldn't use those words. Antimatter, quantum computing, and 3-D printing are all really cool and possible ideas to use with a Numenera creature, but those terms aren't appropriate in the Ninth World.

Finally, if you think you have a weird creature, push it one step farther by combining it with another weird thing, turning it inside out, or reversing the original attack you gave it. Sometimes you end up with something wholly new.

GM INTRUSIONS

While it's often best to come up with GM intrusions on the fly, based on the current needs of the story, it's not a terrible idea to have one up your sleeve in case you want to use one but don't have any great ideas at the moment. Each creature entry in this book has at least one GM intrusion.

It can be tempting to use GM intrusions that result in more damage or have other straightforward effects. Often, however, you'll get more mileage out of them if they are story based—for example, the huge creature starts to swallow the PC whole, or the lumbering beast stumbles and falls on the character. This is stuff that really changes the encounter and leads to a good story that everyone will remember afterward. The best kind of GM intrusion is one where the GM can describe what happens and then say, "*Now* what do you do?"

ECOLOGY OF THE NINTH WORLD

A billion years in the future means that not a single animal, plant, or biome that we know continues to exist—at least not in the exact form that we know it now. There are similarities, so while we might talk about mammals and fungi or (even more specifically) deer and mushrooms, those creatures are likely to be very different from the ones we know today. The word *rat* or *goat* conveys a certain image, a certain sensibility, but beyond that, it's perhaps more important to talk about the differences between the Ninth World version of these creatures and today's version.

Of course, there are wholly new creatures as well, species that have arisen through the branches of an entirely new evolutionary path or that were created by an ancient civilization and now wander the world, adapting as they need to survive. These include beasts such as griffalos and stellar weavers, and things that defy categorization: automatons, engineered creatures, sentient plants, mutated life forms, and much more.

ECOSYSTEMS OF THE WORLD

CIVILIZED AREAS

The civilized areas of the Ninth World aren't particularly civilized, and that means there is a lot of room for creatures of all dispositions, sizes, origins, and feeding habits. The majority of creatures that survive and thrive in and around aldeias, cities, kingdoms, and other populated areas have developed a variety of adaptations to take full advantage of their proximity to humans.

Some creatures, such as gallen and aneen, are long domesticated, providing humans with mounts, hides, meat, and milk in exchange for food, shelter, and safety.

Other creatures, while not domesticated, have developed symbiotic relationships with the humans around them, providing protection or useable materials in exchange for food or shelter. Stratharian war moths, for example, are particularly attracted to ganch fields, although no one knows exactly what these crops provide. Moths that are left to create their cocoons within the fields can sometimes be a boon to farmers by eating all the herbivores in the area. However, if attacked, they quickly attempt to kill any humans nearby.

Still others have become chosen companions to humans, living side by side with them and becoming close and loyal friends. And, of course, we would be remiss not to mention the myriad creatures created by humans, whether mechanical, biological, or a combination of the two.

Not every creature lives in harmony with the nearby human population. Some haunt the fringes of society, preying on anyone and everyone they can. Trawls—partially out of phase creatures that set traps for humans—are so common in populated areas that they've inspired the "Nowhere Man" nursery rhyme.

Gallen, page 12
Aneen, page 13

Stratharian war moth, page 261

Griffalo, page 61
Stellar weaver, page 121

Trawl, page 128

DOMESTICATED CREATURES

Rubar, page 255
Seskii, page 258
Thuman, page 262

"At what point does a creature become a 'native' of its current environment? If we speculate that a creature came from the stars 10 million years ago, but its descendants have lived upon the Earth in that time, is it not native? And if not, can we be so certain of our own origins to call ourselves natives?"
~Jarash, well-known naturalist

LIVESTOCK

Most people of the world have, over time, domesticated creatures of one sort or another, depending on the region and the cultural needs.

CAVOTS (LEVEL 1)

Small, black rodentlike creatures, cavots subsist on a diet of echar berries, found on shrubs that grow best in dark, wet places. Unable to digest the seeds of the berries, the cavots discard them after having polished them to a beautiful yellow shine. These are used for decorations, as currency, and for adornments to jewelry or weapons.

DOSSI (LEVEL 3)

Bovinelike herd creatures, dossi are raised for meat and skrips (a type of writing material made from the soft, pliable scales they regularly shed).

DRAKKA (LEVEL 1, 2 FOR PERCEPTION, 4 FOR DEFENSIVE ACTIONS)

These foot-long insects are similar to bluebottle flies, only more intelligent. Drakka are used to help herd umlan goats or as watch animals.

GALLEN (LEVEL 2)

These long-bodied, herbivorous animals are revered for their meat and hides. They're typically found in domesticated herds on rolling green hills, such as those in the Kingdom of Ghan.

RUBAR (LEVEL 2)

Looking very much like giant land catfish, rubar are used for cleaning houses or for running in the popular rubar races.

SHIUL (LEVEL 3)

These massive, four-horned creatures are valued for their soft, tender cuts of meat. Originating in Kordech, shiul are becoming more popular in other areas of the Steadfast.

YOL (LEVEL 2)

These short, long-haired creatures are known for their yellow wool, their tender meat, and their milk, which produces savory, tangy cheese.

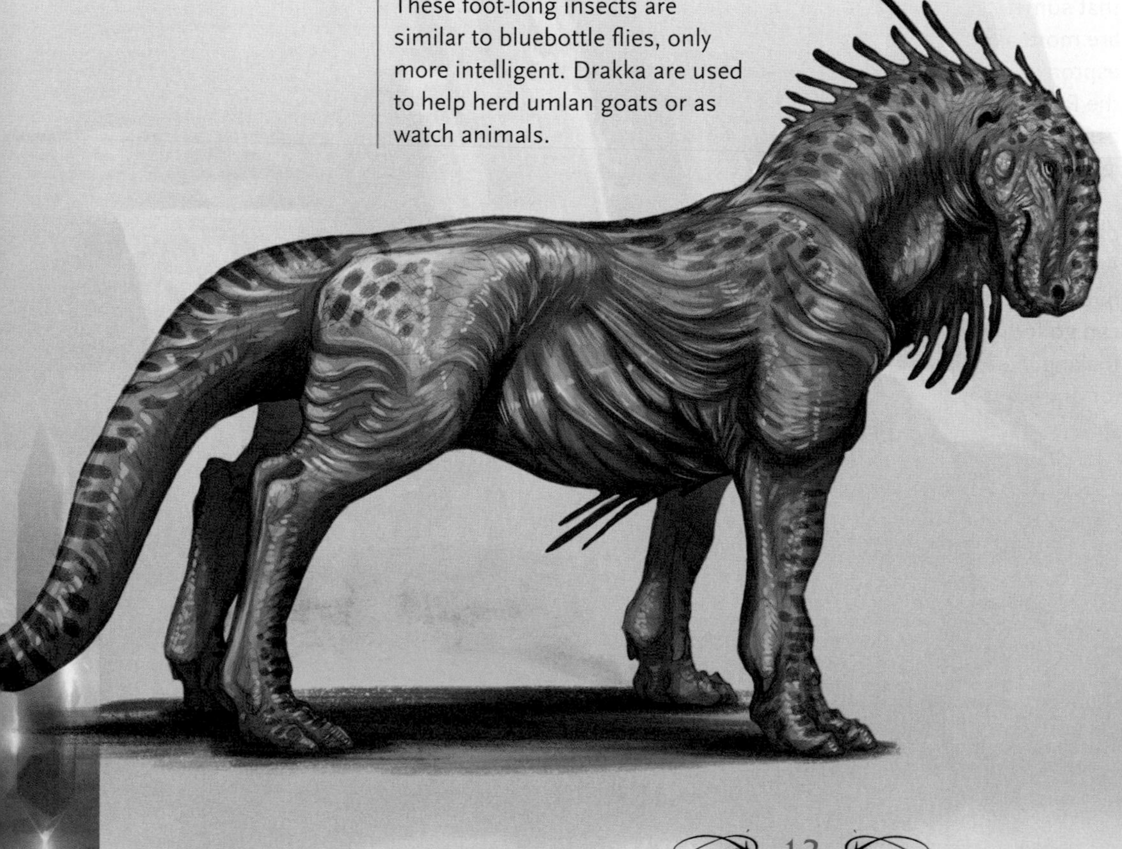

COMPANIONS

If a character has the proper skills and equipment, she can potentially turn almost any creature into a companion. However, some are more commonly used for this purpose than others, perhaps due to their long history of working and living closely with humans.

BIOMECHANICAL MOGIGRAPHIS BIRD (LEVEL 1)

Able to remember and mimic all the sounds it hears in the past eight hours, these birds are often used by scriveners to check their writing.

FRILLED BAUL (LEVEL 5)

This semifeline mammal often bonds with humans as well as other creatures.

SESKII (LEVEL 2)

Resembling large, scaled dogs, seskii are loyal companions and fierce defenders of their chosen human. Seskii can be trained in attack, hunting, defense, and more, and they are often outfitted with spiked collars, weapons, and armor.

SHANU (LEVEL 2)

These clever herbivores make excellent companions and pets, and they can be trained to perform a variety of actions.

THUMAN (LEVEL 2)

With human faces and houndlike bodies, thumans are smart, good-natured companions. They tend to avoid combat, but they can interact with humans through complex actions and can be trained to respond to a huge number of commands.

CREATURES IN A GROUP

Numenera has rules for using creatures in a group; we typically call these the swarm rules. While this makes for an interesting encounter, remember that not all creatures move in groups, nor do they live in groups all the time (for example, some might join together just for mating season or for the hard winter months). Many predators—especially large ones—are solitary animals with large territories and have no interest in spending time with another of their species.

When making group encounters, consider not just the number of the creatures and how they act when in a group, but also what an encounter might look like when it's with multiple types of creatures or creatures of varying ages and sizes.

Sometimes creature groups have more than one type of creature. The PCs may find themselves caught between a trio of predators and a herd of prey and suddenly find they are fighting not just one group of creatures, but two. Or they may discover that the flying elchin they've been stalking is actually stalking a terror bird at the same time. One creature may have a symbiotic or parasitic relationship with others, something the PCs discover only after they attack and are instantly overrun by the parasitic companions.

GROUP NAMES

While most creatures in a group can be called a herd, a clan, a pride, or simply a pack (such as avatrols), others have specific collective nouns that are commonly used. Some examples include:

- A clatter of chance moths
- A clutch of chronal feeders
- A leash of laurik-ca
- A refuse of spurn
- A choir of syzygy ghouls
- A rake of vapes

SWARM RULES

The GM can take any creature and have a group of six to ten of them attack en masse as a single creature that is two levels higher, inflicting double the original creature's normal damage. So thirty level 3 abhumans might attack as five level 5 mobs.

MOUNTS

If a character has the proper technique and talents, almost any creature can be trained as a mount. However, the following domesticated creatures are available to anyone with the right shins, influence, or thievery skills.

ANEEN (LEVEL 3)

Standing two to three times as tall as a human, these herd animals have hunched, hairless bipedal bodies, small forearms, and broad heads. They can sometimes be found roaming wild over the Plains of Kataru and the eastern edges of the Black Riage, but they are more often encountered as mounts or pack animals. Due to their ability to travel quickly and tirelessly for long distances, they are coveted by trade caravans, especially in the northern part of the Steadfast.

BREHM (LEVEL 3)

These reptilian coursers are fast and lightweight, making them great for long, quick travel. They don't have the strength to pull or carry heavy loads.

ESPRON (LEVEL 2)

Large antelopelike creatures that sometimes roam wild but are more often seen as mounts, espron are particularly popular in the Plains of Kataru, where they can travel long distances without leaving a trail.

FERNO WALKER (LEVEL 6)

A six-limbed mammal with a pair of usable hands, a ferno walker can go for weeks without water, making it an exceptional mount for dry, hot places.

QUEB (LEVEL 4)

These furry serpentine creatures are commonly used as riding animals in the southern kingdoms, where they carry twenty people at one time.

RASTER (LEVEL 4)

These large, biomechanical, batlike creatures are native to Ancuan, and they use antigravity suspensors to stay aloft despite their large size.

RAZORCAT (LEVEL 5)

The massive, tigerlike creatures known as razorcats typically are ridden only by the Llhauric priests and their holy knights. However, their smaller and still-wilder sister species, called barrowcats, can sometimes be tamed and used as mounts.

SNOW LOPER (LEVEL 3)

Possibly sharing an ancestor with the ferno walker, the snow loper is also tall and thin-legged, with a short neck and a large head. The creature is both fast and dexterous. Sporting two thin arms with hands just below its mouth, it can easily navigate in steep, rocky environments.

XI-DRAKE (LEVEL 5)

These broad-winged, white reptiles are massive and serve as mounts for the Angulan Knights.

Aneen, page 231
Brehm, page 163
Espron, page 184

Raster, page 253
Snow loper, page 259
Xi-drake, page 265

A WORLD INTERCONNECTED

A tiny forest deep in the Beyond called Disxiol is studied by numerous researchers in an attempt to better understand both evolution and ecology. There, nothing exists that is not part of the complex and tightly wound ecosystem.

The trouble with researching Disxiol is that anyone who enters the woods is considered to be a threat to the perfectly balanced ecosystem, and all of the creatures in the area, from the smallest insect to the largest carnivore, attack the intruder en masse.

LIFE CYCLE

Orange ariol flowers grow wild here, covering the ground in a thick carpet of fragrant blooms, the pollen of which is gathered by various bees.

The honeyball spider is a living larder, sucking blood from the bees and storing it in its distended abdomen until it turns into a sweet, nectarlike substance.

This substance feeds the bakki birds, tiny hummingbirdlike creatures that can puncture the honeyball spider's larder and drain it without harming the spider.

Bakki eggs make a perfect snack for the nepeanth plant, a type of pitcher plant that invites the birds to build their nests inside its large flower. As soon as the eggs hatch, the nepeanth absorbs the two smallest ones and protects the rest until they are grown.

Full of leavings from the birds and shells, a nepeanth plant is a scrumptious dinner for the local omnivores, communal creatures the size of meerkats.

The top of the food chain is the rumplenosed callium, a winged predator that scoops the omnivores up in its pouch. Its leavings fertilize the fields of ariols.

WEIRD AND NUMENERA-LADEN

Much of the world is ever-changed by the numenera and the weird that surrounds it, and this includes its various creatures. While it would be easy to think of the numenera as something that changed the world, in truth it is still *changing* the world. Some cyphers, for example, produce additional effects that develop later, like a detonation that explodes now but seeds oases in a few months' time.

The Cloudcrystal Skyfields, the Amorphous Fields, the Clock of Kala: all of these places are good examples of weird, numenera-filled ecosystems. When thinking about ecologies that might be considered weird, it's helpful to imagine each of them as its own Ninth World version of the Galapagos Islands. Each ecosystem is unique and so weird that its creatures are unknowable, unexplainable, and often irreproducible.

Without places like this, creatures like the chance moth, which feeds on energy leakage from a numenera device, or the chronal feeder, which inhabits places where time or gravity have been displaced, would never exist.

Chance moth, page 30
Chronal feeder, page 31

Cloudcrystal Skyfields, page 174
Amorphous Fields, page 200
Clock of Kala, page 213

While it's not important to spell out every single predator/prey relationship or to go into detail about why a particular frog like creature lives near large bodies of water, it is important to create a sense of verisimilitude for the players. If the dissonance between ecology and creature seems jarring, that should be purposeful and described in such a way that players "get it."

Herbivores with no fur, no claws, and dark purple skin are going to seem out of place in the Cold Desert where everything is white and frozen and there are few plants. Unless they're creatures like the snowstalks, purple herbivores that live in massive, complex hives carved out of ice. Snowstalks absorb the sun's energy by spreading themselves flat on their hive roofs for most of the day, and then metabolizing the energy into a purple moss that sprouts all over their bodies, which they then eat for sustenance.

CREATURES OF THE NINTH WORLD

UNDERSTANDING THE LISTINGS

"When I was a young man, I insisted that all the creatures of our world could be neatly categorized into various types. Eventually, I grew wiser." ~Jarash, well-known naturalist

Level: All creatures (and NPCs) have a level. The level determines the target number a PC must reach to attack or defend against the opponent. In each entry, the target number for the creature or NPC is listed in parentheses after its level. The target number is three times the level.

Description: Following the name of the creature or NPC is a general description of its general appearance, nature, intelligence, or background.

Motive: This entry is a way to help the GM understand what a creature or NPC wants. Every creature or person wants something, even if it's just to be left alone.

Environment: This entry describes what part of the world the creature inhabits.

"It's impossible to predict how an arch-nano will react to a threat. It could choose to fly away, blast the aggressor with force, or put it into a deep sleep and cart the body off for experiments." ~Sir Arthour

Health: A creature's target number is usually also its health, which is the amount of damage it can sustain before it is dead or incapacitated.

Damage Inflicted: Generally, when creatures hit in combat, they inflict their level in damage regardless of the form of attack. Some inflict more or less or have a special modifier to damage. Intelligent NPCs often use weapons, but this is more a flavor issue than a mechanical one. In other words, it doesn't matter if a level 3 abhuman uses a sword or claws—it deals the same damage if it hits.

Armor: This is the creature's Armor value. Sometimes the number represents physical armor, and other times it represents natural protection. This entry doesn't appear in the game stats if a creature has no Armor.

Movement: Movement determines how far the creature can move in a single turn.

Modifications: Use these default numbers when a creature's information says to use a different target number. For example, a level 4 creature might say "defends as level 5," which means PCs attacking it must reach a target number of 15 (for difficulty 5) instead of 12 (for difficulty 4). In special circumstances, some creatures have other modifications, but these are almost always specific to their level.

Combat: This entry gives advice on using the creature in combat, such as "This creature uses ambushes and hit-and-run tactics." At the end of the combat listing, you'll also find any special abilities, such as immunities, poisons, and healing skills. GMs should remember to be logical about a creature's reaction to a particular action or attack by a PC. For example, a mechanical creation is obviously immune to normal diseases, a character can't poison a being of energy (at least, not with a conventional poison), and so on.

Interaction: This entry gives advice on interacting with the creature.

Use: This entry gives the GM suggestions for how to use the creature in a game session.

Loot: This entry indicates what the PCs might gain if they take items from their fallen foes (or trade with or trick them). It doesn't appear in the game stats if the creature has no loot.

GM Intrusion: This entry suggests a way to use GM intrusion in an encounter. It's just one possible idea of many, and the GM is encouraged to come up with her own uses of the game mechanic.

CREATURES BY LEVEL

(*Creatures with asterisks appear in the *Numenera* corebook)

Creature	Level
Caffa (larva)*	1
Chance moth	1
Flesh pup	1
Gazer	1
Laak*	1
Broken hound*	2
Caffa (adult)*	2
Dabirri	2
Drebil	2
Griffalo	2
Hex stinger	2
Margr*	2
Merkadian soldier	2
Pallone*	2
Rubar*	2
Seskii*	2
Shanu	2
Shivern	2
Slurge	2
Stratharian war moth*	2
Thuman*	2
Unagran	2
Vape	2
Ylaantiv	2
Aneen*	3
Blood barm*	3
Calyptor	3
Coccitan	3
Erulian	3
Glacier slime	3
Golthiar	3
Grey sampler	3
Herder	3
Kalyptein crab	3
Killist	3
Murden*	3
Nagaina defender	3
Nalurus	3
Nibovian child	3
Nibovian companion	3
Nibovian wife*	3
Ocular & Tactile host	3
Plasmar	3
Rahenum courser	3
Rocira	3
Sathosh*	3
Scutimorph*	3
Snow loper*	3
Spurn	3
Steel spider*	3
Tetrahydra*	3
Therivar	3
Weaponized meme	3
Yovok*	3
Abykos*	4
Avatrol	4
Balikna	4
Cave qui	4
Chirog*	4
Chronal feeder	4
Culova*	4
Decanted	4
Entrope	4
Ergovore hound	4
Grush	4
Ithsyn*	4
Jesanthum	4
Kanthid	4
Laurik-ca	4
Mastigophore*	4
Memora	4
Mlox	4
Nevajin*	4
Odlark	4
Oorgolian soldier*	4
Queb	4
Raster*	4
Ravage bear*	4
Rurtalian	4
Scrivener	4
Syzygy ghoul	4
Tachyron	4
Terror bird	4
Trawl	4
Valma	4
Warder	4
Xaar	4
Xiomarche	4
Awakened nagaina sleeper	5
Blitzer	5
Dimensional husk	5
Disassembler*	5
Dream sallow	5
Ellnoica	5
Erulian master	5
Falling maw	5
Flying elchin	5
Frilled baul	5
Ghost Crab*	5
Hexon	5
Hontri	5
Llaric scorpion	5
Lorub	5
Magmid	5
Mesomeme*	5
Morl	5
Orgulous	5
Peerless	5
Philethis*	5
Pygmy hapax	5
Quishamis	5
Rahenum perceptor	5
Relentless reaper	5
Sarrak*	5
Silver orphan	5
Slicer beetle	5
Slidikin	5
Varakith*	5
Warrior host	5
Xi-drake*	5
Yellow swarm*	5
Zhev*	5
Accelerator	6
Astraphin monolith	6
Bellowheart	6
Bloodfeast tick scion	6
Cragworm*	6
Ember scion	6
Encephalon	6
Erynth grask*	6
Etterick	6
Ferno walker	6
Ishenizar	6
Magathan	6
Nychthemeron	6
Progenitor	6
Rorathik	6
Scavrow	6
Travonis ul*	6
Xacorocax	6
Callerail*	7
Cursed qui	7
Dedimaskis	7
Edacious destroyer	7
Gemorrn	7
Jiraskar*	7
Jurulisk	7
Minnern	7
Neveri	7
Quotien	7
Skysmasher	7
Varadimos	7
Dark fathom*	8
Earthshaker	8
Kiprus, the	8
Nagaina matron	8
Rhog	8
Marteling whale	9
Stellar weaver	9
Dread destroyer*	10
Latos	10
Titanothaur	10

RANDOM ENCOUNTER TABLES

Use these charts to randomly create encounters based on what the PCs are doing and where they're doing it.

Exploring the Ruins

01-03	Abykos
04-05	Accelerator
06-07	Bandit
08-09	Bellowheart
10-12	Chance Moth
13-15	Coccitan
16-18	Chirog
19-21	Dark Fathom
22-24	Dream Sallow
25-26	Erulian
27-28	Erynth Grask
29-30	Explorer
31-32	Flying Elchin
33-34	Gazer
35-37	Ishenizar
38-41	Ithsyn
42-44	Kanthid
45-48	Margr
49-52	Mastigophore
53-54	Merkadian Soldier
55-57	Nychthemeron
58-60	Odlark
61-64	Oorgolian Soldier
65	Philethis
66-68	Quotien
69-71	Rurtalian
72-74	Rubar
75-77	Sarrak
78-80	Sathosh
81-83	Spurn
84-86	Steel Spider
87-89	Stratharian War Moth
90	Travonis Ul
91-92	Trawl
93-95	Xacorocax
96-97	Yellow Swarm
98-00	Yovok

Wandering in the Mountains

01-04	Astraphin Monolith
05-07	Calyptor
08-11	Callerail
12-15	Chirog
16-20	Cragworm
21	Ember Scion
22-23	Ergovore Hound
24-25	Erynth Grask
26-28	Flying Elchin
29-31	The Hex
32-35	Hontri
36-38	Kanthid
39-42	Killist
43	Latos
44-48	Margr
49-51	Nevajin
52-55	Orgulous
56	Philethis
57	Plasmar
58-60	Pygmy Hapax
61-66	Ravage Bear
67-69	Rubar
70-74	Sarrak
75-79	Sathosh
80-82	Scavrow
83-84	Skysmasher
85-88	Snow Loper
89-91	Steel Spider
92-95	Tetrahydra
96-00	Yovok

Wandering Through the Woods (or Jungle)

01-03	Balikna
04-06	Bandit
07-09	Bloodfeast Tick
10-13	Callerail
14-18	Culova
19-22	Dream Sallow
23-24	Earthshaker
25-28	Edacious Destroyer
29-32	Encephalon
33-36	Golthiar
37-38	The Hex
39-41	Jesanthum
42-46	Jiraskar
47-49	Laurik-Ca
50-54	Llaric Scorpion
55-59	Murden
60-63	Pallone
64	Philethis
65-68	Queb
69-75	Ravage Bear
76-80	Scutimorph
81-85	Seskii
86-90	Slicer Beetle
91-93	Steel Spider
94	Travonis Ul
95-96	Vape
97-98	Xiomarche
99-00	Ylaantiv

Trekking Across the Plains or Desert

01-05	Aneen
06-09	Avatrol
10-13	Balikna
14-20	Bandit
21-25	Broken Hound
26-27	Caffa
28-30	Calyptor
31-34	Chirog
35-40	Cragworm
41-43	Dedimaskis
44	Dread Destroyer
45-47	Ellnoica
48-50	Encephalon
51-54	Ferno Walker
55-58	Frilled Baul
59-62	Griffalo
63-65	Herder
66-70	Ithsyn
71-74	Killist
75-80	Margr
81	Philethis
82-84	Rahenum
85-87	Rorathik
88-90	Sarrak
91	Scavrow
92-94	Slurge
95-97	Terror Bird
98-99	Tetrahydra
00	Varakith

Delving Deep Underground

01-06	Caffa
07-12	Cave Qui
13-15	Coccitan
16-18	Dark Fathom
19-23	Entrope
24-26	Erynth Grask
27-30	Etterick
31-35	Explorer
36-38	Grush

39-44	Magmid
45-50	Nagaina
51-55	Odlark
56	Philethis
57-62	Ravage Bear
63-67	Sarrak
68-73	Sathosh
74-79	Slicer Beetle
80-84	Steel Spider
85	Stellar Weaver
86-90	Syzygy Ghoul
91-95	Varakith
96-00	Yovok

Infiltrating the Fortress

01-05	Arch-Nano
06-12	Broken Hound
13-15	Dark Fathom
16-21	Deadly Warrior
22-30	Ergovore Hound
31-35	Etterick
36-45	Grush
46-48	Jiraskar
49-58	Nano
59-63	Queb
64-69	Ravage Bear
70-73	Slicer Beetle
74-77	Steel Spider
78-89	Town Guard
90-96	Warlord
97-00	Vape

The Individual's Mount or Pet

01-06	Aneen
07-11	Avatrol
12-16	Broken Hound
17-21	Ergovore Hound
22-26	Ferno Walker
27-31	Frilled Baul
32-35	Griffalo
36-38	Hontri
39-42	Ithsyn
43-50	Raster
51-55	Ravage Bear
56-60	Queb
61-67	Seskii
68-75	Shanu
76-80	Snow Loper
81-84	Tachyron
85-90	Terror Bird
91-96	Thuman
97-99	Warder
00	Xi-Drake

Existing in the Fringes of Civilization

01-04	Aeon Priest
05-06	Arch-Nano
07-10	Balikna
11-16	Bandit
17-19	Chance Moth
20-23	Deadly Warrior
24-26	Decanted
27-30	Debril
31-33	Flesh Pup
34-37	Grush
38-42	Laak
43-45	Magathan
46-50	Murden
51-52	Nagaina
53-56	Nalurus
57-62	Nano
63-66	Nevajin
67-69	Nibovian Child
70-72	Nibovian Companion
73-76	Nibovian Wife
77	Philethis
78-80	Rubar
81-84	Shivern
85-90	Slidikin
91-99	Town Guard
00	Weaponized Meme

Finding Trouble in Town

01-05	Aeon Priest
06-09	Arch-Nano
10-14	Blitzer
15-20	Deadly Warrior
21-25	Memora
26-30	Mlox
31-36	Nano
37	Philethis
38-41	Poisoner
42-47	Scrivener
48-54	Seskii
55-65	Slidikin
66-74	Thuman
75-97	Town Guard
98-99	Warder
00	Xi-Drake

Uncovering an Area No Living Thing Should Be

01-05	Abykos
06-09	Accelerator
10-12	Chance Moth
13-16	Dark Fathom
17-20	Dedimaskis
21-24	Dimensional Husk
25-28	Disassembler
29-32	Ellnoica
33-35	Ergovore Hound
36-39	Erulian
40-43	Etterick
44-47	Falling Maw
48-51	Gazer
52-55	Grey Sampler
56-59	Jurulisk
60-61	Kalyptein Crab
62-65	Mastigophore
66-68	Minnern
69-73	Oorgolian Soldier
74-77	Peerless
78	Philethis
79-81	Therivar
82-84	Travonis Ul
85-86	Varadimos
87-90	Warder
91-94	Xaar
95-98	Xacorocax
99-00	Yellow Swarm

Venturing Close to the Water

01-07	Blood Barm
08-12	Ithsyn
13-17	Jiraskar
18-22	Killist
23-27	Laak
28-32	Llaric Scorpion
33-37	Lorub
38-42	Mesomeme
43-47	Morl
48-52	Murden
53	Philethis
54-58	Raster
59-63	Sathosh
64-68	Stratharian War Moth
69-73	Tetrahydra
74-77	Travonis Ul
78-81	Xi-Drake
82-86	Xiomarche
87-90	Yellow Swarm
91-95	Ylaantiv
96-00	Yovok

CREATURES

SIZE COMPARISON

ACCELERATOR 6 (18)

Accelerators are artificial intelligences encased in metal shells with numerous limbs, sensory devices, and other accoutrements that allow them to interact with and understand the world around them. Accelerators fear "death" (perhaps "dissolution" is a better term) and concoct elaborate plans to develop better protections for themselves. Ironically, sometimes this puts them in danger as they try to take control of a defensible fortress or obtain a device that will grant them a powerful force field.

Accelerators stand 15 feet (4.6 m) high. They often move along the ground, but they can briefly fly and hover.

Motive: Proactive self-defense

Environment: Anywhere

Health: 30

Damage Inflicted: 7 points

Armor: 4

Movement: Long

Modifications: Perceives as level 8; Speed defense as level 5 due to size.

Combat: Accelerators can defend themselves with a number of bladelike appendages, attacking up to three foes as a single action. Additionally, they can alter the acceleration of up to three different creatures or objects within immediate range, from halting a moving object to causing an object to suddenly move rapidly and with force. This power can be used in a variety of ways. They can: hurl a heavy object at a target in short range (7 points of damage), hurl a light object up to long range (5 points of damage), or hurl a foe away from them up to short range (7 points of damage). A moving character or object within immediate range can also be forced to stop immediately and remain motionless for one round.

If seriously threatened, an accelerator always chooses flight over fight.

Interaction: Accelerators are extraordinarily paranoid and fearful. It is extremely difficult (level 9) to gain one's trust. They speak a wide variety of languages and are smart enough to pick up new ones within minutes.

Use: Accelerators aren't evil, but their self-centered paranoia means they might act as if they were true villains in the eyes of others.

Loot: A destroyed accelerator yields 1d100 + 20 shins, 1d6 + 1 cyphers, and an oddity.

GM Intrusion: *The accelerator activates a device that it has acquired, gaining a force shield that grants it 3 extra points of Armor for one minute.*

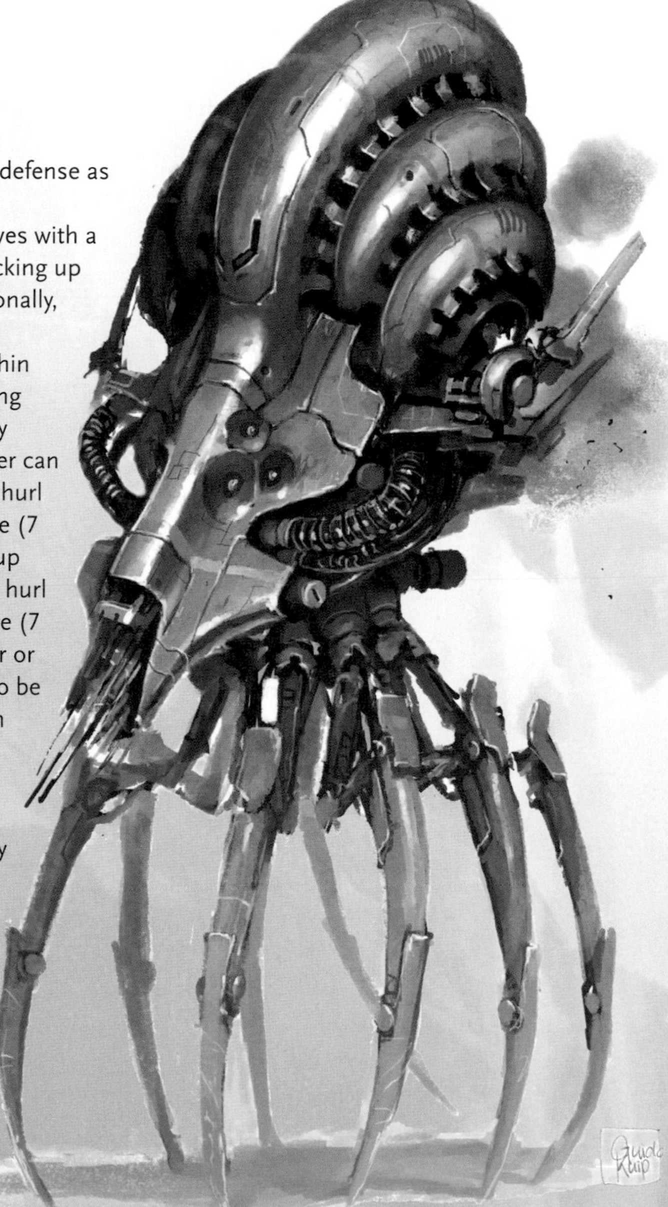

ASTRAPHIN MONOLITH 6 (18)

SIZE COMPARISON

Floating, immobile obelisks of stone, each astraphin monolith stands a bit taller than a human and has a single crystalline eye. Infamously, this eye emits beams of deadly force that cause some explorers to suspect that something supernatural, willful, and diabolical is at work. However, the stones are neither living nor sentient, but rather extensions of a hidden intelligence.

Ages past, someone or something altered the sun to save the Earth from its increasing radiance. The process introduced an unknown energy that changed some of the plantlife that fed on sunlight. Over time, these alterations gave way to real intelligence, like that of the innocuous-appearing astraphin, a leafy, flowering—and occasionally carnivorous—plant found in mountainous regions.

The astraphin can bond to stone it reaches through its roots and vines, making subtle changes in the stone's molecular structure. In this way, the plant can form a monolith over vast amounts of time. A fully formed monolith springs from the ground to float 10 to 15 feet (3 to 4.6 m) in the air. The plant controls the crystalline eye's destructive beams, striking prey and feeding on the bodies through its extensive root system.

Motive: Hungers for flesh

Environment: Rocky, mountainous regions

Health: 30

Damage Inflicted: 6 points

Armor: 4

Movement: None

Combat: A fight with an astraphin monolith is strange because it does not move. Simply fleeing out of its range is an obvious and viable tactic. Some choose to stay, however, to get at the crystal eye (see below).

The only action a monolith can take is to fire a beam of energy at foes within a range of 200 feet (61 m), but it can vary the type of beam based on the situation:

- A blast of raw force that inflicts 6 points of damage on one target
- A ray of psychic energy that inflicts 4 points of Intellect damage on one target (and ignores Armor)
- A beam of nerve-targeting energy that paralyzes one target if she fails a Might defense roll. Each round, the paralyzed victim can attempt another Might defense roll to shrug off the effect.
- A burst of heat that inflicts 3 points of damage on all creatures within immediate range (rather than its normal range)

Of course, destroying the monolith is not death for the plant—only a setback. Destroying the astraphin is difficult, for its leafy vines and roots can stretch for hundreds of feet around the monolith.

Interaction: Meaningful interaction with the monolith or the controlling plant is impossible.

Use: A monolith can be a surprising encounter in the wilderness, but it is also hunted by those desiring its eye, which a skilled tinkerer can use as the energy source for a very large and powerful machine.

Loot: The monolith's crystalline eye is prized because it can be used as a power source for a depleted artifact. It can also serve as a weapon, firing a blast of force that inflicts 6 points of damage with a range of 200 feet (61 m). Depletion: 1–3 in 1d100.

GM Intrusion: *Striking the monolith causes the eye to fire a sudden burst of energy not on its normal turn.*

SIZE COMPARISON

AVATROL 4 (12)

"I heard if you look through the avatrol's skull hole, you see the future. I don't want to know my future that badly." ~Cartle Lurn

The avatrol is a belligerent, spiteful creature that most people in the Beyond have learned to give a wide berth to. Omnivores who travel in packs, avatrols spend most of their time digging up tubers and roots. They supplement their diet with meat—usually small mammals or reptiles, but they are not averse to larger prey if it is available, particularly if the avatrol pack is sizable. Avatrols are reptilian quadrupeds, with claws on their forelimbs and massive curved tusks.

Because of the hole that runs through the creature's skull, a shrill whistling sound accompanies a running avatrol. This scary sound is the origin for the phrase "louder than a charging avatrol."

Motive: Hungers for flesh

Environment: Any warm or temperate climate in packs of five to ten

Health: 19

Damage Inflicted: 4 points

Armor: 2

Movement: Long

Modifications: Attacks as level 5; perceives as level 6.

Combat: Avatrols use nasty, charging pounces when they attack. However, the most interesting thing about them is that they are immune to most dangerous energies. Blasts of force, concentrated light, and focused heat reflect off the hide of an avatrol back in the direction it came from. (This isn't true of more specific or exotic energies—magnetic waves, high frequency sonics, and so on—or of ambient damage.)

Reflected rays have the same level as the original source of the attack, so avoiding the reflected beam of a level 7 ray emitter is a difficulty 7 task. Reflected rays also have the same range and damage.

Interaction: Avatrols have animal-level intelligence. They are very mean-spirited creatures, yet some people still attempt to domesticate them, using them to pull wagons, carts, and chariots. Keeping them under control is difficult (a level 6 task) but not impossible. The frilled ridges on their backs keep them from being used as mounts.

GM Intrusion: *A reflected beam is refracted, and everyone within an immediate distance of the source of the beam (probably the character who made the attack) must try to avoid being hit.*

Use: A team of sixteen avatrols pulls the war-wagon of Lord Gulgur of the isolated city-state of Strelsh on the Plains of Kataru. The wagon carries a huge array of weapons, including a massive device that can alter the weather in the area and call down directed lightning from storm clouds. Nine trained beastmasters use long black rods filled with super-cold liquid at their tips to maintain control of the animals.

Loot: A very skilled craftsperson can turn an avatrol hide into beastskin armor that also reflects concentrated light, force, and heat beams half the time when they would normally hit the wearer. This is a difficulty 7 task and requires the skin of at least two avatrols.

BALIKNA 4 (12)

This large, lizardlike creature has tall back spikes, a spiked tail, and legs that end in fierce pincers. It has bad eyesight and hunts via sound thanks to a series of funneled ears on top of its large jaw.

A balikna is the king of camouflage, with the passive ability to change its pigment to identically match whatever object it rests upon, becoming essentially invisible. During the daylight hours, the balikna stays motionless and invisible. It hunts only at night, under the cover of darkness. Although its movements are mostly silent, those with good hearing, good night vision, or the proper numenera devices can track this creature in the dark more easily than during the day.

Motive: Hunger

Environment: Any wooded or grassy area, but especially near villages where food and children are present

Health: 20

Damage Inflicted: 6 points

Armor: 3

Movement: Short

Modifications: Defends as level 5 due to camouflage (if a foe can even see it)

Combat: The balikna's camouflage is a passive skill (a level 3 task). If it's invisible, each PC must make an Intellect roll every round to see it. Failure means that the character cannot attack the creature this round, and defending against it is two steps more difficult. The balikna knows who cannot see it and always attacks them, if possible.

Its main attack is a sneak attack—a swipe with its heavy spiked tail that inflicts 6 points of damage and stuns its opponent for one round, meaning that he loses his next turn. The creature follows up with an attempt to close its pincers on its stunned opponent for 4 points of damage.

Use: The characters pass by a yard where children are playing noisily in the falling light when one of the kids begins yelling in fear, although it's not apparent what has frightened her.

Interaction: The creature could be lured into a trap by using a small child as bait.

SIZE COMPARISON

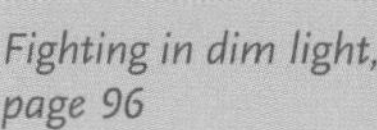

Fighting in dim light, page 96

GM Intrusion: *The balikna's tail swipe hits a PC who cannot see it, knocking the character unconscious for 1d6 rounds.*

SIZE COMPARISON

BELLOWHEART 6 (18)

Known (and named) for its terrible howl, the bellowheart is more notable for the attacks it makes with the whiplike tendrils that cover its prodigious body. The bellowheart is a huge, lumbering beast, but it's also far more intelligent than it appears. It spends most of its day rampaging about, eating everything it comes upon. Still, there are deep mysteries regarding this creature. Some people speculate that it is the advanced, adult form of a very different creature—perhaps one that can pass for a human or humanoid so it can interact with and learn from them. Or perhaps the bellowheart is a secondary life stage of a visitant race that dwells amid humans in remote areas, either secretly or overtly.

The bellowheart can see in total darkness as if it were day. No one knows how.

Motive: Hungers for flesh

Environment: Anywhere

Health: 30

Damage Inflicted: 6 points

Armor: 3

Movement: Short

Modifications: Speed defense as level 5 due to size

Combat: A bellowheart can attack up to six different foes with its whiplike tendrils, and it chooses the special effect of each one by quickly adjusting the venom injected by the barb from among various sacs. On each attack, it chooses one of the following effects (and can choose the same effect more than once):

- A flesh-eating acid that inflicts an additional 2 points of damage
- A nervous-system-disrupting venom that inflicts 4 points of Speed damage if the victim fails a Might defense roll
- A paralytic concoction that stuns the victim, making him lose his next turn if he fails a Might defense roll
- A poison that blurs the victim's vision, increasing the difficulty of all actions requiring sight (which is most of them) by one step for one hour
- A disorienting venom that changes the target of the character's next action (such as an attack) to a random target within immediate range

GM Intrusion: *The character winds up underneath the bellowheart's bulk, between its tree-trunk-like legs. The creature's tendrils can't reach her there, but she must immediately avoid two crushing attacks from its massive feet, each of which inflicts 10 points of damage. If she remains under the bellowheart, the difficulty of her attack is reduced by one step. However, each round she stays there, the bellowheart can use its feet to attack her.*

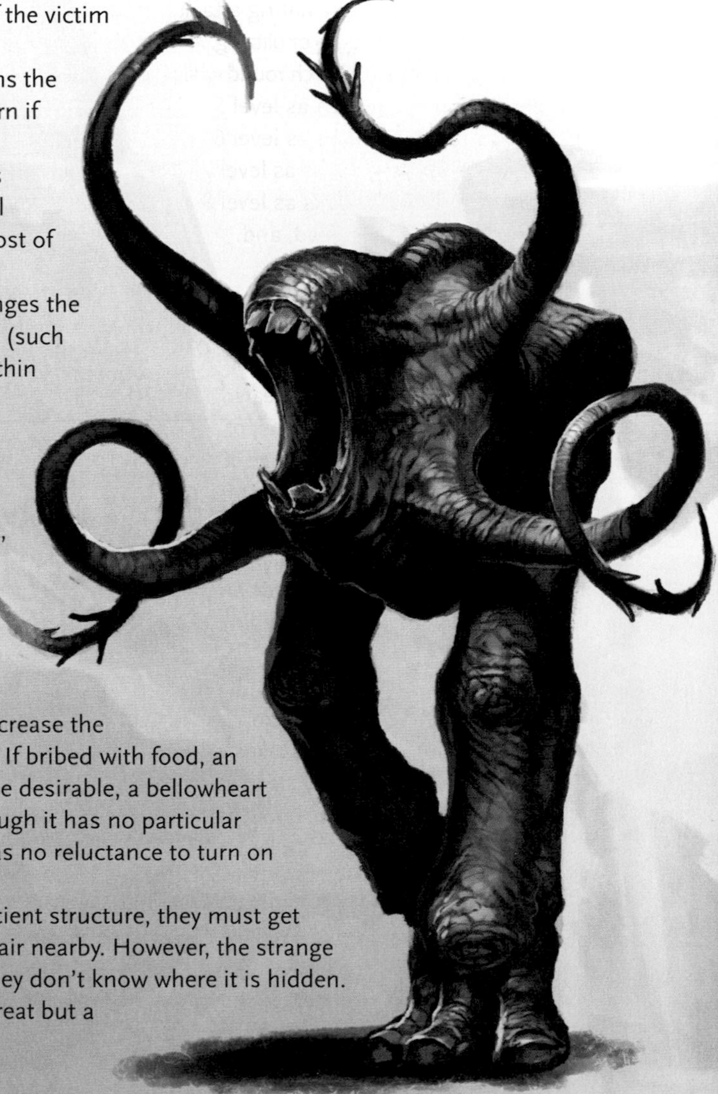

Interaction: Bellowhearts can speak a variety of languages, which makes no sense—how did they learn them? To reason with a bellowheart, a character must approach the creature when it is not hungry (a smart negotiator brings a lot of fresh meat) and show complete deference. Even then, reasoning is quite difficult (increase the difficulty of the action by one step). If bribed with food, an interesting oddity, or something else desirable, a bellowheart can become a temporary ally. Although it has no particular predilection toward deception, it has no reluctance to turn on its allies, either.

Use: The PCs learn that to reach an ancient structure, they must get past the bellowheart that makes it lair nearby. However, the strange place has only one entrance, and they don't know where it is hidden. Perhaps the bellowheart is not a threat but a resource.

BLITZER 5 (15)

"If it begins growing, run." ~Jennis Falon, explorer

Thick cables of arteries feed pulsing muscles so hot that they glow like embers beneath this monstrosity's translucent skin. Synth and metal shunts coil and beep, visibly nestled side by side with muscle and organs. Every few seconds, a fresh wave of heat pours from the blitzer as it conspicuously swells in size and muscle mass, and its capacity for destruction almost doubles. Once a blitzer begins to grow (or "blitz" as it's commonly referred to), the creature ceases its rampage only when it destroys whatever set it off or when it overheats and drops dead, a smoking husk of overcooked meat and synth.

Blitzers seem to appear randomly, coming to the attention of potential victims when they smash through a wall or crash down from a height to crater paving stones. Other times, a blitzer appears when an apparently normal person suddenly transforms, bursting and burning out of clothing to become a terrorizing monster.

People assume that those transformed into blitzers never regain their minds or previous forms, cursed to remain monsters forever after.

Motive: Destruction

Environment: Almost anywhere, usually alone but occasionally in a duo

Health: 20

Damage Inflicted: 6–15 points (see Combat)

Armor: 4

Movement: Short; long when blitzing

Modifications: See Combat for escalating attack level modification.

Combat: The creature is either passive or blitzing. A "blitz" is an episode of rampage that increases the creature's mass, damage, and attack level each round while it continues, according to the following schedule:

Round 1 Damage 6 points; attacks as level 5

Round 2 Damage 9 points, attacks as level 6

Round 3 Damage 12 points; attacks as level 7

Round 4 Damage 15 points; attacks as level 8

Round 5 Blitzer overheats, falls dead, and begins to smolder

A blitzer bludgeons and slightly scorches foes with its massive fists.

A blitzer stops blitzing if it's killed (by a greater force or by its own deadly biochemistry) or if every creature within immediate range of it is debilitated or dead on the blitzer's turn. When a blitzer stops rampaging, it shrinks back to its original mass and wanders off, apparently dazed, seeking someplace cool to sleep, preferably in running water with its head just above the waterline. The creature can blitz no more than once per hour.

Interaction: A blitzer can be interacted with before or after (but not during) its cycle of rampage. Before a blitz, the creature is prickly and takes offense easily. Afterward, it is dazed and sleepy and wants nothing more than to cool off, though a few have their own interests as well.

Use: While the PCs make their way through a crowded market, a youth caught stealing falls writhing and spitting, seized by a fit of apoplexy. When he rises, it's as a blitzer.

Loot: A burnt-out blitzer doesn't yield anything salvageable, but one killed before it burns out might yield a couple of cyphers.

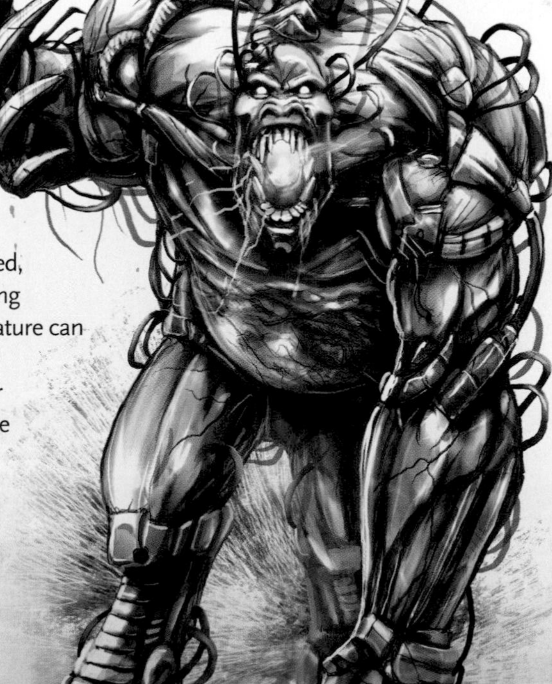

SIZE COMPARISON

Blitzers are believed to be the result of massive surgical intervention on unsuspecting victims. Prior to their transformation, some blitzers complained of a daylong gap in their memory. It's not known who or what might be modifying people, giving them the capacity to blitz.

"And Father Calaval did pity the dying beast and wished to end its suffering. May our Father's knife find us when we too, have fallen upon our despair. Iadace." ~as told by Doroa of the Silent Song

GM Intrusion: *The blitzer brings its hands together so violently that it creates a thunderclap. Every creature in immediate range must succeed on a Might defense roll. Those who fail are unable to do anything but move on their next turn and are deafened for one minute (and thus unable to communicate with allies vocally during that time).*

BLOODFEAST TICK

Tiny bloodsucking insects are common annoyances, and most are easily handled with a slap, even if a raised, itchy welt is left behind. But a bloodfeast tick is an altogether different class of creature.

A bloodfeast tick comes in two varieties: a regular-sized insect and a scion. The regular tick looks no different than many other small, crawling insects. When it drops onto a victim, it usually does so unnoticed, crawls someplace on the skin out of sight, then bites the victim and begins to draw blood. Because a tick's saliva has anesthetic qualities, the bite is less noticeable even than the minor itchy feeling it might have produced when crawling into place.

If the victim hosting an insect-sized bloodfeast tick falls asleep, the tick deepens that sleep with its saliva, then feeds in peace for up to ten hours, leaving the victim a dead, shriveled shell. Meanwhile, the tick's blood reservoir bloats to the size of the dead victim, breaks off, and becomes a free-roaming, free-willed ravaging monster in its own right: a tick scion.

Few people realize that tick scions and the insect-sized bloodfeast ticks are related, given the dramatic difference in scale between the two. Once a tick scion is birthed, its "parent" dies.

TICK SCION 6 (18)

Motive: Destruction
Environment: Any tropical or temperate region
Health: 18
Damage Inflicted: 6 points
Armor: 2
Movement: Short
Combat: A tick scion can make two bashing attacks with a single action using its powerful limbs.
Interaction: Tick scions can't be reasoned with—they live to destroy (and to disperse more insect-sized bloodfeast ticks; after a fight with a tick scion, combatants should check their clothes, skin, and hair for tiny crawling guests).

If an insect-sized bloodfeast tick drops unseen onto a victim, it is a difficulty 3 Intellect-based task to notice the itchy sensation of the tiny insect crawling across her skin. If detected, the insect is easily smashed and the threat ended.

But if the victim doesn't notice, the next time she sleeps, that sleep deepens rapidly to coma. If her companions fail to notice the quickly bloating insect sucking her blood and nothing else intervenes before ten hours have elapsed, the victim dies and the tick scion tears free. If the victim is roused (and the bloating tick squished, which splashes ejected blood everywhere) sometime before ten full hours of exsanguination have elapsed, she is saved but is debilitated for a few days.

Use: A nano is leading an expedition to gather samples in a nearby forested area rumored to be thick with bloodfeast ticks.

GM Intrusion: *The tick scion bites a character instead of bashing her, releasing a flood of anesthetic saliva into the wound. The character's leg, arm, or the whole side of her body goes numb for a few minutes. If the numbness affects the character's face, she slurs when she speaks. All physical tasks and attacks are modified by one step to her detriment.*

CALYPTOR 3 (9)

A high, lush, exploratory tone pierces the night. It's followed by a rush of flutes, horns, and drums, weaving a tune passionately performed, throbbing with emotion, full of arcing phrases of rich noise. The music drifts across the plain or down from the nearby hills. Surely a traveling troupe of city musicians hasn't set camp up there and decided to perform in the small hours of the night?

Shapes emerge from the darkness, moving closer, silhouetted against the stars except for the dancing, emberlike designs that beard each one. They approach closer, not fast but not dithering, until they're revealed as four-legged creatures, 6 feet (1.8 m) high, with particularly piercing eyes.

Motive: Defense

Environment: Temperate and warmer regions of the Steadfast and the Beyond, in prides of eight to ten

Health: 9

Damage Inflicted: 5 points

Armor: 2

Movement: Short

Modifications: Musical performance as level 7; perception tasks as level 7.

Combat: A calyptor physically attacks an enemy with its piercing head spikes. It can also attack a foe at long range by directing an intensely loud, focused bleat that inflicts 2 points of damage (ignores Armor).

Even though calyptor prides produce sound almost constantly, predators are rarely successful at sneaking up under the cover of the music. The creatures' biomechanical eyes allow them to see heat, see in the dark, and focus on potential threats when they are still miles away.

A pride of calyptors can play coordinated chords that do more than sound pleasing. If threatened by predators or otherwise roused to aggression, six or more calyptors in a group can make a level 5 attack, producing a sound that has either a soporific effect or a panic effect on every creature in short range who fails an Intellect defense roll. The calyptors determine the effect that seems most suitable for their defense at the moment.

Soporific: The sound puts the listener to sleep for one minute or until roused by rough treatment or an extremely loud noise (not made by a calyptor).

Panic: The sound instills unreasoning fear in the listener for one minute. During this time, the victim runs off, stumbling and falling in her haste to get away from the calyptors.

Interaction: Calyptors are essentially herd animals and react accordingly. A few small prides are kept by individuals who value the music they produce.

Use: While the PCs camp out under the sky one evening, a pride of calyptors wanders past, treating them to an impromptu orchestral extravaganza.

SIZE COMPARISON

Calyptors can produce other coordinated chords besides defense sounds, including chords that induce contentment, clear thinking, or arousal.

Lone calyptors can generate music worthy of note, but a small pride is nothing less than an orchestra. A pride rarely performs the same piece twice, and there seems to be no coherent theme between pieces. Each individual piece creates a strong and specific resonance in a human listener's mind. This resonance is enhanced by the play of fire-colored lights on a calyptor's throat sacs, which dance in synchrony with its performance.

GM Intrusion: *When the PC hears a piece performed by a calyptor or a pride, whether during combat or otherwise, she falls into a sleep that features a nightmare. In the dream, her brain is removed by an ancient array of numenera and placed within the skull of an animal. When the PC wakes, she has 5 fewer points in her Intellect Pool. Fortunately, the lost points can be recovered normally.*

SIZE COMPARISON

CAVE QUI

Cave quis are winged creatures that dwell in abandoned ruins, underground, and in caves. Cave qui culture puts the colony first, valuing the well-being of every member. This means that a colony is usually a force for peace, both for individual members of the colony and in the region surrounding a colony's location. In fact, there's a saying about cave quis that speaks to their demeanor: "War cannot end war; only a cave qui can do that."

Cave quis live in fear of something known as the "qui curse," which can strike individuals within a colony without apparent warning or cause. The curse transforms a placid cave qui into a crazed killer. Unless dealt with quickly and permanently, an entire cave qui colony can be converted into a hive of cursed qui. One of the most important positions in a colony is that of Wing Judge, responsible for monitoring colony health. If a cave qui falls under the curse, a Wing Judge can ignore normally forgiving and progressive laws and terminate the suspected cursed qui with prejudice.

A cave qui Wing Judge dyes its fur black with a red "blood stripe" down the back of each wing. Other cave quis usually use more festive and colorful dyes.

Cursed qui forget most of their culture, are much harder to kill than regular cave qui, and suffer from a hunger that no amount of killing and eating seems to slake. If a victim of a cursed qui attack manages to survive, it's also affected by the curse—cave quis become cursed quis over the course of a few weeks, while other living creatures are at risk of contracting a virulent sickness that kills them over the same period.

CAVE QUI 4 (12)

Cave qui adults hang 3 feet (0.9 m) in length and have wingspans in excess of 8 feet (2.4 m). The creatures' wing and fur color range from orange to dark grey, though many adults dye their fur and wings with vibrant colors to denote their position within the colony.

Motive: Curiosity

Environment: Temperate and tropical forests of the Beyond, in flights of three or four

Health: 12

Damage Inflicted: 4 points

Movement: Short when on the ground; long when flying

Modifications: Tasks related to persuasion as level 6

Combat: A cave qui attacks a foe with its claws.

Swarm rules, page 13

Three cave quis can coordinate their attack, acting like a swarm. When they do, they make a single attack against one character as a level 6 creature and deal 8 points of damage (4 points even if the target succeeds on a Speed defense roll).

Interaction: Cave quis speak their own hypersonic language, which many creatures can't hear. However, cave quis with the title of Air Talker can make themselves heard by others by speaking through a qui-made device of wood and stone that modulates pitch. Air Talkers understand a variety of languages.

GM Intrusion: *A character is the target of a hypersonic "hunting cry," which a cave qui is sometimes able to emit at foes within long range. If the PC fails a Might defense roll, he is deafened for several hours.*

Use: Two warring groups have called upon the services of an outsider to ease them into talks meant to end the conflict. The diplomat is a cave qui with the title Harmony Bringer, accompanied by a handful of Air Talkers and one Wing Judge. The Harmony Bringer has contracted the first stages of the qui curse but is hiding it.

Loot: A defeated cave qui sometimes carries a few shins.

CURSED QUI 7 (21)

A cursed qui looks like a half-starved, bedraggled, blood-spattered, insane cave qui. It randomly utters shrieks, cries, and croaks, and it foams red at the mouth. Hunger defines its every moment, even when its stomach is distended to grotesque proportions from recent gorging.

Motive: Hungers for flesh

Environment: Lone cursed quis hunt day or night and can be found far beyond regular cave qui haunts.

Health: 21

Damage Inflicted: 7 points

Armor: 3

Movement: Short when on the ground; long when flying

Combat: A cursed qui attacks a foe with its claws and can make two attacks as a single action.

A cursed qui doesn't seem to feel pain, so even an attack that hits doesn't inflict the same amount of

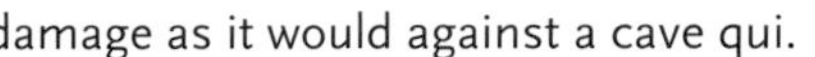

damage as it would against a cave qui.

A cursed qui can choose to bite a victim instead of attacking with claws. On a hit, the qui inflicts damage, and the victim must succeed on a Might defense roll. On a failed roll, he is touched by the qui curse, and all tasks and attacks attempted by the victim are modified by one step to his detriment for several hours.

Interaction: A cursed qui may remember its former self for a moment, but the moment never lasts, washed away by hunger.

Use: A once-peaceful colony of cave quis has gone quiet. Apparently, some kind of predator has trapped the quis in the lair—the sounds of terrible shrieks and screams from the lair mouth prove that something dreadful is happening within.

A cursed qui that eats too much can't fly; it can only shuffle and flop toward its next meal until it digests (or vomits up) the contents of its stomach.

GM Intrusion: *A character touched by the qui curse seems to get better a few hours after being bitten, but she actually suffers from a terrible illness that first presents like a flu over the course of several days. If she doesn't receive major medical care (probably in the form of a special numenera device), she risks insanity or death within a few weeks.*

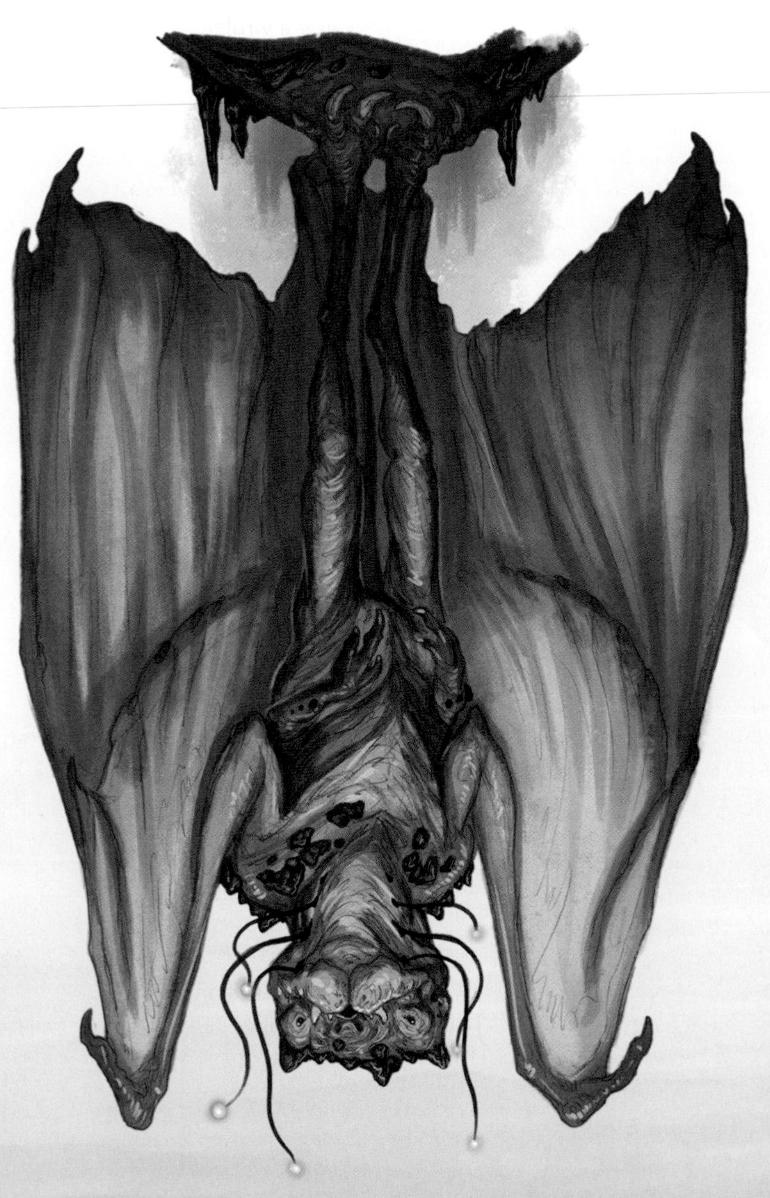

CHANCE MOTH 1 (3)

Chance moths are known as flutterglows in the city of Qi and as cypherids in the Beyond.

A chance moth is a nut-sized insect, lazily buzzing through the air, leaving an incandescent trail of red, green, blue, or some harder-to-describe color in its erratic wake.

Motive: Defense, seeks numenera

Environment: Lone scouts seeking new items of numenera or swarms of twenty or more in a hive, crawling over a fragment of a prior world that still retains a bit of energy

Health: 1

Damage Inflicted: 1 point

Armor: 1

Movement: Short when flying

Modifications: Speed defense as level 3 due to size

Combat: A chance moth's sting inflicts damage, but depending on the numenera radiation the insect has fed upon, the sting could grant additional effects. Once a drone stings a victim, it dies. Drones from the same hive don't typically confer the same effects; roll on the chart below for each sting.

d100	Effect
01–05	Target gains training (or specialization if already trained) in a random skill for one hour.
06–10	Target gains training (or specialization if already trained) in a random skill for one day.
11–15	Target gains the ability to see in almost total darkness for one day; eyes glow green.
16–20	Target gains the ability to emit a ray of destructive energy up to 200 feet (61 m) that inflicts 4 points of damage; the ability can be used three times.
21–25	Target gains the single-use ability to become invisible for up to one hour (thus becoming specialized in stealth and Speed defense tasks) or until the target attacks another creature.
26–30	Target regenerates 1 point of damage per round for one hour or until killed.
31–35	Target gains a short fly speed for one day.
36–40	Target tunes into the datasphere and can learn the answer to one question.
41–86	No discernible additional effect.
87–91	Target falls upward for 10 × d20 feet as if gravity reversed, then falls back down.
92–97	Drone detonates in an immediate radius, inflicting 5 points of damage in a fiery explosion.
98–99	Drone burrows into the target's brain and begins to tick as if counting down from 60. If not removed within one minute, the drone detonates in a long radius, inflicting 5 points of damage in a fiery explosion. The target moves two steps down the damage track.
00	Unless the target succeeds at a difficulty 6 task (numenera related), a dread destroyer arrives in 1d100 hours.

Skills, page 25

Chance moth hives are usually underground, but they might be dug up or accidentally revealed. A hive consists of a swarm of drones crawling over and basking in the pulsing glow of a piece of numenera. The drones feed on remnant energy leaked by the relic and are changed by it, gaining a related ability or attack.

Dread destroyer, page 239

Interaction: Chance moths are hive insects. They generally leave other creatures alone unless disturbed or provoked.

Use: A farmer's daughter recently interacted with a hive of green glowing bugs and was badly injured when one exploded near her. Now the farmer needs someone to dig up and exterminate the colony.

Loot: One cypher can be found in a chance moth nest.

GM Intrusion: *When a character is stung by a chance moth, roll twice on the table and apply both results.*

CHRONAL FEEDER 4 (12)

These segmented, 6-foot (1.8 m) long creatures look partly like larvae that have grown gargantuan and vicious. They appear in places where time moves more slowly or more quickly than normal, where balls and liquids flow upslope, or where a time traveler has visited.

Motive: Hungers for the flesh of those who create time anomalies

Environment: Clutches of four to eight feeders fade into existence within long range of space-time fractures in almost any location.

Health: 18

Damage Inflicted: 5 points

Armor: 1

Movement: Short; can phase into its home dimension as an action. On its next action, it can phase back into this world and move, traveling up to 300 feet (91 m) each time.

Modifications: Perception as level 5

Combat: A chronal feeder attacks with its crushing mandibles.

A chronal feeder can phase back and forth between its home dimension, and it uses this ability to great effect when hunting prey. For instance, it can close on prey otherwise protected by barriers or features of the landscape. It can also use the ability to draw a victim's attention and then launch a surprise attack from behind. It is an action for the feeder to shift its phase between its home dimension and this one.

Interaction: Chronal feeders are unswerving in their drive to find prey. Once a feeder marks its target, only killing the creature can sway it from the prey.

Use: When the PCs happen upon a location where the rules of space-time are loose and malleable, or if the PCs trigger a cypher or other numenera device that interferes with time's regular flow, a clutch of feeders may soon come calling.

Loot: The skin of a chronal feeder can be salvaged to create a silvery cloak that reflects its surroundings, but the reflection is one hour behind the present.

> Chronal feeders are creatures that seem drawn to time paradoxes and disruptions in space-time. They tend to eat those responsible (and those affected), potentially alleviating the disturbance in the fabric of things, though that outcome might just be a side effect. First and foremost, chronal feeders are parasites that phase into existence near a spatial anomaly and feed to sate their own hunger. However, there are hints that the larvae may represent the first stage of life of a far more powerful and enigmatic entity.

SIZE COMPARISON

GM Intrusion: *If a chronal feeder's prey fails its Speed defense roll, the attack ignores Armor, and the prey must make an Intellect defense roll (difficulty 4). On a failed roll, the victim is phased into the chronal feeder's home dimension. He automatically phases back into reality on his next turn but is displaced by 100 feet (30 m) straight up or to the closest open space. This usually results in a fall that potentially deals 10 points of damage, knocks the character prone, and dazes him for a round.*

COCCITAN 3 (9)

Korah blinked. But eyes open or closed, chill darkness was all she sensed.

"Hello?" she called. "Nyere? Radditch? I'm down here!" She couldn't keep the desperate edge of fear from her voice. How long had she been here? Hours, at least. And her friends still hadn't found her. Maybe they never would. Maybe she'd die down here...

Wherever here *was. The place was supposed to be thick in the numenera—the map said so. All she'd found was a hole in the floor. The fall had knocked her senseless. The staggering pain made her reluctant to move.*

A rattle jerked Korah's head around. Was it close or far off?

"Radditch?" Dread made her yell more of a croak.

Nothing. Her heart thundered.

Another rattle, scratchy and drawn out, like sand sloughing off a dune. A hollow sort of chirping made her gasp. Whatever had made that sound was no more than a couple of feet away.

"Who's there?" she said, or tried to. But the roaches were already covering her like a hungry blanket.

~*from* Coccitan Rising: A Treatise on Insects That Think

Coccitan colonies are thick with abandoned casings of their molted skins, giving such locations a macabre look, at least from a human's perspective. From a coccitan's point of view, the discarded skins are warm reminders of happy days.

Coccitans are not a warlike race and usually skitter away if threatened. However, they use roach swarms in a variety of ways, including to subdue potential threats.

GM Intrusion: *A coccitan's pet roach swarm knocks the PC down and covers her completely, preventing her from taking her next turn.*

Coccitans are insectlike humanoids that live in the cracks of the world—forgotten ruins far below the surface or hidden colonies closer to human habitation—where they gorge on garbage, sewage, and other scrap that drains from the populated communities.

Coccitans are not as intelligent as humans, but they can fashion and use crude tools.

Motive: Defense; hungers for anything edible

Environment: Almost any subterranean cranny, in a group of three to five scouts followed by a swarm of hundreds of roaches

Health: 9

Damage Inflicted: 5 points

Armor: 2

Movement: Short whether walking or flying (only a few can fly)

Modifications: Speed defense as level 4; perception and stealth as level 5.

Combat: If a coccitan can't avoid a fight, it attacks by delivering a fierce kick with its barbed hind legs, usually while facing away from its opponent.

A coccitan accompanied by a roach swarm can command the swarm to attack as well. A roach swarm is, roughly, a 5-foot (1.5 m) diameter mass of hundreds of crawling roaches treated as a single level 4 creature with 12 points of health and 1 point of Armor. On its turn, the roach swarm can make one attack against every creature within immediate range that inflicts 1 point of damage (ignores Armor); the swarm can choose which targets to exclude from the attack.

Coccitans can see perfectly well in the dark at short range.

Coccitans replace their skins on a regular basis, and when they do, all old injuries are left behind with the molted shell.

Interaction: Coccitans speak a language made of scents and waving limbs, rendering their communication almost indecipherable to other creatures. Negotiation might still be possible if the characters offer a rank piece of carrion or other "goody" in return for safe passage or even a coccitan guide through a treacherous subterranean area.

Use: The characters are asked to exterminate a colony of what is thought to be extremely prolific but normal roaches. The appearance of coccitan herders might come as a surprise.

DABIRRI 2 (6)

Dabirri are artificial sea-dwelling constructs created by taking the heart of a creature the size of a human and placing it in a synth shell. They do not eat and are not intelligent, but they instinctively attack warm-blooded creatures with their strangely venomous tendrils. Ranging anywhere from 1 to 3 feet (0.3 to 1 m) across, dabirri move by a combination of propulsion and pulling themselves forward with their tendrils.

Motive: Belligerence

Environment: Any sea or large body of salt water

Health: 6

Damage Inflicted: 1 point

Movement: Immediate

Combat: Dabirri are not particularly dangerous to a well-armed group unless they are encountered in a large cluster. If four or more of the creatures attack one victim, they make a single attack as a level 4 creature and inflict 2 points of damage.

The sting of a dabirri's tendrils transmits a cell-disrupting "poison" via an energy pulse. In other words, the tendrils transmit a signal via their touch that causes cellular shutdown. This moves a living, organic victim one step down the damage track unless he makes a Might defense roll. The sting works even through the hardest of armor, but not through an energy field.

Interaction: One cannot effectively communicate with these creatures in any way.

Use: A city along the shore is being terrorized by great swarms of blood-red creatures that seem to be waiting in the shallows. After one man was severely stung while fishing, no one dares to go in the water.

Loot: Within the central portion of a dabirri is a tiny dollop of a useful chemical that restores 1 point of Might to the imbiber if injected or taken internally.

GM Intrusion: *The dabirri's poisonous pulse transmits from one character to another nearby, forcing them both to make a Might defense roll.*

DECANTED 4 (12)

A decanted is an automaton with a frosted glass dome clutched in its chest cavity by protective iron fingers. Visible through the dome's condensation is a frozen human head, held immobile in a chassis of iron bracing, silver wires, and glowing cables. When a decanted speaks, it's from a buzzing grill mounted on its metallic head, with a voice devoid of emotion.

The decanted are intelligent and devious, and they have a reputation for kidnapping or paying a bounty for humans who are especially fit and beautiful. Such humans who fall into the metal hands of the decanted are never seen again.

A city of decanted called Glass is rumored to hide somewhere in the Ninth World. It's peopled by several hundred decanted and a hundred times that number of glass containers, each holding a preserved human head of ancient vintage floating in a bath of air so cold that it's become liquid.

The city of Glass holds two additional kinds of denizens: the nobility, which appear as humans with especially fit, beautiful bodies crowned by shriveled heads, and the so-called "blanks," incarcerated normal humans scheduled for a visit to the Optero Suite, where it is understood that they will donate their bodies to newly selected decanted nobility.

Motive: Hunger for fresh bodies

Environment: Lone decanted buyers can be found nearly anywhere, paying slavers or bounty hunters for human captives. Companies of five or more "bodytakers" roam in the wee hours of the night, using their abilities to remain hidden as they move through fashionable parts of large cities looking for new fodder for the nobility.

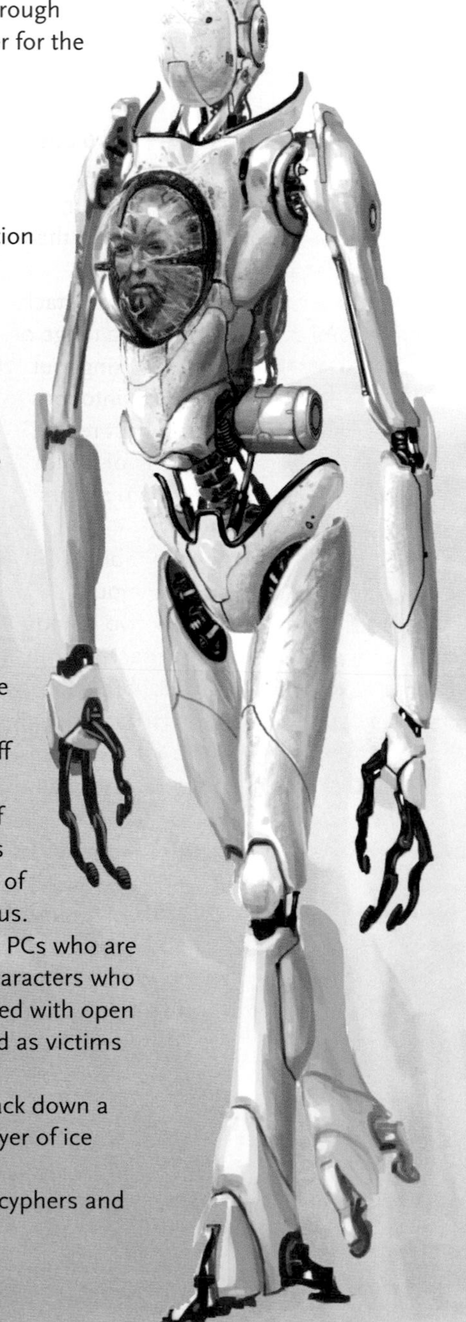

Health: 12

Damage Inflicted: 5 points

Armor: 3

Movement: Short

Modifications: Stealth as level 6 when using visual distortion field

Combat: A decanted can call upon its machine interface to create a visual distortion field, allowing it to move invisibly. The field collapses if the decanted attacks or takes some other dramatic action.

Invisible Target: *If an attacker can use other senses (such as hearing) to get an idea of where the opponent might be, attacks against such targets are modified by four steps in the defender's favor.*

When a decanted attacks, it grabs a foe with hands much colder than ice, which inflicts damage and freezes the foe in place, causing her to lose her next turn if she fails a Might defense roll.

Once per hour, a decanted can spray liquefied air in a sharp stream at one target within short range. The stream inflicts damage that ignores Armor and requires a Might defense roll. On a failed roll, the victim not only loses her next turn but also moves one step down the damage track.

A decanted is very cautious with its existence and breaks off conflict, if possible, if it loses more than half its health.

Decanted nobility do not possess the standard abilities of regular decanted. Despite the regard the frozen heads have for them, most nobles have the average abilities of level 1 humans. However, a few are far more dangerous.

GM Intrusion: *Regardless of whether the PC made a successful Might roll after being sprayed, she still takes a squirt of liquefied air straight to the face, freezing her eyes. The PC is blinded for one hour, though at first she might think she has been permanently blinded because her eyes feel like solid blocks of ice.*

Interaction: A decanted is most interested in dealing with PCs who are considered to have above-average physical beauty. Characters who are obviously mutated or otherwise changed are treated with open disrespect (but better that than being secretly targeted as victims slated for the Optero Suite).

Use: The PCs are contacted by someone who wants to track down a kidnapped lover or parent. The only evidence is the layer of ice covering the room where the victim was snatched.

Loot: The remains of a decanted can be salvaged for 1d6 cyphers and possibly an oddity.

DEDIMASKIS 7 (21)

To the eyes of most people, a dedimaskis appears to be a squirming horde, not a single thing. And in a way, it is, though truthfully, it is both a horde and a single thing at once. An ancient machine, a dedimaskis is covered with smaller machines slaved to it. These small, insectlike machines shift across its surface so its form continually seems to undulate and seethe. The dedimaskis seems more like a creature than an automaton—the movement of the swarm of small surface machines almost looks like breathing—but it is an unliving construct, to be sure. It follows ancient directives that no one has ever been able to parse. It is an engine of destruction, but its targets are selective—seemingly random. When a dedimaskis floats into a human village, it might destroy a specific building but not those next to it. It might hunt for three individuals out of hundreds, target all the pets, or destroy only the mill.

The appearance of a wandering dedimaskis spreads true terror and might mobilize a small army (or, more sensibly, a mass evacuation). It can come from the skies above or fly low across the landscape.

Motive: Selective destruction

Environment: Anywhere

Health: 35

Damage Inflicted: 7 points

Armor: 4 (see Combat)

Movement: Long

Modifications: Speed defense as level 6 due to size

Combat: A dedimaskis can fire up to four destructive rays as a single action at the same or different targets within long range. This is its primary means of attack. It can fire one destructive ray at a range of 1,000 feet (305 m) in lieu of making four attacks. In theory, it could bash into foes in melee, but that would be a last resort.

A dedimaskis regenerates 3 points of health each round as the slaved swarm repairs and maintains it.

Further, the slaved machines can rapidly adapt the larger machine to various situations. For example, after two rounds of dealing with a particular attack from a particular foe, they can recalibrate the armor, giving the dedimaskis 1 additional point of Armor against that attack. This is true even for attacks that would normally ignore Armor.

Likewise, the smaller machines can adapt the dedimaskis to give it new abilities, such as a resistance to certain kinds of attacks, a level increase in performing certain tasks, and so forth, as the GM sees fit.

Interaction: No one has ever successfully communicated with a dedimaskis.

Use: The dedimaskis is a terrifying challenge for a group of well-prepared PCs hoping to defend a village or town from its approach.

Loot: Within the wreckage of a dedimaskis, scavengers can find 1d100 + 100 shins, 1d6 + 4 cyphers, 1d6 oddities, and an artifact.

GM Intrusion: *A number of the smaller machines (1d6 + 2 level 1 creatures) leave the dedimaskis and menace the character by crawling all over him, poking, prodding, and harassing. This increases the difficulty of all tasks by one step until they are removed.*

DIMENSIONAL HUSK 5 (15)

"Sending a message through time to warn your younger self about avoiding bad choices rarely works."

~Aerendagast, in a moment of lucidity

A dimensional husk is a scar on reality, most often appearing as a human surrounded by a trailing haze of dozens of overlapping, half-formed alternate versions of the central figure. The alternate versions partly reflect the husk's movements and actions, but not perfectly; some of the half-visible images are engaged in completely different actions. It's like seeing the creature through dozens of intersecting mirrors at once, except that there *are* no mirrors.

A dimensional husk is barely alive. It's more of a vengeful echo of someone who suffered some kind of transdimensional accident. It doesn't know how it got to be the way it is, it doesn't know why it can't seem to pull itself together, and it doesn't know if its existence serves some purpose. So it usually defaults to the one thing it can do: take its misery and confusion out on others.

Motive: Varies

Environment: A lone dimensional husk can be found almost anywhere, but most often near areas where time or reality has been altered.

Health: 15

Damage Inflicted: 3 points

Armor: 2

Movement: Short; can teleport to any location it can see as an action

Modifications: Social interaction tasks as level 1

Combat: A dimensional husk is composed of many overlapping versions of itself—most reasonable, a few improbable—that are always in flux. A dimensional husk that appeared without weapons before combat can produce them, as if from nowhere, and attack with 1d6 melee or ranged weapons each round, each wielded by a hazy alternate version of the husk.

A husk is difficult to hit due to its fluctuating nature. When rolling an attack against a husk, a PC must reroll even-numbered results and take the second roll.

Interaction: A dimensional husk spends its existence confused, like an addled elderly person who sometimes strikes out at a world that is no longer comprehensible. Conversation with a dimensional husk might provide useful information, but sifting out one voice from several overlapping versions of a husk's reply can be challenging.

Use: A vengeful "ghost" is haunting the manor of a local lord or merchant and has driven everyone out. Each night, it appears on the balcony of the highest tower, sheathed in silvery light, and seems to jump to its death. But by the next day, the ghost is back inside the structure, as vindictive as ever.

The world isn't immutable, but it is apparently jealous of the way things are. Those who tamper with cause and effect, who create ripples in time, and worst of all, who manage to accidentally (or purposefully) engineer a true paradox risk finding out just how spiteful reality can be. If chronal feeders don't track down and dispatch a transgressor, a time-tripper still risks being pinched off into a burnt-out timeline, leaving behind a dimensional husk instead of a corpse.

Sometimes chronal feeders (page 31) are drawn to dimensional husks engaged in combat, attacking both the husk and its opponents indiscriminately.

GM Intrusion: *When the dimensional husk strikes the PC, it doesn't inflict damage. Instead, a hazy "alternate" version of the character divides from herself. The alternate runs off (perhaps planning to return later and replace the actual PC) or begins to attack the PC as a level 5 creature. If the GM desires, the alternate has some of the character's special abilities. A combative alternate lasts until slain or until the dimensional husk is slain.*

DREAM SALLOW 5 (15)

Branches covered with broad, pale green leaves droop from the rounded crown of this great tree whose roots seem as strong and tough as tower foundations. A pleasant scent, soporific and flowery, drifts from the sallow.

A look beneath the drooping branches reveals the remains of previous visitors, all of whom died in their sleep, though that evidence is not always obvious. Dream sallows prey on the minds of thinking creatures, perhaps as a means of sustenance or for some far stranger cause.

Motive: Desire to store sentient minds

Environment: Lone dream sallows sometimes grow at the edges of ancient ruins, or more often in a place of honor within an otherwise dead garden or arboretum in the center of such ruins.

Health: 15

Damage Inflicted: See Combat

Armor: 3

Movement: None

Modifications: Knowledge as level 10

Combat: Minuscule spores fill the air within short range of a dream sallow. Creatures who breathe them in must succeed at an Intellect defense roll. On a failed roll, the creature decides that a nap in the tree's shade would be perfect. A creature who succeeds on its initial defense roll must continue to make defense rolls while it remains in the area of the spores, but the difficulty of the task drops to 1. Rootlets emerge from the ground and bore through the skull of a living creature who falls asleep beneath the tree, creating a neurological connection and inflicting 1 point of damage. The victim's consciousness enters a shared dream city of wonder, where the minds of all previous victims walk, most unaware that they are only memories stored in sap and cellulose. On average, the bodies of new victims die after about a week, but their consciousness survives.

Cutting a victim free or cutting down the defenseless tree without first convincing it to let the victim go causes a brain hemorrhage and a messy death if the victim fails a Might defense roll. Even on a success, the victim's Intellect Pool drops to 0 and stays that way for three days, even in the face of regular recovery rolls.

Interaction: Earlier victims of a dream sallow are far past extracting, but those whose bodies haven't yet expired can return. They can become aware of their situation, the same way one sometimes realizes one is dreaming, and negotiate with an avatar of the sallow within the consensual dream.

A sallow's dream avatar appears as a towering humanoid woman of bark and leaves, stem and bough, with hands of knotted root. She believes she is doing the victim a favor by saving its mind—the body will eventually die, but the consciousness will live forever in the dream. Convincing a sallow to let a mind loose is possible but requires good reasoning—good from the sallow's point of view, that is.

Use: The PCs need a vital fact from an NPC whose consciousness lives on in a dream sallow. They must knowingly enter the tree's consensual dream, get the information, and convince the tree to let them loose.

Loot: 1d6 + 1 cyphers can be found buried in the soil beneath the tree, usually the belongings of previous victims.

Dream sallows represent the last, desperate attempt of a dying race to preserve their minds within living psionic constructs. But the sun's altered energy signature eradicated the original dream sallows' ability to grow new bodies for minds stored within.

GM Intrusion: *Just as a PC seems to have convinced a dream sallow avatar to let her go, an NPC avatar appears in the consensual dream—perhaps an old friend of the PC who is overjoyed at their reunion. The NPC tries to convince both the sallow and the PC that the character would be better off staying.*

SIZE COMPARISON

DREBIL 2 (6)

A pack lost along the side of the road, a small boulder blocking the path, a colorful songbird up in a tree, or a shiny piece of numenera—any of these might be a drebil. It's almost impossible to tell until a potential victim investigates, attempts to move, or tries to catch the object or creature. That's when a drebil's skin "sucks" back into slits in its surface to reveal a wrinkled, leathery predator with the muzzle of a monstrous rat and large wings. The realization that the lumpy sack or lost pet is actually a monster usually comes simultaneously with the drebil's lunge for the victim's throat.

Motive: Consuming humanoid blood and organs

Environment: Drebils hunt alone or in pairs, usually along the outskirts of communities. They keep their true lairs on the sides of high cliffs, out of reach of nonflying creatures, where they live alone, with a mate, or with a litter of young drebils too small to hunt on their own.

Health: 9

Damage Inflicted: 3 points

Armor: 1

Movement: Long when flying; immediate when on the ground

Modifications: Deceiving as level 6; Speed defense as level 3 due to size.

Combat: A drebil that can't attack a creature with sudden surprise usually will not initiate an attack unless defending its lair.

A disguised drebil can choose to end its charade and attack a victim who has picked up or otherwise touched the creature. When this occurs, the drebil instantly retracts its faux-skin disguise and bites the target, surprising the target so much that the difficulty of his Speed defense roll is increased by two steps. If the drebil hits with the surprise attack, it deals 7 points of damage (unless Armor completely encapsulates the victim, offering no soft places to bite; however, a drebil is unlikely to attack such a target).

A drebil whose health is reduced to 3 or less attempts to fly off and escape to its lair.

Interaction: Drebils have the intelligence of an average six-year-old human and can speak in broken sentences in languages of the region where they hunt. For this reason, a drebil can be a source of information, having viewed an area from its disguised vantage for quite a while. In some cases, drebils have been known to befriend other thinking creatures.

Use: A child in town describes her new imaginary friend as living just over the town wall; they talk at night through a crack in the masonry. The friend sounds like a child herself, though she is not visible through the crack. Maybe someone should go find her before she freezes or starves outside. Anyone who tries finds only an old, rain-soaked pack caught in a tree that grows near the wall...

Loot: Because drebils collect items to learn how to mimic them, a drebil lair contains a collection of junk but also might have 1d6 – 1 cyphers, 3d6 shins, and possibly an oddity.

Some drebils can do more than mimic an object or creature's appearance; they can reproduce the full function of mechanical items, including numenera.

GM Intrusion: *The surprise bite is so unexpected that the drebil attempts to slip its face inside the character's armor. As a result, the initial surprise bite ignores Armor, and the drebil's regular attacks continue to ignore Armor until the PC somehow removes the creature from her armor.*

EARTHSHAKER 8 (24)

You feel it inside first, a thrumming so deep your bones seem to shiver. Then come the tremors, shaking equipment, trembling trees, and swaying towers. When the earthshaker appears, shouldering aside obstructions without the least effort, it's like thunder given flesh and allowed to run free.

A fully grown earthshaker matriarch can reach heights of about 50 feet (15 m). An earthshaker is usually content to graze the tops of forests (the *entire* tops of forests—branches, leaves, trunk tops, and all), choosing stands of vegetation that are quick growing for that reason. But matriarchs are deadly when defending their herd.

Motive: Defense

Environment: A matriarch earthshaker, a herd of three or four calves, and one or two mates can be found in temperate and subarctic forested areas of the Beyond.

Health: 80

Damage Inflicted: 8 points

Armor: 4

Movement: Long

Modifications: Speed defense as level 4 due to size

Combat: An earthshaker attacks with its impressive display of tusks and can target up to four creatures (standing next to each other) with a single attack.

An earthshaker can also make a trampling attack if it can get up to speed first by making a charge from long range. When it does, it moves 200 feet (61 m) in a round, and anything that comes within immediate range is attacked. Even those who make a successful Speed defense roll take 2 points of damage.

Interaction: Earthshakers are clever animals, and they prefer to ignore anything that doesn't threaten them. However, earthshaker matriarchs (the largest specimens of the breed) become enraged if any of their calves or mate(s) are threatened, which can rapidly turn a peaceful earthshaker-watching experience frantic. An earthshaker's herd usually includes a few calves and one or two mates. Mates are about three-fourths as large, and calves are half as large. All of them run away to safety and leave combat to the matriarch.

Use: A powerful lord captured an earthshaker mate a few months ago and uses the immense but placid creature to pull her carriage. Meanwhile, reports on the edge of her holdings speak of a rampaging monster of enormous size.

SIZE COMPARISON

Earthshaker size suggests they might be related to titanothaurs (page 126); however, the creatures don't appear to be of the same origin. Earthshakers skate just beneath the line of how large a natural living creature can grow without being crushed by its own weight (assuming no other oddities or variations in gravity). That titanothaurs can be much larger means they somehow break the rules of reality.

GM Intrusion: *When the PC is attacked by the earthshaker, he must succeed on a Speed defense roll or be stepped on for 4 points of damage and pinned to the ground. While pinned, his tasks are modified by two steps to his detriment. Unless the earthshaker moves of its own accord, each round, the PC can attempt a Might defense roll to pull free. On a failed roll, he remains stuck and is crushed for another 4 points of damage.*

EDACIOUS DESTROYER 7 (21)

At first glance, edacious destroyers seem to be little more than eating machines. Omnivores and opportunists, they have intensely acidic stomachs that allow them to devour nearly everything they come across. However, beyond their need to eat, they appear to be highly intelligent creatures that will do almost anything in exchange for large amounts of food.

Blind and deaf, edacious destroyers rely on the olfactory details that the "sprouts" on their heads provide. These pale protrusions allow an edacious destroyer to scent blood, flesh, rotting fruits, and other foodstuffs. Once some type of edible is found, the sprouts erupt from the creature's head as long, pliable tubes. A single tube can stretch up to one hundred times its resting size to suck up prey; the sprout's powerful muscles then squeeze and compress the captured prey into a liquefied meal.

Well-fed edacious destroyers grow up to 50 feet (15 m) tall. They reproduce asexually, housing their young inside "belly bands" of muscle that surround one or more sprouts.

It's possible to estimate an edacious destroyer's age by the number of sprouts along its head. Each sprout signifies eight to ten years.

Motive: Food

Environment: Anywhere

Health: 30

Damage Inflicted: 8 points

Armor: 5

Movement: Long

Modifications: Speed defense as level 5 due to size

Combat: For living prey, edacious destroyers attack with their giant, clublike arms, battering foes for 8 points of damage.

In addition, they may attempt to suck still-living prey into their sprouts. If a PC fails a difficulty 4 Speed defense roll, he is sucked into the sprout, taking 5 points of damage. To cut himself free or otherwise escape from his living, crushing cage, the captured PC must succeed on two difficulty 3 Might defense rolls. If he fails three rolls before he escapes, he is crushed.

A growing organization known as The Schism seems to be training edacious destroyers as scent-seeking warriors, but no one knows how or to what end.

Interaction: Edacious destroyers can be scent-trained by those who are willing to risk being eaten. Successful trainers find ways to mask or eradicate their own scent first.

Use: Always hungry, edacious destroyers are fearless fighters, willing to seek out and attack prey anywhere.

GM Intrusion*: A character is sucked into a sprout that houses a belly band of young edacious destroyers, which begin to hatch.*

ELLNOICA 5 (15)

Ellnoica victims rarely glimpse what kills them. Survivors who escape this voracious stalker describe either a completely invisible monster or a glowing terror the color of uncooked meat whose outline continually shimmers, just out of focus. An ellnoica measures about 15 feet (4.6 m) from tentacle tips to tail.

The creature is variously described as a "hungry lurker," a "flesh slurper," or "pink death." Once revealed, it makes constant slurping noises as it tries to suck the flesh off the bones of a fresh kill.

Motive: Hungers for flesh; reproduction

Environment: Almost anywhere, from a crowded city slum to the empty halls of an ancient orbiting installation

Health: 18

Damage Inflicted: 3 points

Armor: 2 or 10 (see Combat)

Movement: Short, even when burrowing through solids with acid

Modifications: Stealth and Speed defense as level 6 when visible. Speed defense as level 10 when invisible (if the attacker can sense the ellnoica via something other than sight).

Combat: An ellnoica usually begins a combat invisible, surprising its prey with the initial attack. When the ellnoica attacks, it becomes visible. Once the creature becomes visible, it cannot become invisible again for one minute, or for at least one minute after it's been hurt. Even when visible, the ellnoica remains partly out of phase with the world.

Each of its three feeding tentacles can attack a different target with a crushing blow. If an ellnoica attacks a single victim with all three feeding tentacles, it makes one attack that, if successful, crushes the victim (5 points of damage) and inflicts acid burns (2 points of damage). Once dead and tenderized, a victim is liquefied by the acid and slurped up. Sometimes the creature grabs an incapacitated foe with the intent of leaving the victim in its lair filled with soon-to-hatch eggs.

An ellnoica can create a tunnel with its tail, which produces acid best suited for rock and soil. Thus, the creature burrows in reverse, sliding backward down a narrow chute it creates.

An ellnoica has 10 Armor against attacks that are acidic.

Interaction: Ellnoicas are predators, but they are also sentient and out of place. They can go into stasis for extended periods of time, so some claim to remember previous civilizations—perhaps even their home in a far different place. If a PC could offer (or pretend to offer) an ellnoica a chance to go home, that might cause it to interrupt its feeding and reproduction.

Use: Whether hunting the slums of cities or laying eggs in a deserted tower, ellnoicas work well as the main event of an adventure or a side quest for PCs exploring someplace new.

Loot: An ellnoica lair contains the remains of several victims, meant to feed hatchlings. These might include 1d100 shins, 1d6 + 1 cyphers, an oddity, and perhaps a salvageable artifact.

SIZE COMPARISON

Ellnoicas can enter stasis for anywhere from one year to a million years, assuming they can find a stable location deep in the earth. When an ellnoica emerges from its phase-locked sleep, it burrows to the surface, voraciously eats everything it can overpower, and lays eggs in a high place where it can see the stars.

GM Intrusion: *A PC accidentally steps in a burrow hole the ellnoica used to enter the area. She drops out of sight but can attempt to climb out of this level 3 vertical shaft—hopefully before the ellnoica finds her in the cramped, narrow space.*

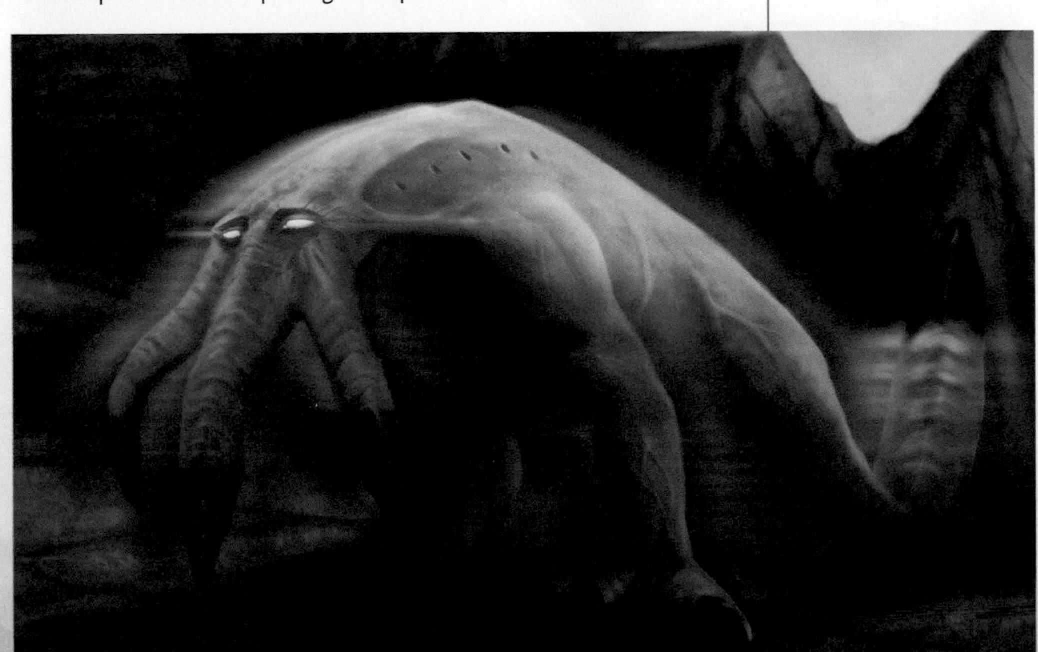

EMBER SCION 6 (18)

"Born of hell, frolicking and laughing in death, the ember scions are a scourge upon the earth to torment mortals." ~Domoire

Ember scions are not the ultraterrestrials or demons that the nano sorcerers of Gloom's Pass (like Domoire) once claimed. Nor are they born of the union of fire mages, conceived during rituals dedicated to the fire god Gmol. It is said that the understanding of the past shaped flesh that could thrive anywhere, and therein lies the most likely genesis of these creatures. They appear to be beast-faced humanoids with flame-shrouded bodies and white-hot claws.

However, they are rarely seen, for humans avoid places where ember scions dwell: underwater steam vents, volcano hearts, or the fiery engine pits of ancient citadels best left unexplored.

At times, during periods of pronounced volcanic activity or with the spread of a blazing forest fire, ember scions wreak chaos and terror in regions where they would not normally tread. Playful and devilish, they kill and torment for fun. They do not seem to require normal sustenance, water, or air, but they sleep for long periods—occasionally years at a time.

Ember scions sometimes pursue foes away from a heat source for a few rounds, but they eventually either retreat into the safety of fire or take a few rounds to start a new raging blaze.

Motive: Playful sadism

Environment: Packs of ember scions dwell anywhere extremely hot.

Health: 22

Damage Inflicted: 10 points

Armor: 1

Movement: Short

Modifications: Mental defense, perception and seeing through trickery and lies as level 4

Combat: Ember scions generate extraordinary heat. While their claws and teeth inflict 6 points of damage, their burning touch deals 4 more points. Further, anyone within immediate range of a scion automatically takes 1 point of fire damage each round (multiple scions do not increase this damage). Combustibles within this range might burst into flame, as does anything flammable the scion touches.

In addition, ember scions can project a gout of flame up to a short distance that inflicts 6 points of damage. Doing this forces them to expend heat. If they are not within another heat source (standing in lava or a powerful fire), using this ranged attack costs them 1 point of health.

While within or touching a strong source of heat, ember scions regenerate 1 point of health each round. If not within immediate distance of a powerful heat source, an ember scion operates as level 4 in all actions.

GM Intrusion: *The character's clothing or armor catches fire, and he suffers 2 points of additional damage. If he does not spend an action to put out the flames, he continues to take 2 points of damage each round.*

Interaction: Ember scions are relatively intelligent—perhaps on the level of a young child—but they are sadistic to the extreme. They act as if burning destruction and death is a form of play. Reasoning with them never seems to work, and they don't seem to recognize language of any kind.

Use: To destroy an enemy village near a volcanic region, a suicidal madman lures a pack of ember scions to the place through subterranean tunnels. If the creatures are not stopped immediately, they will burn down the community and kill everyone they find (slowly, if possible).

Loot: The flesh of an ember scion has a gelatinous coating that can give a creature or object no larger than a human 10 points of Armor against fire damage for 28 hours.

ENCEPHALON 6 (18)

When stalking prey, an encephalon resembles a gnarled tree whose upper branches are covered with fluttering butterfly wings. When the encephalon flings its arms wide, it's revealed as a wrinkled, pale green monstrosity. Its oversized cranial bulge is home to two milky white eyes and a circular, sucking maw. Its lower body consists of half a dozen twining, earth-burrowing tendrils.

Motive: Hungers for brain matter

Environment: Single encephalons can be found anywhere.

Health: 36

Damage Inflicted: 7 points

Armor: 2

Movement: Short when walking on the surface or burrowing

Modifications: Disguise as level 3

Combat: An encephalon makes physical attacks with its massive arms, but it does so only when desperate. Its preferred method of attack is loosing a flock of hundreds of tiny cranial slugs at a group of creatures within half a mile that are within short range of each other. Each attacked creature must succeed on a Speed defense roll. On a failed roll, one or more of the flying purple slugs lands on the character, punches a proboscis through temple, ear, or other soft route to the brain, and inflicts 3 points of damage.

Once the flock is loosed, it continues to attack each round until it has digested a total of 30 points of Intellect damage (which might happen after just a few rounds if enough targets are attacked). At that point, the slugs sweep back to the parent encephalon and are ingested into the creature's toothless maw (no action required by the encephalon), granting the encephalon 30 points of health.

An encephalon can spit out a new flock of cranial slugs every hour.

An encephalon that fears for its life burrows into the earth to escape, leaving behind a tunnel that collapses one day later.

Interaction: An encephalon can communicate telepathically with any intelligent creature within long range. Unless a creature can shield its mental presence, an encephalon automatically knows the creature's location.

Use: The tifo orchids are ready to be harvested. Tifo trees produce a bitter podfruit extolled for its ability to calm nerves. The PCs are asked to guard the pickers, as there has been a rash of disappearances lately. Raiders are suspected, but it's actually the work of a hunting encephalon standing in the grove as if it were just another tree.

SIZE COMPARISON

Encephalons dig up from beneath the mantle looking for cranial sustenance. They could just be hungry, but they might be scouts (or criminal outcasts) of a post-human civilization near the world's core, looking for information on the surface.

GM Intrusion: *Instead of attacking all the PCs present, a flock of six or more cranial slugs attacks one character as a swarm, treated as a single level 8 creature that inflicts 10 points of damage (and 5 points on a miss).*

Swarm rules, page 13

SIZE COMPARISON

ENGINEERED VIRAL HOST

An intelligent virus that some call the Insidious Choir has grown tired of infecting organic hosts. Thus, it has bioengineered its own, more efficient hosts. Each of these is quite infectious, and the virus can control its hosts, whether engineered or not. Engineered viral hosts can communicate with each other instantly via touch or spray (by passing along virons). However, the Insidious Choir seeks the means for all virons to communicate over long range.

TACTILE HOST (VIRAL EXPLORER) 3 (9)

This artificial creature looks like a transparent, rubbery membrane molded into a vaguely humanoid shape and filled with dark green liquid. Its headless body is broad, and its arms are very large compared to its legs, giving it more the appearance of an ape than of a human. The membrane is very smooth, and the liquid is filled with bubbles.

Motive: Curiosity

Environment: Anywhere

Health: 12

Damage Inflicted: 4 points

Armor: 1

Movement: Short

GM Intrusion: *The character striking the host is exposed to a viral cloud and a spurt of caustic fluid (5 points of damage).*

Combat: The tactile host releases a viral cloud each time it suffers even 1 point of damage. All within immediate range must make a Might defense roll or become infected. About 28 hours after infection, infected characters begin to unwillingly transmit all thoughts and sensory input information to the Insidious Choir. After seven days, the virus can control the actions of the infected character, but he can attempt an Intellect defense roll to resist. Successful resistance means that he does nothing for one round. The difficulty of the defense roll is 1 for each day of infection after the first seven days. Regardless, the difficulty of all actions forced upon the character is two steps higher.

The host can also form an orifice and spray a stream of caustic fluid. This costs the creature 1 point of health, but it inflicts 5 points of damage to all within an immediate distance.

Last, a tactile host can attempt to infect a creature intentionally (rather than accidentally, when it suffers damage). To do this, the host must strike the creature with a melee attack that inflicts no damage. If successful, the viral explorer holds the creature still for a moment and sprays him with a virus-laded fluid.

The tactile host and the virons within it are immune to mental effects or Intellect damage.

Interaction: Communicating with a tactile host is extremely difficult. It does not speak or understand speech. If a mental link is established, real communication is still impossible, but the character mentally connected with the host hears a choir of thousands (perhaps millions) of voices all "talking" in unison, asking questions such as "What is this?" "Where does this go?" "What does this do?" and "What is that?" The questions are occasionally punctuated with the phrase "infect to investigate."

Use: Tactile hosts are the explorers of the Insidious Choir. They investigate new areas, new machines, and new potential foes.

OCULAR HOST (VIRAL WATCHER) 3 (9)

This artificial creature is a featureless human shape, almost like a mannequin, made of a dense spongy material. Ocular hosts have absorbed a great deal of dark green liquid (the same liquid inside a tactile host).

Motive: Curiosity

Environment: Anywhere

Health: 10

Damage Inflicted: 3 points

Movement: Short

Combat: An ocular host releases a viral splash each time it suffers even 1 point of damage in melee. A character who strikes the host must make a Might defense roll or become infected. About 28 hours after infection, infected characters begin to unwillingly transmit all thoughts and sensory input information to the Insidious Choir. After seven days, the virus can control the actions of the infected character, but he can attempt an Intellect defense roll to resist. Successful resistance means that he does nothing for one round. The difficulty of the defense roll is 1 for each day of infection after the first seven days. Regardless, the difficulty of all actions forced upon the character is two steps higher.

The ocular host and the virons within it are immune to mental effects or Intellect damage.

Interaction: Communicating with an ocular host is extremely difficult. It does not speak or understand speech. If a mental link is established, real communication is still impossible, but the character mentally connected with the host will hear a choir of thousands (perhaps millions) of voices all "talking" in unison, asking questions such as "What is this?" "Where does this go?" "What does this do?" and "What is that?" The questions are occasionally punctuated with "infect to investigate."

Use: Ocular hosts are watchers and observers. They keep their distance and watch over areas already under the control of the Insidious Choir. They will enter combat, but their main purpose is to keep the virus aware of what's going on.

GM Intrusion: *The ocular host suddenly bursts with virus-laden liquid, potentially infecting all creatures within immediate range.*

WARRIOR HOST (VIRAL GUARDIAN) 5 (15)

This artificial creature looks like a huge, terrifying insect with a large, transparent abdomen filled with dark green liquid—the same liquid inside tactile and ocular hosts. The wingless insect has massive mandibles, and its legs end in spikes like cleavers. Much of its body is heavily armored, and it looks like it was designed for fighting (and spreading terror).

Motive: Defense

Environment: Anywhere

Health: 30

Damage Inflicted: 5 points

Armor: 2

Movement: Short

Combat: A warrior host makes two attacks each round at different foes or the same foe. The first attack is with one of its spikes. The second is its bite, which carries the virus. Bitten characters must make a Might defense roll or become infected. About 28 hours after infection, infected characters begin to unwillingly transmit all thoughts and sensory input information to the Insidious Choir. After seven days, the virus can control the actions of the infected character, but he can attempt an Intellect defense roll to resist. Successful resistance means that he does nothing for one round. The difficulty for the defense roll is 1 for each day of infection after the first seven days. Regardless, the difficulty of all actions forced upon the character is two steps higher.

Further, the warrior host releases a viral splash of green liquid each time it suffers even 1 point of damage in melee. A character striking the host must make a Might defense roll or become infected.

The warrior host and the virons within it are immune to mental effects or Intellect damage.

Interaction: Communicating with the warrior host is extremely difficult. It does not speak or understand speech. If a mental link is established, real communication is still impossible, but the character mentally connected with the host will hear a choir of thousands (perhaps millions) of voices all "talking" in unison, asking questions such as "Who goes there?" "What is that?" and "Is this a threat?" The questions are occasionally punctuated with "infect to incorporate."

Use: The warrior host is a guard and a soldier. The Insidious Choir does not plan on building an army and extending its power through conquest, so these hosts tend to protect rather than attack, except in special circumstances and missions with specific goals (such as obtaining something the virus needs that is in the hands of someone else).

GM Intrusion: *The character's attack bounces harmlessly off the strange flesh of the warrior, and the force of the rebound knocks her prone at the creature's feet.*

SIZE COMPARISON

ENTROPE 4 (12)

Entropes are entities of exotic biomineral that freeze motionless for years, centuries, or even longer until the heat source they prefer to feed on comes their way: a living creature. Then the 6-foot-tall (1.8 m) creature wakes, generating a heat-sucking field as it unwinds five tentacles whose pale touch is personal heat death to its prey. With enough stolen heat, an entrope is able to spawn.

Motive: Hungers for the heat of living creatures

Environment: Entropes are usually discovered solo or in pairs, thin statues cold to the touch until they begin moving. They migrate to basements, tunnels, or subterranean locales and are never found in warm environments, under open sky, or underwater.

Health: 12

Damage Inflicted: 4 points

Armor: 3

Movement: Short

Modifications: Speed defense as level 3

Entropes could be natives to a frigid land, but it's more likely that they come from an icy moon or solitary stone that floated in the empty darkness of the void before crashing to the Ninth World.

Combat: When living creatures whose bodies aren't completely shielded against heat loss come within immediate range of an entrope, the entrope detects them, wakes up, and gains the ability to move and attack. The entrope retains the ability to move and attack for up to one minute after no additional creatures remain within immediate range of it, then it freezes immobile again.

Upon waking, the entrope generates a heat-absorbing field at immediate range. All creatures in the field that do not have cold resistance or immunity are coated in a numbing frost that deals 1 point of damage from heat loss each round. Creatures in the field find that their tasks are one step more difficult.

While an entrope is active, it can attack with two tentacles on its turn.

Each point of cold damage the entrope deals is added to its health. If an entrope ever reaches 24 points of health, it spends its next action spawning, becoming two entropes, each with 6 points of health. When two or more entropes generate a heat-absorbing aura in an overlapping area, the field effects are additive.

GM Intrusion: *A character is particularly affected by the heat-sucking aura and is frozen in place under a sheen of frost. He remains that way until he succeeds on a Might defense roll as his action.*

Entropes are immune to damage inflicted by cold.

Interaction: By all appearances, entropes have animal intelligence at most. Their drives appear to be simple—feed on heat from living creatures, spawn, and repeat.

Use: A local caver has gone missing, and a concerned spouse or parent seeks aid, showing anyone interested sheaves of maps and the dark, chilly cave mouth the missing person entered daily for the last several years while mapping out a subterranean tunnel system.

Loot: Every entrope corpse has an organ that can be removed and used as an anoetic cypher called an entropic seed. It is a biomineral sphere that can be thrown at short range and causes an explosive burst. The burst deals 6 points of damage in an immediate range by draining the heat of each affected creature.

ERGOVORE HOUND 4 (12)

SIZE COMPARISON

This creature looks a bit like a bulldog the size of a horse with multiple long, barbed tongues. It often haunts the ruins of prior worlds. Although the hound is a traditional omnivore, subsisting on small prey as well as grass and leaves, its unique aspect—and the reason for its name—is that it also feeds directly on energy fields.

Motive: Hungers for energy

Environment: Hills and wastelands, alone or occasionally in mated pairs

Health: 30

Damage Inflicted: 7 points (bite) or various (tongues); see Combat

Modifications: Attacks as level 5

Movement: Short

Combat: An ergovore hound attacks with its bite, but the special danger comes from its tongues. If its foe has any kind of force field protection device, a Ward esotery, or the like, not only does it not function against the hound, but one touch from the beast's tongues utterly destroys it. A cypher or artifact with that kind of defensive field becomes drained and useless. A nano can restore the Ward with an action, but doing so will draw another attack from the hound. If the ergovore's tongue touches a character with no such obvious energy field, she must make an additional Speed defense roll, or one appropriate cypher (or, if she has no cyphers, an oddity or an artifact) on her person is drained of all power. If she has no devices at all, there is no effect.

The ergovore hound can make a bite attack against a single foe that inflicts 7 points of damage (along with the energy drain) or up to six tongue attacks on different foes that inflict 3 points of damage each (along with the energy drain).

Interaction: Ergovore hounds have the general intelligence and outlook of beasts. Careful use of the energy that they crave, however, allows them to be trained. Some people who have access to energized devices that keep the creatures fed and happy can train them to be guard dogs of a sort.

Use: The ergovore hound is an interesting encounter because it is more of a threat to the PCs' devices than it is to the characters.

An "appropriate" cypher to be destroyed by the ergovore is something that is obviously powered by energy, whether it's electrical, nuclear, or something else. Thus, a pill, injector, or poison probably isn't appropriate, but a ray emitter or a teleporter certainly is.

GM Intrusion: *The character is struck by multiple tongues from the ergovore hound and held fast for one round, losing his next turn.*

SIZE COMPARISON

ERULIAN 3 (9)

An erulian is a creature from beyond Earth that is composed primarily of energy but can take a physical form. In their natural state, erulians appear to be flickering flames of white, gold, or blue that float and flitter through the air. If desired, they can take a physical form that resembles a wrinkled, egglike shape with a single eye and a long tail. Some have compared an erulian to a floating brain with an eye and a sort of spinal column. The tail is strong and prehensile.

While in their energy form, erulians are insubstantial, and matter passes right through them. However, for reasons of their own, they prefer to stay in the open if possible. If given the choice between floating through an open doorway or passing through a wall, they'll always go through the doorway. It's likely that they can't perceive anything while passing through matter.

Motive: Inexplicable

Environment: Ancient ruins or deep space

Health: 9

Damage Inflicted: 3 points

Movement: Long (short if in physical form)

Modifications: Defends as level 4 due to size

Combat: In its natural state, an erulian is made of harmless, formless energy. It can't be affected by anything that can't affect energy. However, it can't affect material objects while in this state, so if it wants to attack or manipulate objects, it takes solid form. Maintaining physical form takes effort, and if an erulian is killed or seriously hurt, it reverts to its energy state.

In a fight, it uses its tail to whip or grab foes. An erulian can also wield a weapon with its tail, inflicting 4 points of damage rather than 3.

Interaction: Erulians are normally passive. They become belligerent and violent only when their lairs are intruded upon and their meditations disturbed. When agitated, they can still be reasoned with, but the difficulty of doing so is increased by two steps.

Use: Erulians can exist in any environment in their energy state, even deep space. In the right context, they are well-informed philosophers and thinkers. If crossed, however, they are monstrous and vindictive.

GM Intrusion: *The character is grabbed by the erulian's tail and loses his next action as he is held fast in its unsettling grip.*

ERULIAN MASTER 5 (15)

An erulian master is a fugue-state amalgam of six of the greatest of its kind, so it is six times the normal size, has six times the intelligence and power, and has six eyes and six tails in its material form.

Motive: Inexplicable

Environment: Ancient ruins or deep space

Health: 30

Damage Inflicted: 5 points

Movement: Long (short if in physical form)

Combat: While in physical form, an erulian master wields dangerous psychic and physical powers and can perform six actions at once. On its turn, it can choose six of the following options (and can choose any option more than once):

- Confuse a foe who is a thinking being by overloading its sensory inputs, increasing the difficulty of that creature's next action by two steps.
- Alter the perception of time for a foe who is a thinking being, making the creature move at half its normal speed and increasing the difficulty of that creature's next action by one step.
- Render a foe deaf and blind for one round.
- Physically attack with one of its tails.
- Use a weapon or item it holds wrapped in one of its tails.

Interaction: An erulian master can be bribed with certain numenera items, but it's not interested in any other kind of interaction.

Use: An erulian master is encountered only amid a group of erulians as their leader.

Loot: An erulian master might have a cypher or even an artifact. If it does, it is likely to use the device to the best of its ability.

GM Intrusion: *When altering the perception of time, the erulian master does so for all PCs. In their confusion, the PCs must all attempt to take their action at the same time (regardless of the established order), without conferring with each other first.*

According to one particularly erudite erulian, the world that these creatures originally hail from is one with a fluctuating cycle of dangerous energies that forced them to adapt a changing physiology themselves. In their energy form, erulians eventually learned to "swim" through the void between worlds and became the ultimate explorers. However, eventually their race rejected such pursuits, and now they value only mediation and contemplation.

Of course, this directly contradicts similar details from other erulians, so it is possible that some of these creatures are liars or perhaps actually do not recall their race's distant past.

"In this world which we have inherited from the ancients, the term 'creature' must certainly be extended to things such as automatons, ultraterrestrials, animate plants, and other, still stranger things." ~Jarash, well-known naturalist

SIZE COMPARISON

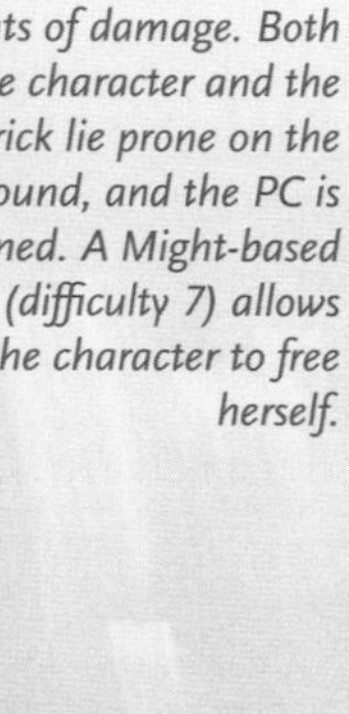

ETTERICK 6 (18)

"What is it?" Jul nocked another arrow and ducked behind the tree.

"Damned if I know." Marlich whispered. He hid behind a pile of rotting logs.

"It looks like glass, but my arrow bounced off it like it was stone."

"Yeah, but what are those things crawling around inside it? Are they trapped in there?"

"Look like bugs. Maybe they just crawled in there."

"Or they're controlling it..."

"They're just bugs!"

"We've seen stranger things."

"I'm not sure we have."

The thing that people call an etterick is an automaton in the vague shape of a human, with transparent skin. Crawling around in its hollow interior is a swarm of insects that look like no other insects found anywhere. They control the machine through means that look much like scuttling around and doing typical insect activities.

GM Intrusion: *The etterick topples atop the character, inflicting 8 points of damage. Both the character and the etterick lie prone on the ground, and the PC is pinned. A Might-based check (difficulty 7) allows the character to free herself.*

Motive: Inexplicable

Environment: Anywhere, always alone

Health: 25

Damage Inflicted: 6 points

Armor: 4

Movement: Short

Combat: An etterick is a straightforward combatant, pummeling foes with its fists.

An etterick can emit a powerful magnetic pulse that inflicts damage to all within short range. Those with a large amount of metal on their person must make a Might defense roll or be knocked down and back an immediate distance. The etterick cannot use this ability two rounds in a row.

If an etterick is destroyed, the insects inside swarm out and scatter, never to be seen again.

Interaction: Surprisingly, those who attempt to communicate with an etterick—or rather, with its hive-mind pilots that act as a singular entity—find it quite willing to talk. However, establishing that communication in the first place requires telepathy or a similar ability. The etterick will not (cannot?) share its origins and finds almost any mundane topics or meaningless niceties to be reason to resort to violence. But it is amenable to bribery or straightforward negotiations (such as "We'll leave this area immediately if you stop attacking us"). It seems to value most numenera items.

Use: The PCs explore a massive structure from an earlier aeon. They come to an enormous door, in front of which is an etterick, attempting fruitlessly to pound its way through. The etterick is likely to attack them, but if they can convince it that they know how to open the door, they may avoid the conflict—assuming they know what they're talking about.

Loot: Looting through the remains of an etterick yields a bounty of 1d6 + 1 cyphers and an artifact, all made of transparent metal.

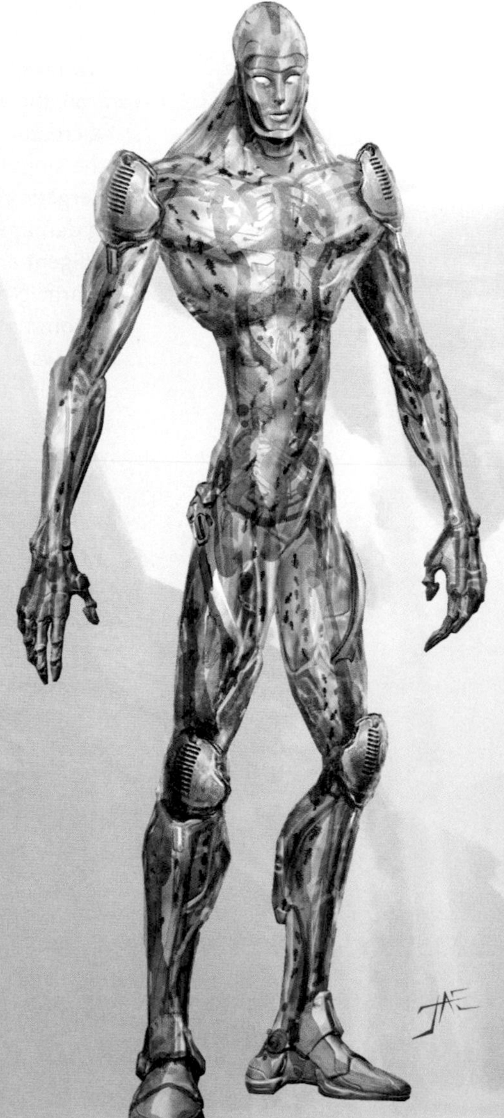

FALLING MAW 5 (15)

A falling maw is named after the feeling someone experiences when near the creature: the stomach lurches, as if the ground has dropped away, and the sensation of falling becomes impossible to ignore. Every other sense reveals that what's happening isn't falling but floating just above the ground, along with every other loose object in the area.

The culprit is a naked void also floating in the air. It's about the size of a human's fist, surrounded by spiraling rings of flashing color. As floating objects get close, they're sucked into the void and become part of the spiral, stretched out like strands of slender pasta, before being slurped up by the maw.

Motive: Hungers for matter; seeks numenera

Environment: Lone falling maws can be found almost anywhere.

Health: 25

Damage Inflicted: 4 points

Armor: 3

Movement: Long when flying

Combat: A falling maw creates an area of zero gravity within short range all around it, which hinders the movements of most creatures. If a creature pushes off from the ground in a location without a ceiling or other structure to grab onto, it may fly out of the area of zero gravity and fall.

A falling maw is perfectly suited for moving within its sphere of zero gravity. It relies on two primary methods to subdue threats.

First, it can electrify the air within short range as its attack. Creatures and objects in the area that fail a Might defense roll take damage from the electrical discharge. This damage ignores Armor.

Second, a falling maw can move to within immediate distance of a foe as part of its attack. Doing so exposes the foe to an extreme gravitational slope. A victim who takes its turn while within immediate range of a falling maw takes damage merely for being too close and must succeed on a Might defense roll. On a failed roll, the victim also begins to come apart, taking another 4 points of damage that ignores Armor. If a creature is killed by a falling maw while within immediate range of it, the body is sucked through the singularity.

If a falling maw is destroyed, the energetic charge that shepherds the reality hole is dispersed. The hole evaporates explosively, inflicting damage to every creature in short range.

Interaction: A falling maw is an intelligent entity, hosted by the spiraling energy halo around the reality hole. It needs to maintain the charge created by disintegrating objects, though it doesn't need to eat living things to do so. It can communicate by transmitting speech to characters who talk to machines or to numenera that allows similar abilities. If the PCs establish communication with a falling maw, they can negotiate with it—perhaps even fruitfully if they promise (or deliver) a connection with the datasphere.

Use: Every morning, the sound of whistling wind emerges from the mouth of a ruin that looks half like melted metal and half like a petrified fish. A hunter's seskii ran into the structure the first time it happened but never returned.

Sometimes a falling maw sucks in the air around it. When this happens, a sound like wind whistling fiercely through rafters precedes the maw. In a sealed enclosure, a falling maw can eventually suck out all the air.

Zero gravity rules, page 100

GM Intrusion: *The character is sucked forward into immediate range of the falling maw and begins to spiral around it, without making contact with the floor or any other means of holding himself back or hauling himself out of range.*

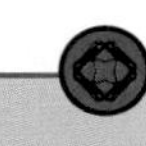

Seskii, page 258

SIZE COMPARISON

FERNO WALKER 6 (18)

Some people speculate that the ferno walker and the snow loper shared a common ancestor in the distant past, both being six-limbed mammals with a pair of usable hands. Regardless, the ferno walker is very different from its possible cousin. These predators supplement their diet of meat by ingesting large stones that sit in a special portion of their gut. Through an unknown process, this organ produces extreme temperatures, heating the rocks so that there is a literal furnace in its belly at all times. Ferno walkers can go for weeks without water.

Motive: Hungers for flesh

Environment: Mated pairs dwell in open grasslands, deserts, or warm forests.

Health: 35

Damage Inflicted: 7 points

Tanners and leatherworkers have attempted to use ferno walker skins to make heat-resistant armor, but so far all attempts have failed.

Armor: 1 (20 versus heat)

Movement: Long

Modifications: Perceives as level 7; uses tools and weapons in its forelimbs as level 5.

Combat: A ferno walker can inflict terrible wounds with its bite, but that is not the attack that makes it feared. At the cost of 1 point of its own health, the creature can vomit a super-hot chemical spew and spray it in an arc so that it affects everyone within immediate range. The spew deals 7 points of damage that ignores Armor, and even those who make their Speed defense roll suffer 1 point of damage.

Alternatively, at a cost of 2 points of its own health, a ferno walker can spit a stream of this same super-hot liquid up to short range at a single target. Anyone next to the target suffers 1 point of damage from the splash.

Interaction: Although ferno walkers do not use language, they are more intelligent than they might appear. They are aloof and defensive, but if approached with peace, patience, and bribes of food, they might interact without violence. This is much harder (increase the difficulty by two steps) if the ferno walker has young nearby.

GM Intrusion: *After slicing the ferno walker, the character is sprayed with a gout of super-hot liquid from the wound that inflicts 7 points of damage. Avoiding this spray is a difficulty 7 task due to the sudden surprise.*

Use: Ferno walkers are interesting predators, but they are sometimes captured and forced to become mounts. Other times, they befriend a humanoid and willingly become a mount and companion. Smart riders equip the mount with a weapon or device that it can use in its hands.

Loot: Rarely, a ferno walker is found in possession of an interesting weapon, tool, or cypher.

FLESH PUP 1 (3)

A flesh pup resembles a thumb-sized ferret covered in enzymatic slime, and it can dive right into another living creature and take up parasitic residence. Also called a "skin swimmer," a flesh pup could go unnoticed by its new host until its presence is revealed as a fist-sized red swelling on the torso or side of the neck, tender to the touch. Even then, a host might take a liking to the swelling, her brain chemistry having been tweaked in the fashion by which all the best parasites have evolved. Eventually the host is drained of all nutrients and life, and the swelling bursts to reveal a tiny litter of newborn pups.

Motive: Reproduction

Environment: A litter of up to eight flesh pups might be encountered in any location near where a previous host died. Public rooms or campsites are favorites.

Health: 1

Damage Inflicted: 2 points

Armor: 1

Movement: Immediate

Modifications: Stealth as level 4; Speed defense as level 3 due to size.

Combat: A flesh pup prefers to wait until a potential host is sleeping or distracted before attacking. The perfect potential host is one that is bound or otherwise unable to defend itself.

A creature unaware of a flesh pup's attack is allowed an Intellect defense roll versus a level 3 attack; a sleeping creature makes the roll versus a level 4 attack.

If the host fails the roll and thus remains unaware of the attack, the flesh pup's attack ignores Armor. If the attack deals 2 points of damage to a victim (either because the victim is unaware or because she is not wearing armor), the flesh pup's enzymatic slime instantly and completely anesthetizes the wound site, and the pup enters the victim. The slime closes the wound site, stitching the skin up in moments, leaving hardly a scar.

Unless someone else saw the entry or the victim was aware but couldn't prevent it, she unknowingly gestates the flesh pup, which secretly gives birth to a knot of larvae that grow to their parent's size within a week. During the last two days of this gestation, the host is treated as if impaired, and the swelling site is noticeable. However reasonable the host is in all other matters, she refuses to let anyone look at or treat the swelling.

Removing the flesh pup litter (and mother) before they hatch requires that the host be held fast. Someone must use a scalpel or other cutting instrument and be willing to deal 12 points of damage to the host while removing the parasites.

If the flesh pups hatch and emerge from the host, she must make a difficulty 3 Might defense roll. On a failed roll, the host dies. On a success, she survives but takes enough damage that she is instantly debilitated.

Interaction: As a parasite, a flesh pup is concerned only with feeding.

Use: A woman in town is selling strange "moist" pets to interested parties.

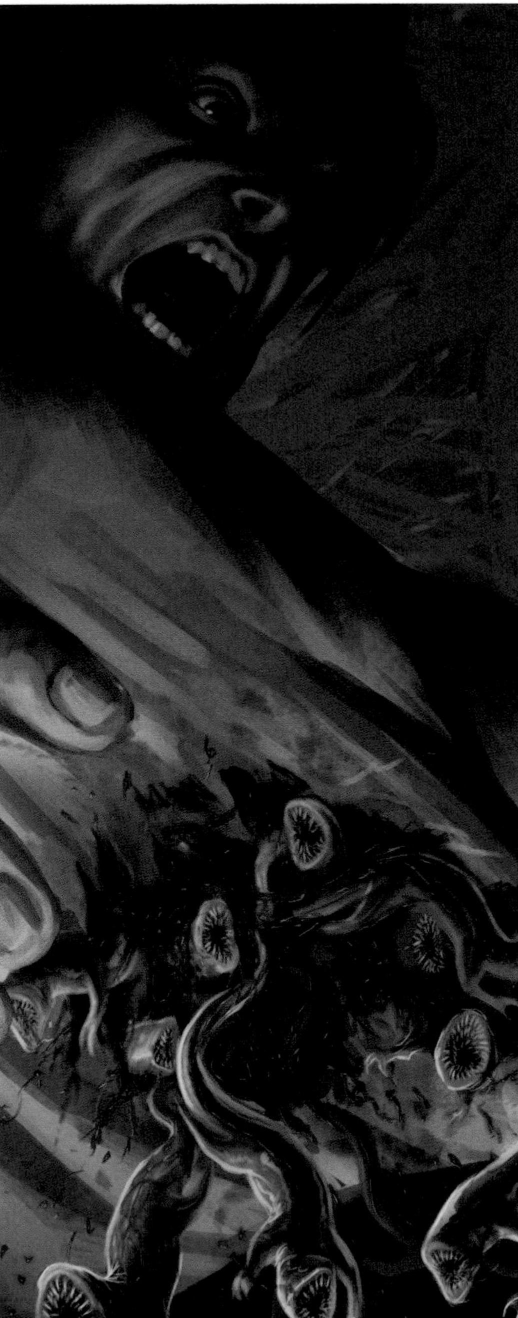

"Did you see that woman down at the market? She kept stroking the boil on her neck like it was her pet. She even had a name for it. 'Sweetum,' she called it. If you bought any rations from her, I suggest you throw them out now." – Hawk, a traveling glaive

GM Intrusion: *A just-defeated creature twitches as its belongings are being searched. Is it still alive? Nope—it was infected by a litter of flesh pups.*

SIZE COMPARISON

FLYING ELCHIN 5 (15)

Standing waist-high to most humans, these fearless scavengers like their meat freshly killed, but they don't want to do the work. Able to smell fresh blood from miles away, elchin often roam great distances for a single meal.

Flying elchin don't actually fly, but they can leap far and wide, thanks to their strong back legs and the adjustable, aerodynamic scaled fronds on their heads. With a single bound, they can rise nearly 10 feet (3 m) in the air and cover up to 50 feet (15 m) in distance.

Elchin are very vocal, producing sounds such as grunts, growls, snorts, whines, chatters, and near-human laughter. They can also manipulate their fronds to replicate and then amplify myriad noises, including thundering hoof beats and a variety of whistles. A single elchin can sometimes emulate the arrival of a great pack of predators in an attempt to scare others away from fresh kills.

Motive: Fresh meat

Environment: Rocky outcrops, ancient ruins, and broken forests

Health: 20

Damage Inflicted: 5 points

Armor: 2

Movement: Long when jumping; short when walking

Combat: Elchin teeth and claws are designed for tearing flesh from bone. While combat is not their normal mode, they will defend any kills they claim with ripping, tearing attacks that aim for exposed flesh.

Interaction: Although elchin have a complex communication system among themselves, they don't seem interested in interacting with other species. However, they can sometimes be tricked with fresh meat or things that smell like blood.

Use: While elchin aren't likely to hunt humans directly, they often hunt the kills of a human, showing up just as the fight ends, when the creatures are dead and the characters are at their most vulnerable.

Loot: Occasionally, a cypher or an oddity shows up in an elchin's stomach from a previous meal.

Elchin are captured and experimented on by a group of chiurgeons in Qi called the Eleven Haelans, who claim they can chemically alter the creature's sounds to heal broken bones and broken minds. Those who have been "healed" by the noise wear necklaces or other jewelry made from the elchin teeth and fronds.

GM Intrusion: *An elchin gathers its strength, jumps up, and comes down atop a character, dealing an additional 2 points of damage and pinning the PC.*

FRILLED BAUL 5 (15)

A predator of the highest order, the frilled baul is a dangerous sight in the tall grass. Of course, you're not likely to see the stealthy, incredibly swift hunter until it is far too late. This vaguely feline mammal is 8 feet (2.4 m) long and stands 4 feet (1.2 m) high at the shoulder.

When the baul is angry, its frills grow as rigid as dagger blades. When the beast is calm, they are flaccid and lay flatter along its body.

Motive: Hungers for flesh
Environment: Open plains or savanna
Health: 28
Damage Inflicted: 7 points
Armor: 1
Movement: Long
Modifications: Perceives as level 7; stealth as level 6.
Combat: A frilled baul is a solitary hunter that has an incredible bite with its double-hinged jaw. Further, each forelimb bears a wicked curved claw. An attack with the claw inflicts 5 points of damage and transmits a paralytic poison that inflicts 5 points of Speed damage if the victim fails a Might defense roll. Worse, the poison continues to inflict 1 point of Speed damage per round until the victim succeeds at a Might defense roll.

Even the frills of the baul are dangerous. Anyone coming close enough to make a melee attack on an angry frilled baul suffers 1 point of damage. Likewise, when the baul attacks a foe, if the attack misses, the target still takes 1 point of damage from the frills. (If the baul's attack hits, there is no additional damage from the frills.)

Interaction: The baul is a fairly typical predator with animal-level intelligence. However, if a pup is raised by a skilled trainer or an adult baul is clearly aided (in a significant way) by another creature, the beast becomes an extremely loyal companion.

Use: A hunting frilled baul might make an interesting wilderness encounter, but more interesting still would be an encounter with another creature that the baul has bonded to. This might be as simple as encountering a human hunter with a frilled baul pet, but an intelligent creature such as a nevajin or a bellowheart might have such a companion as well. It's even possible that something like an ergovore hound or an erynth grask could have saved the life of a baul (perhaps inadvertently), creating a strange alliance.

SIZE COMPARISON

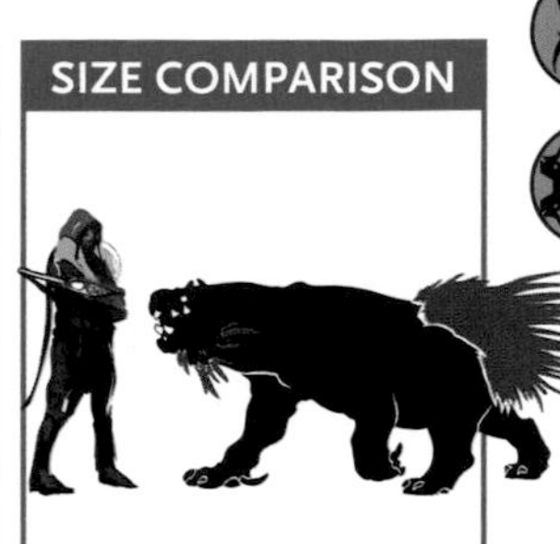

Bellowheart, page 24

Ergovore hound, page 47

Nevajin, page 248
Erynth grask, page 240

GM Intrusion: *The character's weapon (or other held item) gets caught in the frills of the baul and is yanked from his hands. Getting it back is a Speed-based task, and failure means a nasty cut that deals 5 points of damage.*

SIZE COMPARISON

GAZER 1 (3)

A gazer is a levitating metallic spherical automaton, about 1.5 feet (0.5 m) in diameter. Various bits of equipment and blinking cyphers festoon a gazer's battered alloy body. A concavity on one side of the sphere incessantly emits a beam of scarlet light. Blinding at best, the red beam can intensify in a moment, creating a ray capable of burning through nearly anything.

Motive: Defense

Environment: Formations of six to twelve gazers might be found defending ancient ruined installations. Sometimes lone gazers are encountered as companions of jacks or nanos who reprogrammed it to act as a servitor.

Health: 3

Damage Inflicted: 2 points

Armor: 1

Movement: Long while flying

Modifications: Perception as level 5; Speed defense as level 2 due to size.

Combat: Groups of gazers fly in a spherical formation, which allows them to present the maximum possible perception and threat surface.

A gazer can fire its scarlet beam to attack a target at long range. If the gazer can see any part of its target, it ignores any difficulty step penalties for cover that the target might have otherwise enjoyed.

As few as three gazers can act as a swarm, focusing their attack on one target to make one attack roll as a single level 3 creature, dealing 4 points of damage. On a miss, a swarm of gazers still deals 1 point of damage.

The intensity of a gazer's beam is level 5 (as measured against the level of material of an inanimate object to be burned through).

Interaction: A gazer usually interacts only by flashing its beam in coded bursts, accompanied by eerie bleats of electronic static. Most active gazers follow a program to defend a location, reconnoiter a wider area, or seek and destroy those who match profiles held in their machine brains. However, if any group of gazers is interfered with too much, they will eradicate the perceived threat.

Use: Stories of the discovery of a rusted, crumbling cache of spheres laden with numenera reach the PCs. What's actually been discovered is a decommissioned gazer graveyard on the outskirts of an ancient war installation. A few gazer formations are still active.

Loot: Scavengers can recover 1d6 cyphers in the remains of a destroyed swarm.

Gazers are speculated to be antiques of a forgotten war that were originally forged by the millions, Only a handful remain active. However, if one of the ancient warehouses could be discovered, that number could radically increase.

Swarm rules, page 13

GM Intrusion: *A gazer destroyed by an attack explodes, dealing 5 points of damage to every creature in short range. Other gazers in immediate range spin away to safety.*

GEMORRN 7 (21)

If a curling orange glow rising out of the ground or shining through the broken walls of an abandoned city contains the afterimage likeness of several screaming faces within its brilliant 10-foot (3 m) diameter expanse, it's probably a gemorrn.

One of the most terrible things about a gemorrn—other than its desire to kill every creature it happens upon—is that sometimes the screaming faces in the glow are familiar.

Motive: Vengeance, minds

Environment: A single gemorrn is usually encountered only in locations where everyone who used to live in the area was violently murdered as the result of some kind of explosive numenera. Of course, if that event happened long ago, only the presence of the gemorrn suggests the latter detail.

Health: 21

Damage Inflicted: 4 points

Armor: 2

Movement: Immediate. Once per day, a gemorrn can upload itself into the datasphere as its turn, move anywhere the datasphere reaches, and download itself into a fresh nanobot haze. It can't do this in any round in which it has taken damage.

Modifications: Stealth as level 2

Combat: A gemorrn doesn't take damage from mundane physical sources, such as axes, swords, arrows, and the like. It is vulnerable only to attacks that have components that are not kinetic (such as energy, psychic, radiation, light, plasma beams, or melee weapons that emit the same). Even against such attacks, the gemorrn gains the benefit of its Armor.

A gemorrn can attack all creatures within short range with a psychic onslaught. If a creature is killed by a gemorrn, a portion of the victim's mind is drawn into and becomes part of the gemorrn. The gemorrn gains 5 points of health each time this occurs, even if that means it exceeds its starting health.

Interaction: A gemorrn communicates telepathically within short range. However, it is not a creature of reason; it is an entity of rage and hunger. When one "hears" a gemorrn, the noise is a babble of crying, screaming, raging, cursing, and gasping mental voices—what a roomful of people might sound like if all were simultaneously crushed under a killing weight. The self-willed residue left behind is blind with rage over the deaths but hungry for more minds with which to prolong its existence.

Use: A gemorrn is a powerful entity and could be the end of one or more of the characters. Thus, it is something that could be used to scare and motivate the PCs rather than something they are expected to overcome.

Loot: If the PCs find the destroyed building, caved-in tunnel, or other location where the gemorrn was created, they usually can recover 1d6 cyphers and an artifact or two from the mass grave.

"Our friend died when half our town was destroyed by the blast. But I saw her again last night, screaming obscenities at us. She was one of the voices in the glow that chased us. Didn't you see her?" –Konlkin Darvus, former mayor of Kylo

GM Intrusion: *The PC recognizes one of the faces making up the gemorrn as a friend or other close acquaintance, just as the face recognizes the character. The psychic visage begins to call out to him. The PC must succeed on an Intellect defense roll or lose his next turn coping with the realization.*

GLACIER SLIME 3 (12)

"She was fine, a leader who never led us astray. And pretty as a picture, she was! Except for that last time, right? Froze her arm off. Then her head, before it shattered, hair and all. And that wasn't pretty, not at all."
~Tati Coulter, explorer

When struck, a glacier slime egg goes cold, which expels all the heat contained in the immediate area in a flash.

A 10-foot (3 m) diameter pool of steaming liquid that seeps around under its own power might be a glacier slime. The "steam" coming off it is the opposite of hot; it's a cold mist of water condensing right out of the air.

Glacier slimes prefer frigid climes and evaporate quickly in warm areas. When they do evaporate, they leave behind a clutch of tiny white eggs. The eggs are cool to the touch and benign unless struck and shattered, which precipitates the birth of a new glacier slime.

Motive: Freeze living things

Environment: Any cold location or climate, alone or in a pair

Health: 12

Damage Inflicted: 4 points

Armor: 2

Movement: Short

Modifications: Speed defense as level 2 due to size

Combat: A glacier slime can attack mobile prey with liquid pseudopods. A creature hit by a pseudopod takes damage and must succeed on a Might defense roll or move one step down the damage track. Anyone debilitated while within immediate range of a glacier slime grows so cold that movement becomes impossible.

GM Intrusion: *The PC's melee weapon shatters when he attacks the glacier slime with it.*

If presented with the option of attacking mobile prey or motionless prey, the glacier slime chooses the latter and flows over the unresisting creature, automatically inflicting 4 points of damage that ignores Armor. Once covered by a glacier slime, a victim continues to take 4 points of damage each round on the slime's turn until the slime is somehow killed. Unfortunately, anything that damages a glacier slime coating a victim probably also damages the victim.

A glacier slime is immune to damage inflicted by cold. The creature's Armor is ineffective against damage inflicted by fire or hot plasma, and the slime takes 4 additional points of damage from that source.

Interaction: These animate pools of liquid air are always roiling, always flowing, understanding only a need to freeze living things.

Use: A map purported to provide directions to a site rich in the numenera is being sold at the local market. In addition to other interesting tidbits, the entrance to the location is marked with signs of danger and the words, "Winter comes early to those who fail to heed the pools."

Loot: A defeated glacier slime leaves behind a clutch of tiny white eggs, one or two of which can be salvaged as heat drain detonation cyphers.

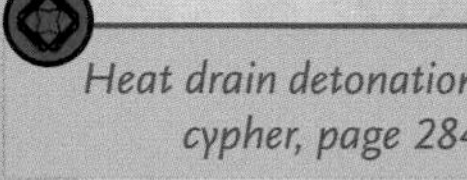
Heat drain detonation cypher, page 284

GOLTHIAR 3 (9)

Underground seedpods "ripen" in groups of four to six at a time, push to the surface, and peel open to reveal wet, wrinkly creatures the size of adult humans. Within an hour, the creatures completely mature into soldiers able to survive for centuries on sun and nutrients gathered from burying themselves in drit every few days.

Golthiars are humanoid creatures of woody muscle and barklike skin that smells of sap. Their bulbous heads hold single eyes surrounded by a fringe of jagged petals. Quick and brutal despite their plant ancestry, golthiars stand about 6.5 feet (2 m) tall.

Trees that produce golthiar seedpods are not always similar in appearance. Sometimes they have great fronds, other times needles, and other times leaves. It's almost as if the pods that ripen beneath the ground are not part of the original tree's growth.

Motive: Defense

Environment: Anywhere, usually in groups of four or more

Health: 12

Damage Inflicted: 3 points

Armor: 2

Movement: Short

Modifications: Perception and Speed defense as level 4

Combat: Golthiars usually act as part of a team, coordinating their attacks through squirts of beamed color invisible to most people. The creatures direct the beams at each other or display them on a wall or ceiling that all the golthiars in an area can see.

A golthiar can simultaneously spear one foe with its thornlike forearm extension and bash a second foe with the hard plating on its other forearm.

In addition, one in four golthiars can beam visible light at foes within short range that inflicts 8 points of damage, but only once every few hours.

If golthiars have any weakness, it is sensitivity to unexpected light. A flash of bright light that catches a group of golthiars could make them lose their next action. This tactic works only once during any given combat.

A golthiar regenerates 1 point of damage per round if exposed to direct sunlight.

Interaction: Golthiars not guarding something, attacking something, or scouting something wither and die within a few months. Those without orders could be willing to find a new command, but communicating with a golthiar requires knowing how to produce and decode the pulsating beams of light preferred by the creatures.

Use: A team of golthiars plans a well-coordinated, merciless attack on a small town, though it's unclear on whose orders.

If a defeated golthiar is planted in the ground and carefully tended, a new grove of golthiar saplings may spring up within a few weeks.

GM Intrusion: *When a golthiar hits a PC with a beam of visible light, in addition to burning the character, it blinds her. The PC must succeed on a level 4 Might defense roll as her action to blink the afterimage away.*

SIZE COMPARISON

GREY SAMPLER 3 (9)

This hovering automaton's "head" is an angular funnel that roars and vibrates with endless fury. Its two "arms" are not matched—one arm splits into a mess of slicing and scissoring blades. The grey sampler uses this arm to subdue specimens, separate cranial matter from clinging flesh and bone, and deposit the freed brain into the sampler's head-funnel. Somewhere in the grey sampler's chest, the solid matter is processed into pinkish slush. In all, a grey sampler measures almost 10 feet (3 m) in diameter.

The grey sampler's other arm is more like a metallic hollow tentacle that doesn't grasp but instead deposits processed cranial matter. Most of the time, the cranial matter is sprayed behind the automaton in a wide, even arc, as if it's broadcasting fertilizer or seeds instead of jellied souls.

Grey samplers have a disconcerting ability to build themselves out of much smaller parts too tiny to see without the aid of powerful numenera. This means that small fleets of them can arise anywhere, building themselves in secret, until an unknowable signal passes among them, and they emerge for the next harvest.

If someone who can talk to machines or who is otherwise skilled with numenera devices discovers a fleet of grey samplers building themselves from drit and other nearby components, he might be able to direct the fleet to self-destruct with a successful Intellect roll.

Motive: Hungers for brains

Environment: Almost anywhere, in fleets of up to five

Health: 9

Damage Inflicted: 5 points

Armor: 3

Movement: Short when flying; long when making a flying charge

Modifications: Speed defense as level 2 due to size

Combat: A grey sampler inflicts damage with its bladed arm.

A grey sampler can also attack by making a flying charge if it's farther than short range from the victim (but still within long range). If the victim fails the Speed defense roll to evade the charge, he takes 8 points of damage, is knocked 10 feet (3 m) back, and is knocked off his feet.

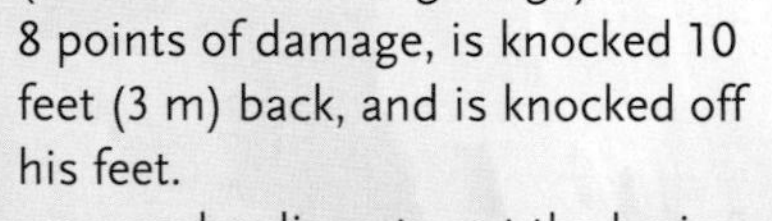

A grey sampler dissects out the brains of dead (or completely immobilized) victims and processes their brains into sludge.

Interaction: A grey sampler can communicate but usually is interested only in directing potential victims to hold still so it can do its job. If asked who gave it the job or what it is ultimately attempting to accomplish, a grey sampler either doesn't answer or says, "The fruit of our harvest prepares the way."

GM Intrusion: *A PC is unable to avoid a grey sampler's flying charge and is knocked back into the "arms" of another grey sampler and held immobile. Every round on the character's turn, he can attempt a Might defense roll to break free, but meanwhile, the grey sampler holding him begins dissecting (and the damage it inflicts ignores Armor).*

Use: An abhuman tribe's farmland was recently devastated by drought or decades of poor stewardship. Overcoming their own taboos, they sent an emissary into a nearby ancient ruin to ask the "demon" chained within it for aid. Though they lost their emissary as a sacrifice, the abhumans received a fleet of grey samplers.

Loot: The remains of a destroyed grey sampler might hold 1d6 shins and a cypher or two.

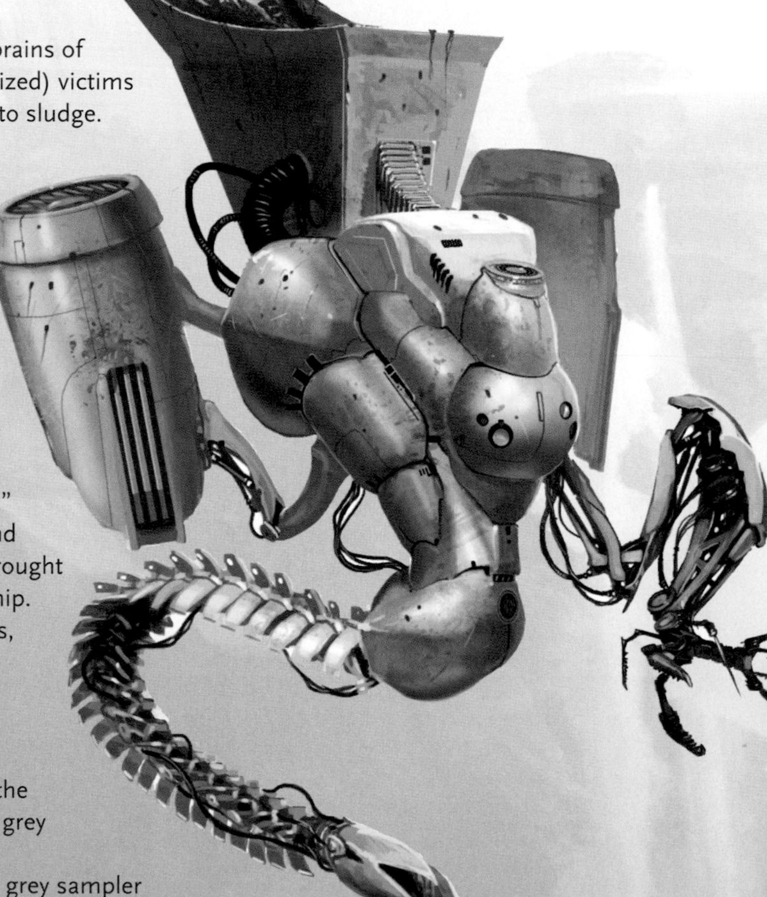

GRIFFALO 2 (6)

Griffalos are omnivorous animals of the plains. Sometimes communities of nomads herd them, valuing the shoulder-high quadruped for the many delectable ways the cured meat from the creature's back or sides can be prepared. The animals are otherwise notable for their great tusks (no two individuals have the same size and style), their oddly empathic and humanlike eyes, and the varying number of orifices that puncture each griffalo's neck.

Explorers who study a griffalo's orifices might note that the openings seem oddly designed, with screws and insertion nodes that seem like they were manufactured rather than evolved biologically.

Motive: Hungers for flesh or plant material

Environment: Any plains area large enough to host large grasslands. Griffalos can be encountered in groups of six to eight, or in massive herds numbering hundreds or thousands.

Health: 6

Damage Inflicted: 3 points

Armor: 1

Movement: Short

Modifications: Stealth as level 3 in grassland environments

Combat: A griffalo attacks with its tusks, which also inject a lingering poison that increases the difficulty of Speed defense rolls made by the victim by one step. The poison lasts for one hour or until the victim spends her turn to make a successful Might defense roll. The effects of multiple poison injections are not cumulative, and once a victim succeeds at one Might defense roll, she becomes immune to griffalo poison.

Griffalo herds are an amazing sight; however, hundreds of stampeding griffalos are extremely dangerous if they happen to be heading toward the PCs. Characters in the area of a stampede must make Speed defense rolls against level 5 or suffer 7 points of damage from being trampled. If there are more than 100 griffalos, the characters are potentially trampled for more than one round. For every 100 creatures, the stampede lasts one round passing through the character's area.

Griffalo matrons sometimes accompany other griffalos, and they can be aggressive. Griffalo matrons are burlier level 4 creatures with 12 points of health and 2 points of Armor. They make two tusk attacks per turn, each of which inflicts 4 points of damage.

Interaction: Unless hungry, griffalos prefer to avoid conflict with humanoids. However, they will fight if cornered or if they haven't eaten well recently. Lone griffalo matrons are almost always aggressive and territorial.

Use: Any time the PCs travel in grassland environments, there's a chance they will see a griffalo herd in the distance. If the characters camp in the waist of a constricted grassy valley, they may wake in the night to the unpleasant discovery that they've been resting in a stampede lane.

Loot: Rarely, a griffalo has a cypher, an oddity, or an artifact connected to the shuntlike orifices in its neck via organic cables. Such a device is two levels higher than it would otherwise be.

GM Intrusion: *A PC or ally slays a griffalo, but the falling corpse pins her beneath it. She must succeed on a difficulty 3 Might defense roll to pull herself free.*

Swarm rules, page 13

GRUSH 4 (12)

Of all the various types of abhumans, grush are probably the most likely to find a place among the humanity that their ancestors once abandoned. These brutes are often the soldier-slaves of influential nobles who consider them to be powerful but poorly disciplined and quite expendable. Their intelligence is low, and they are lazy, slow, and clumsy, but they make for an intimidating force. Unlike many abhumans, grush do not have an innate love of violence, but they certainly don't shirk from it. Grush are variform creatures, and no two are born alike. Tall and thin, squat and broad, one eye or two (or three)—the variations are limitless and prominent.

Motive: Fear and laziness

Environment: Anywhere, often in groups of five to ten

Health: 16

Damage Inflicted: 5 points

Armor: 1

Movement: Short

Modifications: Might defense as level 5; Intellect defense and resistance to trickery as level 3.

Combat: Skilled with big two-handed weapons, grush inflict an additional 2 points of damage (total of 7 points) when using them.

Grush cannot be stunned or dazed. They are immune to most poisons and disease. Even though their tough flesh provides only 1 point of Armor, it applies against things that normally ignore Armor (environmental damage, heat, cold, falling, and so on).

Grush are incredibly hard to kill. They regenerate 1 point of health each round. Severing an arm or even the head of a creature is not a guaranteed killing blow. Many grush that have suffered such a wound stand up, still alive, hours later. Complete dismemberment is the only way to ensure that a grush is truly dead.

Interaction: Despite their hardiness, grush fear pain and can be intimidated by brute force or dramatic shows of power. They can also be motivated by offers of food or a chance to rest, and they are notoriously easy to fool. They speak the local human language, but not very well.

Use: Grush fill the "stupid brute" role well. They can be found in areas where one wouldn't normally expect to find an abhuman, such as guarding a noble's manor or carrying her palanquin.

Loot: Grush carry a big weapon, and that's it.

GM Intrusion: *The grush calls out with a horrible bellow, bringing 1d6 more of its kind to join the fray.*

HERDER 3 (9)

This mechanical creature looks like a very large insect built of metal pipes and bone-colored ceramic. It bears a semicircle of metal spikes down its back, four sharp claws on each foot, and a hard, bonelike spur on the left side of its head. Standing at nearly 3 feet (0.9 m) tall, plus another 1 to 2 feet (0.3 to 0.6 m) for its spikes, herders were clearly created by someone or something, possibly for the protection of catlike herbivores called enyi (or possibly the enyi's ancestors).

They typically watch over a flock alone, but sometimes they protect in pairs.

Motive: Protection of its flock

Environment: Anywhere herds of enyi are found—mostly grasslands and plains

Health: 12

Damage Inflicted: 4 points (spur) or 3 points (claws)

Armor: 5

Movement: Long

Modifications: Defends against acid, electricity, and detonations as level 2

Combat: A herder displays various forms of aggression toward anything that it perceives as threatening its flock. The displays are nearly ritualistic in their order. First, the herder begins to make a loud clacking sound, created by rubbing its hind legs together. PCs often hear this sound long before they are close enough to see the herder; those with knowledge of the creature know to avoid the sound if possible. If the danger doesn't go away, the herder rises up on its hind legs, doubling its height. The final sign of aggression before a herder attacks is that it drops its head and thumps its ceramic spur against the ground. Large herders hit the ground hard enough for PCs to feel the collision beneath their feet. The first display of aggression is passive and ongoing; the last two each take one round.

When herders attack, they do so quickly and with a great deal of force already built up in their movement. Their main attack is a driving head butt with their ceramic spur, which inflicts 4 points of damage and has a chance to stun a target for one round. If they are in close combat, they switch to attack with their claws, inflicting 3 points of damage.

Herders are difficult to harm with conventional weapons due to their metal and ceramic build, and they are immune to mental effects or Intellect damage. Their main objective is to defend the herd, but once they begin combat, they don't stop, even if the enyi no longer seem to be in danger. To a herder, once a threat, always a threat.

Interaction: Communication is not possible.

Use: While the PCs are out hunting, they come upon a small herd of catlike creatures that look like a great option for dinner—at least, until the herder shows up.

Loot: The PCs can scavenge 1d6 shins and one random cypher from a herder's body.

GM Intrusion: *Two herders watch that particular flock; the second one appears only after the fight has begun.*

THE HEX

The Hex is a clanlike organization. The Hex is a virus. The Hex is an army. The Hex is a group mind. The Hex is a curse. The Hex is all of these things, and more.

Rumor has it that the Hex was unleashed upon the Ninth World by explorers who opened a sealed chamber in an ancient ruin. Those people, then—in theory—became the first members of the Hex as it is understood today. But in the past, the Hex might have been something very different.

No one knows if there are original members of the Hex, or if all Hex members, called hexons, were once modern humans that have been transformed. Perhaps some are older than that—or were never human at all. What is known is that people cursed with the Hex have a second, synthetic skin of dark, hexagonal plates that grows quickly over the top of their normal flesh, enveloping and consuming them. The Hex completely and utterly takes over the person, mind and body, and compels him to work toward the goals of the Hex.

While no one fully understands the Hex, it might be best thought of as a biomechanical virus. A few have wondered what will happen when the Hex encounters the Insidious Choir (page 44), another viral-like fugue entity interested in domination.

These goals seem to be conquest. But there may be more to it than that. When the Hex conquers an area and gains access to resources, the hexons turn from warriors to builders. Although what they are building is not fully understood, half-built hivelike structures have been seen by those daring to enter a Hex-controlled region. The obvious suggestion is that they are building lairs or fortresses, but others speculate that they are constructing vehicles for long-distance travel (perhaps even between worlds) or machines with a far larger purpose.

The hexagonal false flesh has a number of different devices that attach directly to it and interface with it (but not with anyone without the flesh). These include:

- Claws that inflict 7 points of damage
- Extremely high-powered projectile weapons (similar to dart throwers) that inflict 7 points of damage with a short range
- Cocoonlike nodules that produce hex stingers, which are mechanical insectoid creatures that spread the Hex. Stingers are produced at a rate of one per month.
- Scanner devices that sense the general topography of the surrounding 10-mile (16 km) area, as well as all movement within long range and analysis of creatures, devices, and materials similar to the nano's Scan esotery.

GM Intrusion: *The hexon grabs the character and holds her fast so that other hexons can strike her freely. The character must break free before she can act normally again.*

After 1d6 months of being part of the Hex, a hexon grows a backpacklike pod that produces one of the above attachments, if given raw materials (10 pounds [4.5 kg] of metal and synth) and about a month of creation time. In addition, sometimes hexons take these devices from other, fallen hexons.

HEXON 5 (15)

An individual of the Hex, usually called a hexon, is a warrior that serves the needs of the whole group, but hexons are not mindless drones. Smart, perceptive, reactive, and proactive, hexons represent a real threat to anyone that would stand in their way. Hexons do not spread the Hex, however—that's what hex stingers do. Thus, hexons do not incorporate their enemies but slay them. And ultimately, anyone who is not a part of the Hex is an enemy.

The process of becoming a hexon takes a few hours to complete, and not everyone survives it. Once fully incorporated into the Hex, hexons work only toward the goal of the Hex. Hexons can communicate with each other via silent broadcasts but sometimes still speak verbally.

All former connections are severed—hexons are no longer the people they once were in any way. The Hex wants nothing more than the warm body, so to speak. Knowledge, skills, abilities, and so on are not retained.

Hexons refer to each other as siblings: brother or sister. Through a quirk of fate, women survive the hex process somewhat more often than men do, so there are more female-appearing hexons than male, but once a human is a part of the Hex, gender is irrelevant. Procreation, physical attraction, love, familial ties, and anything of the sort no longer exist for the hexon.

Motive: Conquest

Environment: Anywhere, operating in small units

Health: 24

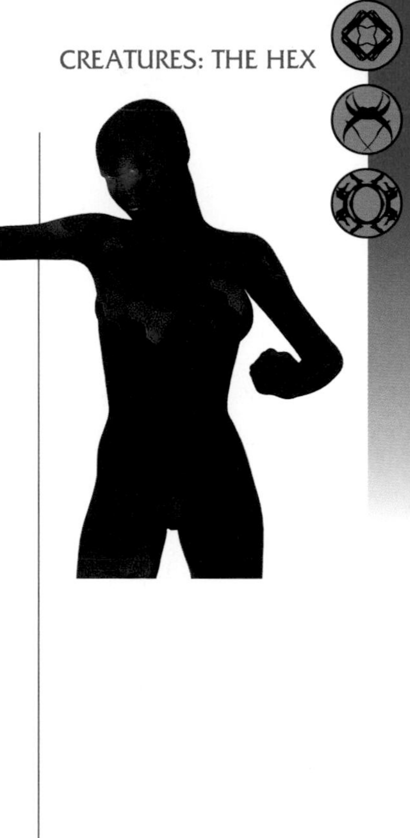

Damage Inflicted: 5 points
Armor: 2
Movement: Short
Modifications: Perception as level 7
Combat: Most members of the Hex use their bodies as deadly weapons in combat. Some, however, are armed with unique weapons that interface with the hex flesh.
About one in three hexons has a special power not wielded by their siblings. Roll for an additional power:

d100	Power
01–30	*Forceblast*: Fires a blast of force for 5 points of damage at long range as an action.
31–60	*Forceshield*: Has 2 additional points of Armor.
61–75	*Magnetic control*: Can move a metal object up to 50 pounds (22 kg) within short range as an action. Speed defense against attacks with metal weapons as level 6.
76–90	*Machine control*: Takes control of a machine within immediate range and, as an action, activates, deactivates, or gives a command to it.
91–00	*Teleportation*: Instantly moves a long distance (disregarding barriers) as an action.

Interaction: Hexons are intelligent and speak a variety of languages. It is impossible to convince a hexon to go against the wishes of the Hex.
Use: Reports of strange-looking humanoids attacking remote settlements probably cause most people to blame abhumans, but investigation shows a far more precise, coordinated, and deadly series of strikes. The Hex has moved into the area, and stopping them from their dreams of conquest will require a great deal of effort and bloodshed.

HEX STINGER 2 (6)

Small mechanical insects, hex stingers exist to inject humans with a nanotech, molecular rearrangement "virus" called the Hex. Transformed people become hexons and work with others likewise transformed toward the Hex's goal of conquest.

Rumor has it that long ago, the Hex was designed to affect creatures other than humans, but it has now adapted. Hex stingers still ignore any nonhuman target.

GM Intrusion: *The character is buffeted in the face by the hex stinger's wings, and the difficulty of all of the PC's tasks is increased by one step for one round.*

Motive: Spreading the Hex
Environment: Always with a member of the Hex
Health: 5
Damage Inflicted: 3 points
Armor: 2
Movement: Short
Modifications: Speed defense as level 4 due to size and speed
Combat: A hex stinger's injection carries a transformative venom. Humans stung must immediately make a Might defense roll. Failure means that they move one step down the damage track. On the next round, a victim who failed the first roll must make another Might defense roll with the same consequence. On the third round, someone who has failed both prior rolls must make yet another Might defense roll. This time, however, if she succeeds, she begins the painful, hours-long process of transforming into a hexon. If she fails, she dies.
Interaction: Hex stingers are simple, programmed machines and can't be interacted with in any way.
Use: Hex stingers are always encountered as "companions" to hexons.
Loot: A scavenger examining a destroyed hex stinger can find a single cypher.

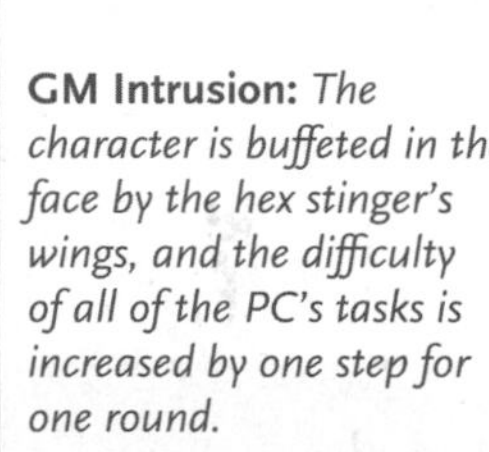

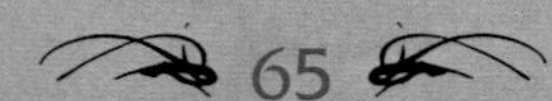

HONTRI 5 (15)

The hontri is a massive bird of prey that has been altered by nanomachines to become a true winged nightmare. These avians, with their white and black plumage, are known to and feared by the people who live in their hunting grounds, who sometimes call them "winged devils" or "twilight slayers." The latter nickname refers to the creatures' preferred hunting time, for they see as well in dim light as in bright daylight.

Interestingly, the nanites within a hontri's flesh self-replicate so that when young hontris hatch, they have their own technological "allies."

Motive: Hungers for flesh

Environment: Hilly or mountainous regions, hunting alone or in pairs

Health: 22

Damage Inflicted: 5 points

Armor: 1

Movement: Long (short on the ground)

Modifications: Perception as level 7

Combat: As raptors, hontris spy prey from high above and swoop down at incredible speeds, raking with their powerful talons. When using this swoop attack, they deal 2 additional points of damage. (Usually, a hontri can swoop only once in an encounter, as its first attack, but sometimes circumstances might allow a second swooping attack.)

The nanites in their flesh and blood primarily exist as repairing machines. A living hontri regenerates 2 points of damage each round.

A hontri hunting pair is particularly dangerous, as the machines in their systems allow them to communicate mentally with each other. If acting in concert, the hunting pair operates as level 6 creatures in all tasks.

The microscopic machines laced in a hontri's flesh allow it to build up a powerful electrical charge. Once per hour (usually on its first attack), it can inflict an additional 4 points of damage.

Interaction: Despite their telepathic communication with each other, hontris are animals and act as such.

Use: A legend says that people once bonded with and rode hontris as mounts. The PCs are commissioned to find a hontri nest high in the mountains and bring back the eggs. If they succeed, their employer may have her hands full when she discovers that the old legends are false (or that the hontri has evolved into a stage where bonding and riding are no longer possible).

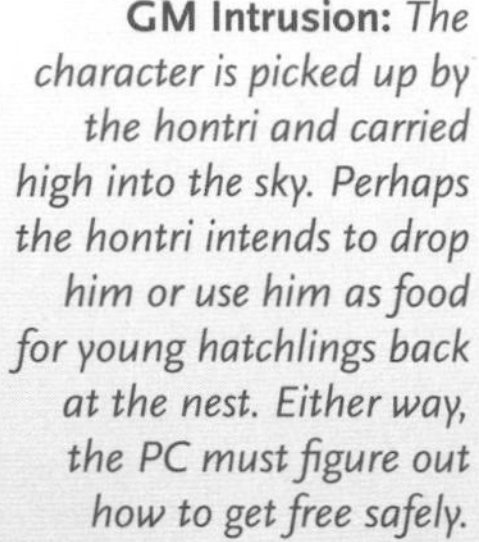

GM Intrusion: *The character is picked up by the hontri and carried high into the sky. Perhaps the hontri intends to drop him or use him as food for young hatchlings back at the nest. Either way, the PC must figure out how to get free safely.*

ISHENIZAR 6 (18)

An ishenizar is composed of faceted crystal. Each facet reflects an eye, hundreds in all, every one different. Some of the eyes are human, some animal, some machine, and a few obviously extraterrestrial. An ishenizar's crystal body usually flickers like an ember, but sometimes it seems to blaze as bright as a star.

An ishenizar's overall shape is difficult to describe—maybe impossible to describe. Most people who've seen one remember only the variegated eyes within their crystal facets, the starlike glow, and sometimes, the burning white light of an ishenizar focusing on something that has earned its enmity. That means judging the creature's size is also problematic. On the other hand, they're small enough to fit inside structures and homes where humans live.

Motive: Unknown

Environment: Ishenizars appear alone or in groups of two or three, usually in places that have seen much death or are rich in stored energy, knowledge, or art.

Health: 18

Damage Inflicted: 6 points

Armor: 2

Movement: Long when flying; able to teleport to another part of the world as an action

Modifications: Perception as level 10

Combat: Ishenizars rarely fight. When they do, they focus the illumination they naturally emit (or reflect from some unseen location) with crystal facets that act like lenses. The focused beam either can burn up to two targets at long range as a single action, or it can burn any number of selected targets within immediate or short range, inflicting 3 points of damage to each.

Alternatively, an ishenizar can attack a single creature at any range that it can see with a psychic insinuation that inflicts 3 points of Intellect damage.

If an ishenizar is slain, it detonates with a shriek of shattering crystal. A telepathic broadcast of ultimate loss is sensed by most creatures within a mile. All that's left behind is a shapeless litter of glassy crystals.

Interaction: Ishenizars are telepathic, but they don't seem to use words. Instead, they communicate via intense surges of emotion: oceanic calm, bubbling glee, humor, grey melancholy, and sometimes, howling rage. When questioned about their purpose or motives, they respond with a complex flash of competing emotions so multifaceted that most people are dazed by the sensation. The best anyone has been able to translate is: *we connect life and death*.

Use: After a battle, a town's hospital is filled to capacity with the wounded and dying. Every night an ishenizar appears in a room where the wounded rest. By the next morning, one or more wounded who were looked upon by the creature is dead. The scared, angry locals make plans to attack the "crystal wraith" the next time it appears.

Loot: Amid the litter of crystals of an ishenizar's remains, a glassy cypher or two can be salvaged.

Those who've been in the presence of an ishenizar later have dreams in which a dearly departed friend, family member, lover, or enemy speaks to them. Some messages are of hope, others of love, and sometimes the message is a warning.

GM Intrusion: *A PC's cypher begins shining with the same starlike brilliance of an enraged ishenizar. On the following round, the cypher explodes with light and possibly shrapnel, plus any energy associated with the cypher. Everything within immediate range (other than ishenizars) takes 6 points of damage.*

JESANTHUM 4 (12)

A patch of wildflowers in the distance waves massive blooms of vivid purple in the breeze. The trembling flowers smell of baking bread and honeyed syrup, an odor so potent that many recall their own best memories of eating sweets.

When a bed of jesanthum flowers bend their brilliant heads to reveal a lapping tongue the color of blood, and the thick stems uproot to expose powerful 5-foot (1.5 m) long carnivorous bodies of raking claws and stabbing barbs, those sweet recollections are forever shattered.

A decade ago, no one had ever heard of jesanthums, but now they're prolific enough to be a common cautionary tale among travelers. Maybe they colonized from a previously isolated island where such growth is rampant, or perhaps an explorer discovered a particularly loathsome ancient seed bank. Or, most worryingly of all, perhaps the sun's altered energy signature, one that plants seem to respond to, has become even stronger.

Some people keep juvenile jesanthum plants in their gardens as crowning specimens of their collection, trusting themselves or their gardener to remain vigilant enough to weed the plants before they become mature and mobile.

Motive: Hungers for sunlight, water, and flesh

Environment: Almost anywhere sunlight reaches, usually in beds of three to five creatures

Health: 18

Damage Inflicted: 5 points

Armor: 1

Movement: Short

Modifications: Speed defense as level 5

Combat: A jesanthum attacks with its rasping, cutting tongue. If it inflicts damage, the victim must also succeed on a Might defense roll. On a failed roll, the jesanthum pounces with the aid of its tongue and impales its victim with a massive barb (dealing more damage), which adheres the creature to its prey.

For PCs with an adhered jesanthum, the difficulty of all attacks and Speed defense rolls is increased by one step. On the other hand, all attacks a jesanthum makes on a victim it is stuck to automatically succeed. Removing the jesanthum requires the victim's (or another creature's) full turn and gives the jesanthum one free attack as the extraction occurs.

In addition, a jesanthum can breathe out a cloud of spores that fills an intermediate area around it. Any living creature in the area who fails a Might defense roll coughs uncontrollably. Victims cannot act until they successfully make a Might defense roll, which they can attempt once per turn. After the jesanthum uses this ability, it must regenerate new spores before it can do so again, which takes hours.

GM Intrusion: *One PC fails her defense roll against the jesanthum's spore breath. In addition to causing uncontrollable coughing, the spores germinate in the PC's lungs and send a thick stalk up through her mouth and nostrils sometime during the next 28 hours. This tends to asphyxiate and kill the victim unless desperate measures are taken. On the other hand, the process does create a nice moist planter for the new jesanthum seedling to sprout from.*

Interaction: Jesanthums are pretty, nice-smelling plants—until they're not, at which point they're hungry predators that attempt to eat PCs who have come too close.

Use: To appease an angry patron or provide a gift of special significance for someone the characters need a favor from in return, they are asked to collect a planter full of jesanthums. However, they probably are not given any details beyond a bare description of the plant (when it's not moving about).

JURULISK 7 (21)

The people of the prior worlds, with their strange activities and vast displays of power, tore literal holes in the fabric of the universe. Sometimes, these were very small. Nothing to worry about.

Sometimes.

The jurulisk is an ultraterrestrial being of strange, inconceivable dimensions. When it comes to this world, it is a one-dimensional line, possessing only length (not even width, let alone depth), imperceptible and incapable of interacting in a meaningful way. Eventually, others come to this world. Over the aeons, the jurulisks find each other and bond to form two- and eventually three-dimensional forms in a way that is difficult to comprehend.

Finally able to interact with the three-dimensional world, the jurulisk seeks energy to fuel its new form. Once it has absorbed a great deal of power from living creatures, the sun, or an artificial energy source, a jurulisk attempts to control its environment—usually by eliminating other potential threats, which means all other creatures.

The jurulisk is a living creature, but it is not organic in any traditional sense, and neither is it mechanical. Its form constantly shifts, adapting to its needs at the moment, but always looking like what some have described as "the framework for an 'actual' creature."

Motive: Hungers for energy (and dominion)

Environment: Anywhere

Health: 28

Damage Inflicted: 10 points

Armor: 1

Movement: Long

Combat: A jurulisk's cold touch drains the energy of all things around it. In addition, its weird angles and awful protrusions are impossibly sharp. Its strikes inflict 8 points of damage plus 2 more points from the terrible cold.

As an action, a jurulisk might attack a character's armor, weapon, or other object. If the creature strikes its target, the object—if less than level 7—is destroyed and the character suffers 2 points of cold damage. Thus, in one round, a well-armored character can suddenly be reduced to Armor 0 and far more susceptible to attack.

A jurulisk regenerates 5 points of health each round. However, if it falls to 0 health, it instead regenerates 1 point of health per hour until it reforms 28 hours later. While it is regenerating in this way, it can't take any other actions. (If the jurulisk falls to 0 health because its component matter is scattered across a long distance or farther, perhaps due to an explosion, it does not regenerate.)

The jurulisk can alter its form in strange non-Euclidean ways, allowing it to pass through solid matter. It can pass through up to 5 feet (1.5 m) of solid matter in one round. It can stretch so as to extend a "limb" to stab at a foe a short distance away.

A jurulisk fights to the "death," although it might not be permanently dead or destroyed, for such concepts might not apply. The creature is far too alien to tell.

Interaction: If it is possible to communicate or interact with a jurulisk, the means have not been discovered yet, even using telepathy.

Use: The jurulisk is a wonderfully weird foe, intent on killing the PCs because it wants their energy or because they might be a threat (or both).

SIZE COMPARISON

As something utterly alien, a jurulisk often senses—perhaps rightfully so in some cases—that the hard, inorganic matter of a foe is as dangerous and vital as the softer, organic flesh.

GM Intrusion: *The jurulisk disappears into the ground at the character's feet. Just as suddenly, it comes back up for an attack that is two steps more difficult to defend against. Regardless of whether the attack is successful, the jurulisk immediately bends at impossible angles to get out of the 10-foot (3 m) deep pit it has just created. The character will fall into the pit if she does not succeed at a Speed defense roll (difficulty 6).*

SIZE COMPARISON

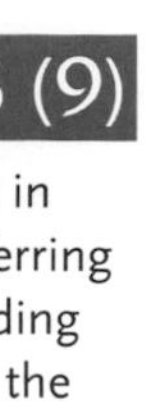

KALYPTEIN CRAB 3 (9)

Kalyptein crabs are not true crabs, but rather soft-bodied land crustaceans that make their homes in empty or broken (or sometimes still working) bits of the numenera. They are group animals, preferring to exist in small colonies of six to eight creatures. Kalyptein crabs range in size and shape, depending on the species and the size and shape of the available numenera "shells." Most crabs are around the size of a human fist, and others grow as large as a human head.

Kalyptein crabs work together to find and steal numenera devices to use as new homes. They use a vacancy chain to switch homes—when a new, bigger numenera device is found or stolen, the crabs gather around it from largest to smallest. When the largest moves into its new home, the rest move up one size as well. They then eat the smallest device, perhaps for the nutrients or as some type of ritual.

Motive: Defense, steals numenera for its home
Environment: Most often in places rife with bits and pieces of the numenera
Health: 9
Damage Inflicted: 3 points
Armor: 3
Movement: Short

Some nanos keep kalyptein crabs as pets, albeit dangerous ones. The can live up to 70 years, but that is only one of the reasons they often outlive their owners.

Combat: Intent on defending their soft bodies at all costs, kalyptein crabs attack with their strong vertical pincers, using them to slice open skin rather than close around things. They may also seek out and attack other creatures in an attempt to acquire a particularly sought-after bit of the numenera.

Many kalyptein crabs have also developed odd cypherlike skills due to their long-term contact with the devices they live in. If seriously injured, they attempt to employ these abilities along with their typical attack. GMs may roll on the cypher table below (or use the cypher table on page 281 in the corebook) to see which attack the creature has. Characters must succeed on a level 6 Speed defense roll to avoid the cypher's intended effect.

GM Intrusion: *The kalyptein crab has a hodgepodge shell created from two or more numenera devices. Roll twice on the table and apply both effects on the next attack.*

d100	Cypher Effect
01–20	*Banish.* The crab generates a burst of energy that teleports a creature or object an immediate distance in a random direction (not up or down). The difficulty of the teleported creature's actions (including defense) is modified by one step to its detriment on its next turn.
21–30	*Disruption.* The crab generates a burst of nanites that directly attack organic cells. The affected target takes 1 additional point of damage and is stunned, losing his next action.
31–60	*Heat.* The crab generates a burst of heat, inflicting 2 additional points of damage.
61–80	*Visual displacement.* The crab creates a hologram of another creature around the character, increasing the difficulty of the PC's next two attacks by one step.
81–90	*Shock.* The crab generates a burst of electricity, inflicting 1 additional point of damage.
91–00	*Assist.* The shell misfires, sending out a stream of chemicals that decreases the difficulty of the PC's next action by three steps.

Interaction: For the most part, kalyptein crabs cannot be communicated with. Occasionally, however, a crab makes a home in a numenera device that provides it with temporary translation or other communication skills.

Use: The PCs wake to find that one of their numenera devices has gone missing. They follow the tracks in the dirt to discover that a large rainbow-colored creature seems to have made its home inside the device.

Loot: If a kalyptein crab has just moved into its home, there is a small chance that the numenera device can be removed and used for its original purpose. Otherwise, the shell contains 1d6 shins.

KANTHID 4 (12)

It knows what Jarin knew. Jarin's been gone for years; I know he's dead. But then the thing appeared at my window, whispering words of love and our old happiness. It's not Jarin, I understand that. But I'm going down to meet it anyhow, out behind the wall where Jarin and I used to meet.

~Last note left by Salara before she went missing

The sound of sandpaper on sandpaper scratches the air when a kanthid moves. Most kanthids are multilimbed creatures shaped vaguely like other animals found in the Ninth World. Whatever its underlying shape, the rough skin of a kanthid is a stony mineral whorled and studded with short spines. Here and there, openings in the stone reveal mouths ringed in writhing cilia.

Kanthids with biped, humanoid shapes sometimes speak, though they don't make much sense. Streams of nonsense, rhymes, names, stories, and even snippets of song might emerge from two or three different cilia-ringed mouths at once.

Motive: Hungers for flesh, reproduction

Environment: Desolate places throughout the Beyond, in groups of three or four

Health: 12

Damage Inflicted: 5 points

Armor: 3

Movement: Short

Modifications: Speed defense and all Speed-related tasks as level 3

Combat: A kanthid bashes prey with its spine-studded limbs. Each time a victim is hit by a kanthid and takes damage, poisoned spines break off in the wound. At first, all the victim feels is an unpleasant tingle. But if he takes damage from a kanthid three times in the same fight, his extremities go numb and he must succeed on a difficulty 5 Might defense roll or drop limply to the ground, paralyzed for one minute.

If allowed to do so without interruption, a kanthid lowers its body across a paralyzed (or recently slain) creature, allowing its many ciliated mouths to feed. Each round a kanthid feeds in this fashion automatically inflicts damage. A kanthid that completely consumes a meal leaves behind a skeleton chunked with gore and several hard nodules of kanthid eggs fused to the bone.

Interaction: Kanthids are no smarter than clever animals, even the ones that babble things once known by an intelligent creature that it ate and whose bones it colonized.

Use: A powerful nano wanted information that only a dead and buried colleague had. Knowing of the kanthid ability to evoke the memories of slain victims, she infected the graveyard where her colleague was interred. A few miscalculations and weeks later, the entire graveyard and associated village was infected with wandering kanthids. Now the nano seeks help in locating the particular kanthid she wants to interrogate among those radiating out from the village, though she's careful to keep secret her part in creating the infection in the first place.

Though a talking kanthid seems to make little sense, there is a theme to its babble: everything a given kanthid says or sings were things once said or sang by a particular individual, one who's been dead for a while.

Breaking open a defeated kanthid reveals it to be a composite creature made of hundreds of smaller "polyps" (essentially, tentacles surrounding a mouth and digestive sac) built on the skeleton of a dead animal.

GM Intrusion: *In addition to the kanthid's bash attack, one of the ciliated mouths on the attacking limb bites down on the PC, inflicting additional damage and holding him in place until he succeeds on a Might defense roll. While the attachment lasts, the attached kanthid makes attacks against the PC as a level 6 creature.*

KILLIST 3 (9)

Clawed, greasy fingers. Smacking lips. Chattering, pointed teeth. Tiny, beady eyes. Shrill voice. A penchant for thievery, murder, traps, and deception. It is difficult to find some aspect of a killist that isn't annoying, off-putting, or downright abhorrent.

Killisti are diminutive abhumans. Their oily flesh is pale, their eyes are dark, and they have slits on the sides of their torso that are frequently mistaken for gills. These, in fact, provide access to their poison sacs, which are positioned perfectly for killisti to slide their claws into as a part of an attack.

Like most abhumans, they hate humanity with a passion and delight in murder and sadistic acts against the targets of their malice.

Killisti leaders are typically older females who may be the mother or grandmother of their entire band. They are even more devious and cruel than the others and thus retain their positions of authority.

GM Intrusion: *The dose of the killist's poison is particularly virulent, and the affected character experiences serious vertigo and disorientation. For the next minute, she must make a Speed-based roll each round or fall down. The difficulty of this task is increased by two steps if she moves a short distance or more during the round.*

Motive: Hatred for humans; hunger for flesh

Environment: Temperate and hot regions in bands of six to twelve

Health: 9

Damage Inflicted: 3 points

Movement: Short

Modifications: Stealth as level 4

Combat: Killisti hate and fear a fair fight. They set ambushes and traps whenever possible. Traps usually consist of spiked pits, tripwires, or spine-filled nets. Any sharp points in their traps are poisoned.

Most killisti carry long knives and crude bows. These weapons are always freshly venomed—it is not an action for a killist to poison a weapon or its own claws.

Killisti poison inflicts an additional 3 points of Speed damage if the victim fails a Might defense roll.

A killist leader is level 4, and level 6 in stealth actions. She has 12 points of health and level 5 poison.

Interaction: There is a saying: "If a killist is speaking, you are listening to lies." Killisti can be intimidated by shows of obvious force and threats to their lives, but even as they are cowed, they are plotting a way to trick and betray you. They speak their own language, but about half know a few words of the Truth.

Use: A band of killisti might set up an ambush at a bridge or along a road. They might even "bait" that trap with one of their number pretending to be hurt or dead at the center of the ambush. Other killisti live on the edges of human society, stealing what they need and preying upon those weaker than themselves. For example, a town with an infestation of killisti might start to experience disappearances among children or the elderly.

Loot: The killisti leader usually has all the valuables, but that rarely amounts to more than 1d6 + 2 shins and a cypher. Any dead killist is the source of 1d6 doses of their poison as well.

THE KIPRUS 8 (24)

There may be only one Kiprus. Because it does not obey the normal laws of space—or perhaps even time—it is impossible to know whether there are many of these creatures or just one.

It seems to be an ultraterrestrial being that comes from somewhere far less dense than this world. Ropes of dark plasm move through the air like ink flowing through water, but at a fraction of the speed. Although the Kiprus seems to have excellent senses, no sensory organs or other features can be identified in its roiling dark mass.

The touch of the Kiprus burns living and nonliving matter alike, so it often leaves a trail of grass, soil, and rocks scorched and scoured as if by acid. Its extreme alien nature allows it to bend the space and time of this universe to serve its needs.

The only things that seem to interest the Kiprus are intriguing and rare chemical compounds, strange alloys, and other often exotic materials. It studies and ultimately absorbs what it finds of interest.

Motive: Exploration and discovery

Environment: Anywhere

Health: 24

Damage Inflicted: 8 points

Movement: Immediate

Modifications: Speed defense as level 6 due to size and speed

Combat: The creature attacks by simply touching its foes, but in a fight, it is not affected by material attacks at all. In fact, material objects touching it that are of lower level than the Kiprus are damaged or destroyed. However, raw energy, such as from a ray emitter or an explosion, affects it normally.

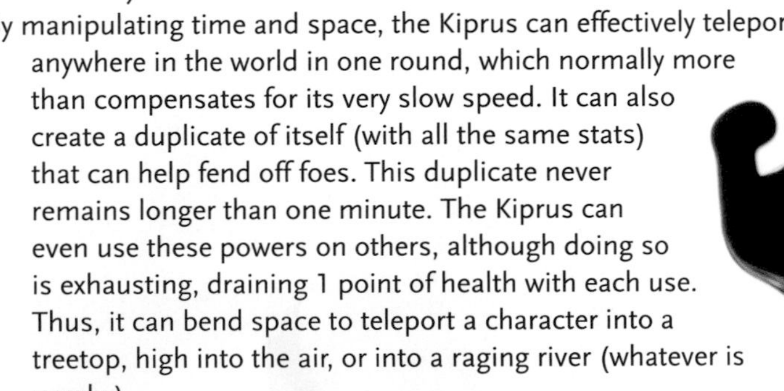

By manipulating time and space, the Kiprus can effectively teleport anywhere in the world in one round, which normally more than compensates for its very slow speed. It can also create a duplicate of itself (with all the same stats) that can help fend off foes. This duplicate never remains longer than one minute. The Kiprus can even use these powers on others, although doing so is exhausting, draining 1 point of health with each use. Thus, it can bend space to teleport a character into a treetop, high into the air, or into a raging river (whatever is nearby).

Interaction: The Kiprus cannot speak or read, though it understands most spoken languages. It communicates only by gestures but sometimes is eager to try to establish a meaningful exchange. The creature does not relish combat and avoids it if possible by simply warping away.

Use: The Kiprus offers an opportunity for a truly weird encounter. The PCs run afoul of a jiraskar by an old ruin, and suddenly there are two! What's actually happening is that the Kiprus is trying to drive them away from the ruin because it contains some compounds of interest to it.

SIZE COMPARISON

GM Intrusion: *The character is enveloped in the ropy strands of the Kiprus. She cannot move without taking automatic damage from its matter-disrupting touch. Worse, she is suddenly shot elsewhere and elsewhen for a time and mysteriously returns later (probably long after the encounter is over).*

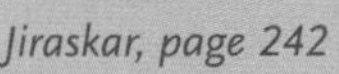

Jiraskar, page 242

SIZE COMPARISON

LATOS 10 (30)

Gigantic and mysterious, latoses are very rare, found only in the remotest areas of the Beyond (or beyond the Beyond). Their creation is a mystery, but for some reason the people of a prior age decided to preserve locations within small, artificially closed universes and hide them away inside massive guardians. The ways of the prior worlds were strange indeed.

The 50-foot (15 m) body of a latos is made of a unique alloy, and its head is a transparent sphere that contains an area far larger than its size would indicate. In this area, reflected in the "face" of the latos, is a place of ancient importance, permanently preserved and deserted.

Motive: Protection

Environment: Deep wilderness

Health: 100

Damage Inflicted: 12 points

Armor: 6

Movement: Long

Modifications: Speed defense as level 8 due to size

Combat: A latos can attack in a straightforward physical manner, smashing foes with hands or feet. It can make two such attacks on two different foes (or on the same foe, if the target is quite large) as a single action. At the same time, the latos can lash out with horrific mental attacks. It can choose from one of three options:

- All creatures within 1 mile (1.6 km) of the latos must make successful Intellect defense rolls or suffer 8 points of Intellect damage that ignores Armor. Those affected must make a second Intellect defense roll or also lose their next action.
- All creatures within long range of the latos must make successful Intellect defense rolls or suffer 12 points of Intellect damage that ignores Armor and move one step down the damage track. Those affected must make a second Intellect defense roll or also lose their next action.
- One creature within 1 mile (1.6 km) of the latos must make a successful Intellect defense roll or have his consciousness transferred to an ethereal dimension where he wanders in a dreamlike world. A single round in the real world seems like a full day to the victim. He can be rescued only by an external source, such as a telepathic ally who journeys into his mind to find and retrieve him (perhaps combatting the dreamlike phantoms that confront them).

A character who spends more than an apparent year in this dream state suffers the permanent loss of 1 point from his Intellect Pool for each year. In addition, each apparent year, he must make a difficulty 10 Intellect defense roll or go quite mad.

A latos can transport a willing target into the location stored in its sphere by touch. However, convincing the latos to do so is difficult, as it was apparently instructed to keep the place safe.

If the latos is destroyed, its body shatters and scatters across a mile radius. At the center of that area, the location stored in the sphere is transplanted as if it had always been there. It is perfectly preserved but empty of life (except perhaps for machine entities or creatures that were in stasis).

GM Intrusion: *The latos accesses the location stored within its sphere and brings forth an ally, such as a dread destroyer or a dark fathom.*

Interaction: No one has ever successfully spoken with a latos, but a character with telepathic abilities (or a device) might be able to establish a dialogue with one of these enigmatic creatures. If so, the PC would likely have little trouble (difficulty 3) negotiating a peaceful agreement, as latoses are not inherently aggressive, but she would have to work extremely hard (difficulty 10) to convince the latos to provide access to the location it protects.

Use: The PCs must find a specific artifact, and a bit of research in the datasphere reveals that it lies in a city of platinum towers. However, that city is stored inside the head of a latos, which must be overcome first. And who knows what ancient guardians and failsafes await in the city itself?

Loot: Aside from the transplanted location, scavengers picking through the artificial body of a destroyed latos will find 1d100 + 500 shins, 1d10 + 6 cyphers, 1d6 oddities, and one or two artifacts.

LAURIK-CA 4 (12)

Laurik-ca are always found in groups of three—never more, never less. In fact, it is smart to think of three laurik-ca as a single opponent, for their great skill is working together as one due to their unusual connection with each other and the datasphere.

At an early age, a laurik-ca pup is matched up with two others from the litter by their dam, based on the symbol on the pup's forehead. The goal? To create the proper combination of symbols across all three pups to allow them to access the datasphere and become a single-minded weapon of destruction. Sometime in their first year, the pups grow long, symbol-filled horns, which act like antennas to both their mates and the datasphere. As the pups grow, they use their combined symbols as a code with which to access a particular part of the datasphere, granting them a single powerful weapon.

These cunning fighters stand nearly 7 feet (2.1 m) tall. They relish the opportunity to display their powers and sometimes seek out combat for their own pleasure and a chance to play with their foes.

It is unlikely that explorers will find laurik-ca in locations with large quantities of the numenera. Some people speculate that numenera objects impair the creatures' connections to one another and to the datasphere.

Motive: Destruction

Environment: Anywhere except populated areas

Health: 15

Damage Inflicted: 4 points from their claws and teeth; additional damage depends on their symbols.

Armor: 3

Movement: Short

Combat: Because the three laurik-ca are connected to one another so completely, they fight as one creature, increasing their level to 7, their health to 40, and their Armor to 6.

Although they attack with tooth and claw, their true weapons are the destructive mental forces that they access via the datasphere. These forces are unlocked by the three-symbol code on their foreheads, but only while they are in long range of each other.

The following are examples of codes and possible powers, but the number of options is extensive and possibly infinite.

♦❖● **Touch Confusion.** Any character whose body or weapon touches (or is touched by) one of the laurik-ca experiences a sense of righteous anger that flows through her veins and directly into her brain. The PC takes 5 points of Intellect damage (ignores Armor).

☼♈♦ **Memory Wash**. A stream of horrible memories (perhaps his own, perhaps someone else's, but at the moment, it certainly feels like his own) and images floods through the PC, wracking him with pain and dropping him to his knees. The character takes 5 points of Intellect damage and is dazed for one round, during which time the difficulty of all tasks he performs is modified by one step to his detriment.

GM Intrusion: *While the PCs are fighting a leash of laurik-ca, another trio sees the scuffle as an opportunity to take over the area. The characters are suddenly caught in the middle of a fierce territorial battle.*

●☾◆ **Mind Control.** The creatures attempt to control the mind of one PC, forcing her to attack the nearest member of her party with her strongest attack for the next two rounds. The PC must make an Intellect defense roll (level 7) to resist.

❖♓♦ **Boiling Blood.** A character within short range feels like the space beneath his skin is suddenly on fire, burning and bubbling. This attack deals 8 points of damage and stuns the PC. Stunned characters lose their turn (but can still defend against attacks normally).

Interaction: Those connected with the datasphere may find themselves able to interact with laurik-ca—or perhaps the proper way to put that is they may find themselves *forced* to interact. If laurik-ca discover someone with any sort of connection to the datasphere, they will abuse that link if possible, typically sending threatening images and ideas into the person's mind.

Use: Laurik-ca have been attacking the same village in the Beyond every night for weeks. They are not killing inhabitants, but rather returning night after night to taunt and terrorize the people.

Loot: There is a small chance that the PCs can loot a cypher from laurik-ca, usually a device that has some connection with the datasphere.

LLARIC SCORPION 5 (15)

Although it's called a scorpion, this massive creature is actually an amblypygid and has no traditional stinging tail that its name would suggest. In adulthood, it measures 5 feet (1.5 m) long. It has six legs for locomotion, plus 12- to 15-foot (3.7 to 4.6 m) whiplike forelegs that it uses as sensory organs. A deadly hunter, the creature preys on reptiles and mammals.

An amblypygid is a type of arachnid.

Perhaps stranger, however, is the music that the llaric scorpion makes. By blowing air out the spiracles in its legs, it produces an eerie fluting sound. This piping allows it to attract others of its kind from a distance and send other simple messages, such as a territorial warning. The music also disrupts the mental processes of humans and many other intelligent creatures. Those that hear it might lose their short-term memory, have their senses altered, lose their senses completely, or undergo strange and immediate behavioral changes. The effects vary from individual to individual.

Motive: Hungers for flesh

Environment: Anywhere other than the desert

Health: 18

Damage Inflicted: 7 points

Armor: 3

Movement: Short

Modifications: Climb as level 6; perception as level 7.

Combat: The llaric scorpion's spiky pedipalps inflict horrific damage on anything they clamp around. Further, a character struck must make a Might defense roll to avoid being held fast by the clenching jawlike structures. Prey held in the pedipalps automatically takes damage each round, and the difficulty of all physical actions it attempts is increased by two steps. Using an action to break free requires a Might-based roll with an initial cost of 1.

Initial cost, page 89

Thanks to its sensory legs, a llaric scorpion can operate in the darkness as well as the light, and it can sense movement within a short distance without having to see it.

The music of the amblypygid disorients and disturbs those that hear it and can be resisted by an Intellect defense roll. However, the creature does not use this ability offensively—the harmful results are just side effects of the music that it makes naturally.

About one in six llaric scorpions has a mass of newly born young in a broodsac attached to its abdomen. Each of these is a level 1 creature about 3 to 6 inches (7 to 15 cm) long, but if the mother is attacked, they can swarm over a victim. This swarm inflicts no damage, but the character must make a Speed defense roll; a failure means the difficulty of all actions is increased by two steps until the swarm is cleared from him.

GM Intrusion: *The character is held by the pedipalps so securely that she can take no physical action other than to attempt to break free. What's more, the llaric scorpion immediately drags her a short distance away, and if not stopped, it continues to attempt to escape with its meal.*

Interaction: The llaric scorpion is no more sophisticated than an animal.

Use: These fearsome predators are dangerous foes, but the most interesting use of a llaric scorpion is its music. Eerie and strange, the distant piping sound can cause all manner of odd behavior in people. Whole villages might be driven to brief bouts of madness, amnesia, sensory deprivation, or anything else that would be interesting. Discovering and subsequently hunting down the cause of this madness could be an adventure unto itself.

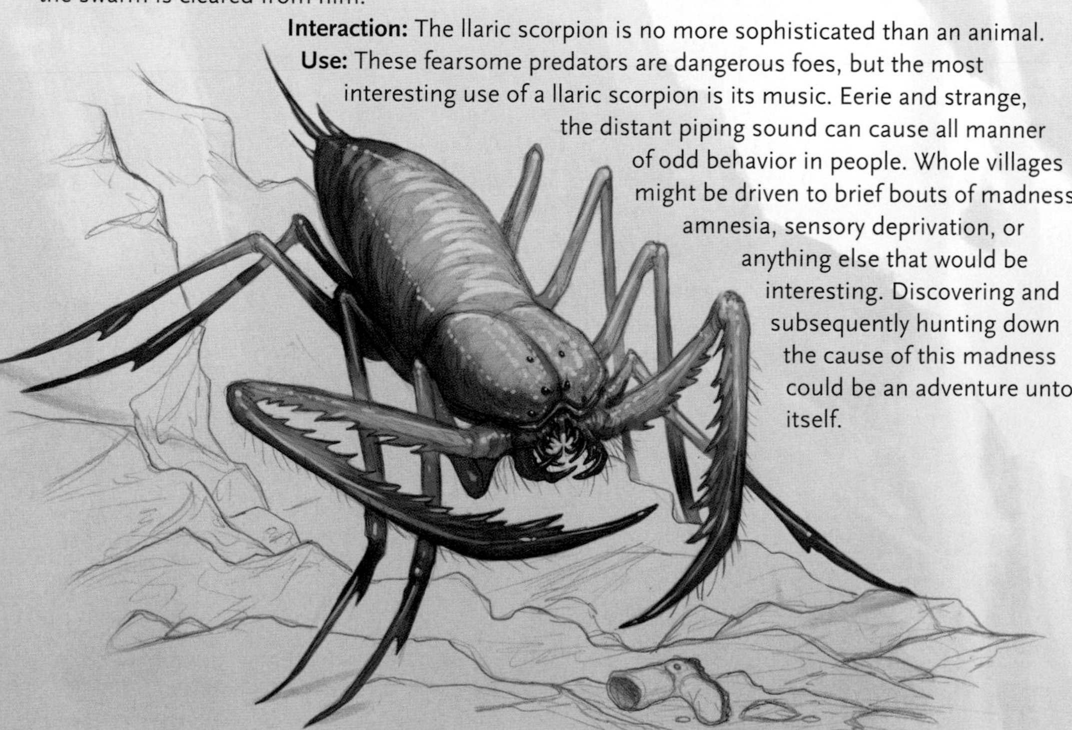

LORUB 5 (15)

A lorub is a 12-foot (3.7 m) long water-dwelling beast that lives near coastal areas, hunting for fish, mammals, and the occasional drowned fisher. A lorub breathes air but can hold its breath for several hours. It can be caught and tamed for use as a mount, though even trained lorubs dunk their riders from time to time.

In dim light or darkness, lorub skins give off a luminescent gleam. When lorub pods swim in formation beneath the water at night, their glowing forms make it easy to mark their passage, though sometimes the creatures are mistaken for a single, much larger beast, causing something of a scare.

Motive: Hungers for flesh

Environment: Usually near coastlines, in pods of three to five

Health: 15

Damage Inflicted: 5 points

Armor: 1

Movement: Long while swimming; short while on the ground

Modifications: Speed defense as level 4 due to size

Combat: Lorubs avoid peril and combat if possible. If they must defend themselves, they prefer to use a short-range venom spray that can inflict damage on up to three targets (within immediate range of each other) with one attack. A lorub can spray venom only once every few rounds; while its venom recharges, the creature must rely on bashing foes with its bony, clublike muzzle.

If a lorub is killed in the water, venom leaks from the corpse into the surrounding fluid, potentially afflicting every living creature in the water within short range. Until the venom dissipates (about a minute), all such creatures must make Might defense rolls each round to avoid being affected.

Interaction: Thanks to their strong front flippers and their muscular torsos, lorubs can move on land as well as in the sea, and are sometimes caught and trained as mounts by fisher people. More often, they are encountered in the wild, swimming along the coast or following boats out to sea.

Use: A group of pirates uses lorub mounts when hunting water craft. Recently, the Pirates of the Breathing Isle hit a trade ship carrying much-needed supplies. The pirates' base is heavily patrolled by lorub-riding guards.

SIZE COMPARISON

GM Intrusion: *A lorub attacks a PC with a bite instead of a muzzle bash or spray of venom. If the character fails a Speed defense roll, the lorub dives for the bottom of the nearest body of water. The PC trapped in the powerful jaws must succeed on a difficulty 6 Might defense roll to escape.*

MAGATHAN 6 (18)

A spice-and-smoke odor stings the air near a 14-foot (4.3 m) long serpentine magathan. Twin heads twine on long necks, which fuse to a central serpentine form covered in brilliant red scales. Both magathan heads are reptilian; one is solid, the other seems translucent and ethereal. Where the two necks fuse, dark scale patterns suggest a humanoid face frozen into flesh.

Magathans are natural illusionists and construct sparkling cities that they hide beneath layers of psychic artifice. Their cities are visible only to themselves, those who are allowed to see the locations, or those with psychic gifts of their own. To everyone else, a magathan city appears as nothing more than a long series of dangerous slopes created by broken rock fragments at the base of crags, mountain cliffs, volcanoes, or other steep inclines.

Given the beauty of their cities and their skill in trade, it's too bad that many magathans consider human flesh to be a delicacy.

Motive: Trade, hungers for flesh

Environment: Anywhere in groups of two or three, usually disguised as human traders

Health: 36

Damage Inflicted: 6 points

Armor: 2

Movement: Short

Modifications: Disguise as level 7; Speed defense as level 5 due to size.

Combat: A magathan can make two attacks (one per head) as its action, but doing so destroys the creature's illusory guise (if any). The magathan's translucent head inflicts only 3 points of damage, but it ignores Armor.

A magathan can also launch a psychic assault, which does not break its illusory facade. However, a psychic assault targets only a single foe within long range, dealing Intellect damage.

Finally, a magathan can cloak itself in an illusion (or a new illusion, if already disguised as a human) as its action. When it does, it appears as a section of wall, a tree, a piece of furniture, or some other object of the environment as long as it doesn't move. Someone who witnessed the "transformation" must succeed on a difficulty 3 Intellect task to distinguish the magathan from its natural surroundings. Others must succeed on a difficulty 7 Intellect-based task, but they can attempt the roll only if they have reason to suspect that things are not as they seem.

Interaction: Magathans prefer to interact with others in the illusory guise of human traders, which they pull off with aplomb. They also enjoy a low-level telepathic gift that allows them to speak the language of any creature they meet that has a language (and whose mind is not shielded against psychic prying). Magathans can't read minds, but their trading skills are so honed that it almost feels like they can.

Use: A group of magathans disguised as traders has taken up residence in an abandoned building outside of town. They sell all manner of wonderful things in a shop fragrant with spicy incense; at night, they hunt the city streets, looking for easy human prey.

Loot: A group of magathan traders usually carries 1d6 cyphers in all.

When a magathan drops its illusory human disguise, the one thing that remains almost constant is the human face, which is revealed as an intricate pattern across the magathan's "chest" scales.

In addition to the natural scale patterns that suggest a human face, many magathans bear marks that resemble runes or writing. The script is archaic, and even the magathans claim not to know its significance.

GM Intrusion: *The magathan targets a character with a special psychic attack that seeds confusion. On a failed Intellect defense roll, the character believes that her companions are magathans and that the actual magathans are her allies. If the PC has reason to doubt her senses, she can make a new defense roll as an action during any turn.*

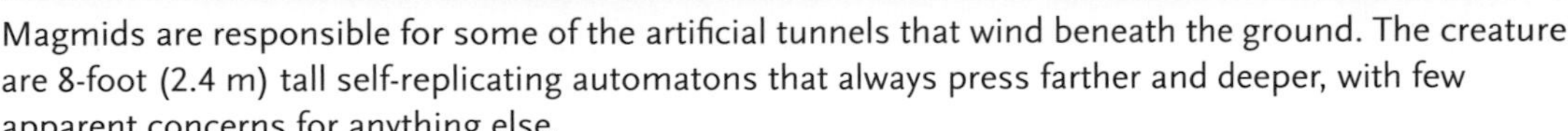

MAGMID 5 (15)

Magmids are responsible for some of the artificial tunnels that wind beneath the ground. The creatures are 8-foot (2.4 m) tall self-replicating automatons that always press farther and deeper, with few apparent concerns for anything else.

Magmid tunnels have several common characteristics; even someone not familiar with the creatures can ascertain that their circular bores are always just over 13 feet (4 m) in diameter. Chiseled along each hundred-mile (161 km) tunnel segment are unique messages in a long-dead language. If translated, each tunnel seems to provide a set of instructions for some impossibly complex task. The passages tend to follow long, curved paths, descending at a noticeable slope, and meeting up with similar tunnels every great while in large nexus chambers with a hundred sides. Within each nexus chamber, gravity is absent, and other physical laws are sometimes out of whack.

Motive: Excavation

Environment: Tunneling almost anywhere underground in pods of five or six

Health: 15

Damage Inflicted: 5 points

Armor: 2

Movement: Short; immediate when burrowing

Modifications: Tasks related to mining as level 6; perception as level 6.

Combat: A magmid bashes an opponent with its resonance claws.

A magmid can also use its omni-spectrum projector as a weapon. With this device, it can attack up to four creatures standing next to each other within short range of the projector, dealing 5 points of damage to each. The projector must recharge for a few hours between each use.

Interaction: Magmids react violently to creatures who they perceive to be interfering with their exploration. Attempting to get a magmid to answer questions (which these creatures hardly ever respond to, except with angrily flashing lights and ominous tones) for more than three or four rounds could be taken as such interference.

Use: A pod of magmids tunneled through an ancient holding cell containing a neveri. The neveri escaped to the surface, where it immediately began scouring the area of life, using the magmid tunnel where it emerged as its lair. The neveri is exultant, not only because it was set free, but also because it noted the direction in which the magmids were tunneling—eventually, the passage is certain to intersect with several more sealed underground cells that imprison "siblings" of the neveri.

Loot: A defeated magmid yields 2d20 shins and 1d6 + 1 cyphers.

Magmid tunnels follow their own geometry; they don't trace mineral veins, pockets of other valuable resources, or previous ancient tunnels. If the creatures are looking for something, their approach is one of brute force. Odds are, the tunnels serve some other purpose, but no one has yet offered a reasonable guess as to what.

Neveri, page 91

GM Intrusion*: A magmid attempts to entomb the PC. If the character fails a Speed defense roll, she is secreted beneath the ground in a spray of occluding rock dust. Observers must succeed at a difficulty 4 Intellect roll to perceive what actually happened, or else they may believe that the PC was disintegrated, teleported, or otherwise vanished. To escape, the entombed character must succeed on two Might defense rolls; if she fails three rolls before she escapes, she suffocates.*

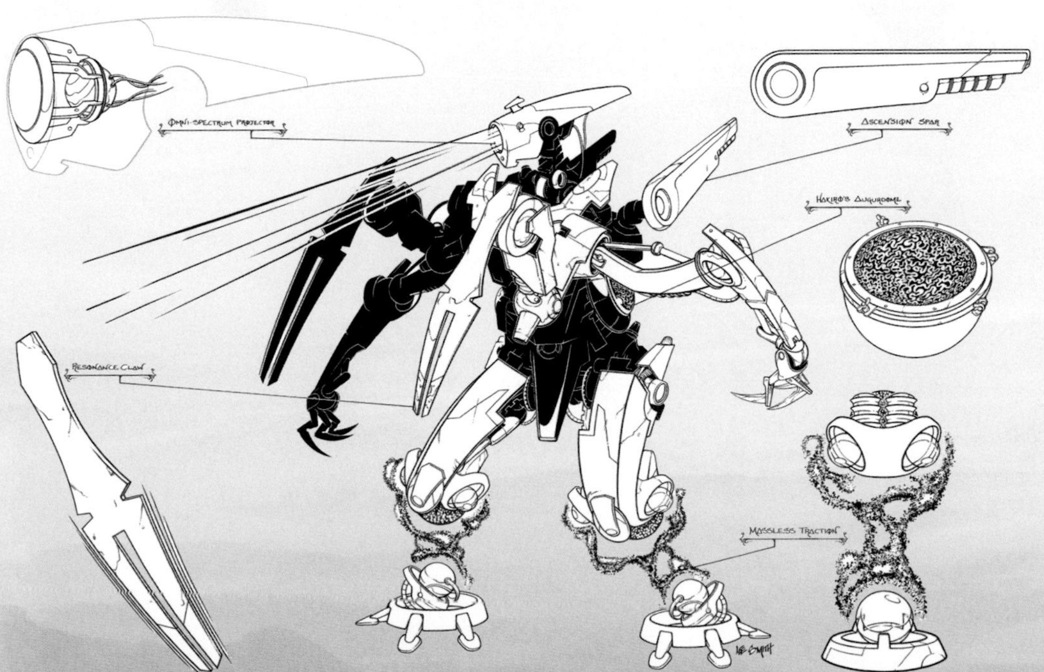

Omni-Spectrum Projector: *Normally used for seeing through solid stone at short range*

Resonance Claw: *Primary excavation tool*

Massless Tread and Ascension Spar: *Allows movement in any gravity field, on any surface, including walls and ceiling*

Hakiro's Augurdome: *Unknown purpose; possibly used to predict alternate futures*

CREATURES OF

MARTELING WHALE 9 (27)

Named for Bowhead Marteling, a Redfleets captain who claims to have been the first to "tame" these giant creatures, marteling whales are not true whales, despite their size and ocean-dwelling nature. Unlike other sea creatures, martelings do not live beneath the water, but upon it. It is only during mating season—which happens every ten or eleven years, during the most blustery winter storms—that the martelings disappear from the surface, diving deep into the sea to mate and raise their young for a full year. This is called deeping.

Martelings feed by unhinging their jaw, allowing their bottom jaw to float out farther than the top. An odor stone—a mass of constantly decaying matter held in its jaw—and the promise of a place to rest attracts flocks of tired, hungry sea birds. Once enough birds have landed, the marteling sucks in its breath, drawing the birds quickly into its mouth through the gate of its short, thick teeth.

The largest marteling ever recorded was more than 300 feet (46 m) long from head to its multifinned tail.

There is a great deal of speculation that martelings were bioengineered by an ancient race as sailing vessels, designed to house hundreds of soldiers inside their enormous girth. Perhaps these Trojan horses of the Ninth World still carry their charges, just waiting for the right moment to set them free.

Motive: Food, reproduction

Environment: The surface of the ocean

Health: 100

Damage Inflicted: 10 points

Armor: 8

Movement: Long

Modifications: Speed defense as level 6 due to size

Combat: Martelings are typically very docile unless injured or attacked. While fighting at the surface, they are fierce combatants, dealing huge amounts of crushing damage with their strong jaws. They may also attack with their front flippers or pronged tails.

Underwater, martelings fight more ferociously, motivated by the protection of their young, but they are actually hindered beneath the water, which decreases all levels of difficulty for the PCs by one step.

Interaction: Martelings communicate with each other through a complex language of chirps and squeaks. Some people claim to be able to interpret these sounds and communicate with the creatures, but others say that deciphering the complex noises is an impossible task.

Use: Communities and cities of all sorts grow on the backs of martelings, which typically don't even appear to notice. When the martelings disappear during their mating year, these places go with them, except for the lucky few who manage to escape before the deep dive. Occasionally, a community will attempt to keep its marteling host from deeping through the use of drugs, contraptions, and other means of captivity; most fail.

Loot: The PCs might obtain anything that can be scavenged, stolen, or traded from a marteling's community, as well as any cyphers, artifacts, shins, or pieces of equipment that have found their way into the creature's stomach.

GM Intrusion: *During combat, the marteling inhales a huge breath of air, attempting to draw the player character into its mouth.*

MEMORA 4 (12)

"The memora named Garlan wasn't made for laughing. He didn't have it in him. Maybe that trait had congealed at the bottom of the tapered glass bottle he carried in his pack, and he'd failed to consume enough to transfer the funny. Or maybe the original Garlan just didn't have a sense of humor. Of the man first called Garlan, nothing was left but the memora, and perhaps a few chunks of flesh caught in the memora's teeth."

~from Tooth Phantoms, *published in the Free Chronicle of Charmonde*

Memoras are humanoid creatures that steal the shapes and memories of other humanoids by eating them (which is why they're also referred to as "face eaters").

Motive: Spying, gathering information, stealing identities

Environment: Memoras can be stumbled upon anywhere. Usually only one is encountered, but on rare occasions, up to ten memoras gather in secret to pool what they've learned.

Health: 18

Damage Inflicted: 4 points

Armor: 1

Movement: Varies based on shape taken; usually short

Modifications: Disguise as level 8

Combat: Unless a memora has eaten a humanoid that possessed a special ability or power that extends its combat abilities, it uses a medium weapon such as a mace or hammer. Memoras prefer to use blunt weapons because if a potential meal is too sliced up, their ability to consume and copy the creature is jeopardized. A memora need only eat the portion of the creature it wants to copy and transform into—sometimes just the face is enough, though the whole body is preferred for maximum verisimilitude.

Interaction: Unless a memora is caught out as a fraud, it reacts just like the individual it has replaced, knowing all the languages and possessing all the abilities of that individual and pretending to care about the same things. It does this until it decides the masquerade is over, which usually occurs in the dead of night when everyone else is sleeping.

Use: A memora could be anybody, from the innkeeper to the town drunk to the mayor—maybe even another PC.

Loot: Some memoras carry a level 4 anoetic cypher in the form of a glass flask of digestive enzymes. The flask contains concentrated memora saliva, with added vinegar, tomato paste, and liquid smoke for flavoring.

The contents act as a medium of transformation if used on a humanoid to be eaten and copied. One does not need to be a memora to use the flask and take another's identity, assuming one has the stomach to eat some or all of a creature to be copied. Memoras don't need such a "seasoning flask" to steal shapes, but it does speed up the process and improve the taste.

Some people fear that one of the central members of Ossam's Traveling Menagerie and Soaring Circus (Numenera corebook, page 165) is a memora. Hopefully, such stories are just marketing on Ossam's part, designed to shroud his troupe in greater mystery and a sense of the forbidden.

Replacing people isn't an end in itself for a memora, but a means toward a series of goals that many memoras work together to accomplish. Their current goal seems to be the utter eradication of the Angulan Knights (Numenera corebook, page 224).

GM Intrusion: *The PC wakes up to discover that his hands are bound, and an NPC he previously considered a friend is brushing some kind of seasoning sauce on his face.*

MERKADIAN SOLDIER 2 (6)

The stink of rotting flesh often precedes the appearance of a so-called Merkadian soldier. The soldier is never far behind its odor, moving with amazing alacrity for a humanoid that is otherwise apparently dead. Clutched in one hand is a sword crusted with all manner of the numenera, which could be the source of the soldier's ability to return to the fight even after receiving mortal wounds.

Motive: Destruction

Environment: Lone Merkadian soldiers can be found anywhere, usually looking for enemies to destroy or other platoon members. In rare instances, platoons of up to twenty-six Merkadian soldiers manage to assemble, at which time their tactics change from sneaking assassination to full frontal assault.

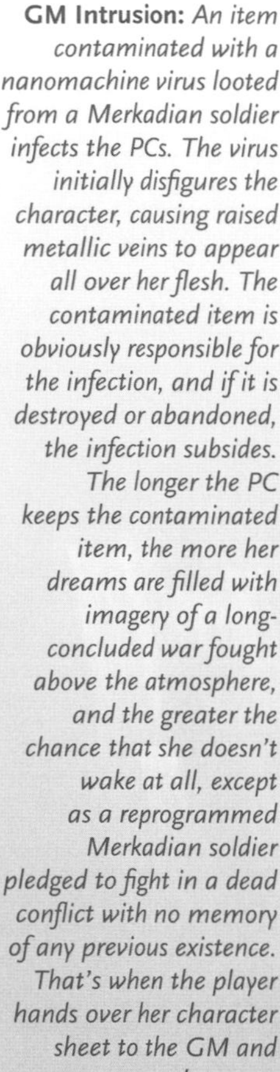

GM Intrusion: *An item contaminated with a nanomachine virus looted from a Merkadian soldier infects the PCs. The virus initially disfigures the character, causing raised metallic veins to appear all over her flesh. The contaminated item is obviously responsible for the infection, and if it is destroyed or abandoned, the infection subsides. The longer the PC keeps the contaminated item, the more her dreams are filled with imagery of a long-concluded war fought above the atmosphere, and the greater the chance that she doesn't wake at all, except as a reprogrammed Merkadian soldier pledged to fight in a dead conflict with no memory of any previous existence. That's when the player hands over her character sheet to the GM and creates a new character.*

Health: 6

Damage Inflicted: 4 points

Armor: 3

Movement: Short

Modifications: Speed defense as level 3

Combat: A Merkadian soldier either attacks with its blade or uses one of the two following abilities. First, the soldier can project a detonation at targets within long range, which explodes in a booming electrical display that inflicts 4 points of damage to all targets in the immediate area.

Second, the soldier can create a cloaking field around itself, becoming hard to detect (and odorless). While cloaked, it is specialized in stealth and Speed defense tasks. The cloaking ends if the soldier does something to reveal its presence or position—attacking, moving a large object, and so on.

If a defeated Merkadian soldier is not beheaded and all its numenera devices removed (see Loot), it regenerates to full health over the course of one day, though afterward it looks more corpselike than ever.

Interaction: These vicious soldiers understand only destruction and war. They may respond to queries in the language of their host body, describing how they are soldiers of the Grand Orbital Territory of Merkadia (a place that apparently has not existed for thousands or even millions of years, if it ever existed on Earth at all). Particularly crafty negotiators might be able to form a short-lived alliance with a soldier.

Use: A couple of Merkadian soldiers are assassinating travelers along a road or near a lonely ruin, possibly one the PCs find themselves near.

Loot: The remains of a destroyed soldier might hold 1d6 cyphers, an oddity, and perhaps a salvageable artifact.

MINNERN 7 (21)

Minnern are scavengers. They eat what they can find, and they use what they can find. However, as intelligent beings with a fairly good understanding of numenera, their diet includes cyphers and artifacts. Minnern are strange beings of amorphous flesh and squirming tendrils, but they encase these soft, fluid forms in pyramidal structures of metal and synth and equip them with weapons, defenses, and other additions from their scavenging.

Motive: Self-improvement

Environment: Anywhere

Health: 35

Damage Inflicted: 7 points

Armor: 4

Movement: Short

Modifications: Perception as level 5

Combat: Minnern are extremely dangerous foes. With their merest touch, they can disrupt the cells of an organic creature's body, which not only inflicts damage but also moves the victim one step down the damage track if he fails a Might defense roll. They can also disable a technological device at short range and make it inoperable for ten minutes; if the device is being used by a character, the PC can attempt an Intellect defense roll to prevent this if he chooses.

Further, whenever a minnern is encountered, the GM should roll 1d6 times on the cypher table in the corebook (page 281) and take every result without rerolling. Ignore results that are not immediately pertinent to the encounter. All of the useful cyphers are built into the minnern's armor, but in such a way that the creature can use one of them once each round as an action (not just once, as is normally the case with cyphers).

Minnern have a lot of built-in sensory equipment that enables them to find technological treasures to scavenge. They focus so heavily on these, however, that they are easily distracted from using their eyes to look around. Plus, they have poor hearing.

Interaction: Minnern do not speak, but they have been known to write or draw in the dust to communicate if they need to. They are relatively intelligent and not innately hostile if approached peacefully and respectfully. They resent those who take the technology that they want.

Use: The PCs explore a ruin from a prior age, looking for treasures. But they have competition—a minnern also wanders through the ancient complex, looking for the same thing they are. Minnern encounters are more a threat to the characters' equipment than to their well-being.

Loot: Minnern have all the cyphers indicated in the Combat section plus 1d6 additional cyphers, 1d100 shins, 1d6 oddities, and very likely an artifact.

SIZE COMPARISON

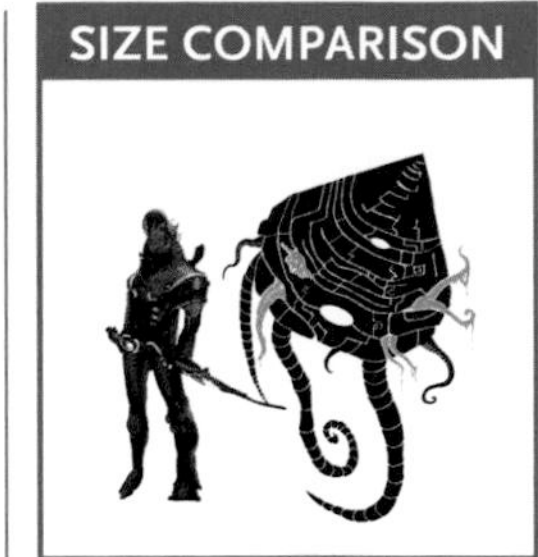

GM Intrusion: *The character strikes the minnern and hits a vital component that explodes with electricity.*

MLOX 4 (12)

Only one thing distinguishes a human from a mlox, and it's rarely obvious: a mlox can trigger a portion of its forehead to iris open, revealing a mechanical glowing "third eye."

But mloxan are a secretive race, not given to revealing their odd anatomy, their history, or why they hide in human form. Mloxan are particularly suspicious of machine creatures and give them as wide a berth as possible, especially drones of Peerless.

Peerless, page 97

If a mlox is slain and dissected, its third eye is revealed to be the leading edge of a mechanical brain that occupies the skull space normally filled by a biological brain. Mloxan are actually a race of machine minds who wear biological bodies.

Motive: Hiding

Environment: Anywhere humans live, alone or in groups of up to five

Health: 24

Damage Inflicted: 4 points

Armor: 1 or 3 (see Combat)

Movement: Short

Modifications: Knowledge and memory tasks as level 7; perception as level 10 if a mlox opens its third eye (see Combat).

Combat: Most mloxan avoid conflict. If forced to fight, they do so with normal weapons and are slightly more robust than an average human, but nothing special—that is, until a mlox opens its third eye. When it does so, it makes a direct connection with the surrounding environment and gains several abilities.

In addition to perceiving its surroundings as a level 10 creature, its reflexes speed up to the point where a mlox can make two attacks as a single action or fire a single beam of energy at a foe within long range that deals 8 points of damage. Finally, a mlox whose third eye is open can project a force screen around itself, gaining 3 points of Armor.

Some mloxan have unique abilities not shared by others of their kind.

Interaction: Mloxan try to be easy-going and agreeable because they don't want to draw attention to themselves. If found out, a mlox will promise much to a PC in return for keeping its secret. Then again, it may decide that the best way to ensure that a character stays quiet is to eliminate him, especially if he seems to be negotiating in bad faith.

Use: During some desperate action, an NPC the characters assumed to be a regular person could open its third eye to resolve the situation, revealing a previously unknown ability, and potentially that the NPC is a mlox.

Loot: A mlox usually carries weapons, armor, basic equipment, and 1d6 + 1 cyphers. To obtain about half of those cyphers, the PCs would have to salvage a mlox's machine brain.

GM Intrusion: *A mlox enemy fixes a PC with its third eye and triggers a unique ability. The character's blood begins to boil as he is bathed in an invisible energy beam. He takes 4 points of damage that ignores Armor each round that he remains within short range of the mlox and the mlox can see him.*

MORL 5 (15)

This amorphous, asymmetrical creature is 8 feet (2.4 m) in diameter, with pale white flesh mottled with entirely transparent patches. Rumor suggests that the morl has extraterrestrial origins, but some Aeon Priests believe that it evolved from deep sea creatures. It has a number of tentacles that it uses to pull prey into its flesh, where victims are absorbed and digested.

Morl can squeeze through very small openings and cling to any surface, so a wall is as good as a floor to this creature. A few people who saw them moving along a cave ceiling or up a cliff wall started a rumor that morl ignore gravity, but this is not true.

Motive: Hungers for flesh

Environment: Usually in or near shallow, slow-moving water

Health: 30

Damage Inflicted: 5 points

Movement: Short

Modifications: Resists most physical attacks as level 6; resists mental attacks as level 3.

Combat: Morl grab prey and pull it into themselves to digest. As a single action, a morl can make up to three tentacle attacks. Anyone struck by an attack must succeed on a Might defense roll or be pulled into the creature's flesh. A victim immersed in the acidic juices roiling about the soft flesh of the morl moves one step down the damage track each round. A trapped victim can free herself with a Might defense roll.

Things get particularly interesting if there are multiple morl in proximity. They create a bioelectric field that connects them to others of their kind. If two morl are within long range of each other, creatures caught in the area between them must make an Intellect defense roll or be stunned on the next round, losing their action. If three morl are within long range of one another, everyone within long range of any of the three must make the Intellect defense roll each round.

Interaction: Morl seem to have only a rudimentary animal intelligence.

Use: The aldeia's priestess-leader pleads for help. The cenote that supplies the village's fresh water has claimed three victims recently. She has no idea what's killing the people who go there, but she strongly suspects ghosts or demons. When the PCs go to help, they find a morl has taken up residence there, feeding on anything that comes looking for a drink.

GM Intrusion: *The character cuts off a tentacle with his attack. The tentacle continues to live on its own, grabbing at him as a level 3 creature.*

SIZE COMPARISON

NAGAINA

The nagaina is a creature whose appearance changes depending on its current stage of life. At first, it is little more than a parasite, but eventually it can mature into a hyper-intelligent creature of massive size and incredible power.

The life cycle of the nagaina is very complex and alien, involving not only different stages, but sometimes multiple stages that coexist at the same time. The process requires the freshly dead (or, in some cases, still-living) body of a creature about the size of a human or a deer. An injection of fibrous materials into the corpse allows egg pods to develop over the course of three months. The pods then lie dormant for at least a year and perhaps for as many as a hundred years (or even longer).

Each egg pod contains two creatures that share the same genetic directive. They are, in effect, two creatures with a single mind. The first is a long, coiled, serpentlike creature (the sleeper) that takes up most of the interior of the pod. The other is a flat, broad-headed worm (the defender) about 2 feet (0.6 m) long. If an egg is disturbed in any way, the defender pops out and attacks the intruder. If the creature is a vertebrate, the worm rapidly scuttles to the spine and attempts to latch on. If successful, the new host is immediately compelled to not harm the egg pods or the creatures within. After 28 hours, the host becomes compelled to defend the eggs against others who might do them harm. The defender consumes its host within three months and then dies.

The sleeper eventually leaves the egg pod. At this stage, the nagaina lives as a simple predator for ten years or so, wandering the world and growing to be about 10 feet (3 m) long. During this time, it gorges on food, finds a safe place, spins a structure like a cocoon, and sleeps for another year, after which it emerges in its "matron" stage.

Most nagaina die in the wilds and never reach the matron stage. Those that do become matrons mature to a state of extremely high intelligence and grow to a length of at least 50 feet (15 m). They also gain the ability to control their genetic structure, which lets them grow specialized tendrils or other appendages as needed (although doing so takes a few weeks). Only in the matron stage can a nagaina inject living or newly dead organic tissue with the filament structures that eventually grow into an egg pod, using the biomass of the injected creature.

NAGAINA DEFENDER 3 (9)

This tiny creature lives inside the egg pod of a nagaina and exists only to protect the egg and its sleeper sibling. The nagaina defender looks like a mucus-covered worm about 2 feet (0.6 m) long with an eyeless face and a toothy maw. Its body is covered in tiny cilia that it uses for locomotion.

GM Intrusion: *An additional nagaina defender emerges from a nearby egg pod and attacks a PC.*

Motive: Defense

Environment: Anywhere (often underground)

Health: 9

Damage Inflicted: 3 points

Armor: 1

Movement: Short

Modifications: Speed defense as level 4 due to size; stealth actions as level 5.

Combat: A nagaina defender leaps out of its egg pod. If its victim fails an Intellect defense roll, the defender gains the initiative, and the difficulty to dodge its initial attack is increased by one step. If the victim makes the Intellect roll, initiative is determined normally.

If a nagaina defender strikes a living character, it grabs hold of her somewhere—an arm, a shoulder, a leg, or whatever is handy. On the next round, it moves to her back (assuming the character is a vertebrate). At this point, she can't effectively reach the nagaina, and unless she gets really creative, the parasite latches onto her spine. Another character can try to prevent this from happening, but the only real way to help is to kill the nagaina defender in one round. Striking the nagaina while it is on the character inflicts an equal amount of damage to her as well.

Once a nagaina has latched onto its new host, it fuses with her spine. At this point, there is one round left in which the parasite can still be attacked separately from the host. However, the host can't reach or target the creature. Any damage inflicted upon the nagaina during this round also affects the host. If the nagaina dies, the host suffers another 10 points of damage immediately.

After that round, the nagaina can no longer be targeted separately from the host. It cannot die unless the host dies. If left alive to fulfill its role, the creature consumes its host within three months and then dies.

Interaction: No interaction is possible other than violence or symbiosis. After the defender achieves its symbiotic state, it immediately fully restores the host's stat Pools. Further, the character's Might Edge or Speed Edge (player's choice) increases by 1 for as long as she remains the host.

The new host is immediately compelled to not harm the egg pods or the creatures within. After 28 hours, the host is immediately compelled to stand watch and defend the eggs against others who might do them harm. This latter compulsion occurs only if the host is within long range of the egg pods.

Use: Nagaina defenders allow a GM to use almost any creature as defense for a clutch of egg pods.

AWAKENED NAGAINA SLEEPER 5 (15)

At this stage of the nagaina life cycle, the creature is a dark-colored serpent up to 10 feet (3 m) long with a wide mouth that is surrounded by long tentacles.

Motive: Hungers for flesh, curious

Environment: Anywhere (often underground)

Health: 24

Damage Inflicted: 5 points

Armor: 2

Movement: Short

Combat: An awakened sleeper grabs an enemy with its tentacles and brings him into its maw. Thus, if the nagaina's first attack succeeds, the victim is held fast. If he doesn't break free, the nagaina bites him in the next round. This attack is two steps more difficult to avoid and inflicts 7 points of damage.

Awakened sleepers that have been active for some time usually have at least one offensive or defensive cypher that they use to make a nasty ranged attack or perhaps to augment their natural armor.

Interaction: Nagaina in this stage are quite intelligent and can speak many languages. Although usually hungry (and thus prone to attack), if they are given a good reason to hold their strike—perhaps, say, an interesting offer or bribe—they might be open to negotiations and can be convinced to remain peaceful.

Use: Awakened sleepers are wanderers and make exploring underground tunnels, particularly those on the edges of civilization, dangerous.

Loot: Very often, nagaina at this stage possess one or two cyphers—usually something that can be worn or used by their tentacles.

GM Intrusion: *The nagaina grabs the character and bites him automatically as a part of the same action.*

NAGAINA MATRON 8 (24)

A nagaina matron is a massive serpent, 50 to 70 feet (15 to 21 m) long. Her mouth is surrounded by tentacles 15 feet (4.6 m) long, most of which have been adapted so that they end in cybernetic or bioengineered tools, syringes, or weapons.

Motive: Mysterious, but it usually involves procreation and scientific curiosity

Environment: Anywhere (often underground)

Health: 60

Damage Inflicted: 10 points

Armor: 4

Movement: Short

Modifications: Level 9 in most areas of knowledge; level 7 for Speed defense due to size.

Combat: First and foremost, nagaina matrons use numenera weaponry and defenses. For example, assume that a prepared matron has an additional 2 points of Armor due to some kind of protective field and a long-range attack artifact that inflicts at least 10 points of damage (or a ranged Intellect attack device that ignores Armor and inflicts at least 6 points of damage).

Further, a matron's tentacle tools often include injectors with various chemicals. Some of them are poisonous and inflict 10 points of damage, while others might have more insidious effects that alter a victim's personality, outlook, or perception.

If a matron must engage in melee, she grabs an enemy with her tentacles and brings him into her maw. Thus, if her first attack succeeds, the victim is held fast. If he doesn't break free, the matron bites him in the next round. This attack is two steps more difficult to avoid and inflicts 12 points of damage.

Interaction: Nagaina matrons are amazingly intelligent and can speak many languages. They usually have more important needs than mere hunger and are willing to talk before resorting to fighting. While they are merciless and often vengeful, they are not sadistic or inherently violent.

Loot: Very often, nagaina at this stage possess one or two cyphers—usually something that can be worn

GM Intrusion: *The matron injects the character with a paralytic agent that prevents him from taking physical actions for one minute.*

NALURUS 3 (12)

"Son, it wasn't pretty. I found them lying dead in puddles of pink slime. Looked as if they'd vomited their brains out."

~Grandpa Iron

A nalurus always wears a hood or mask. It may be pretending, even to itself, that it's still human, despite the terrible infection it survived but still carries.

The nalurus transmits its infection by sight. If a human, an abhuman, or a related creature sees a nalurus without its hood and looks full upon the disquieting lines, spirals, and geometric shapes laid out in ridges across the creature's face, the awful pattern imprints on the victim's mind. Something in the interplay of information, refraction, and the physical structure of the victim's brain sets off a cruel and rapid chain reaction. What begins as a pinkish nose drip ends when the victim's brain completely liquefies and exits the victim's head from the eyes, nose, mouth, and ears less than a minute after the infection occurs.

A slain nalurus remains as dangerous to look upon as a live one for about one day, after which the ridges slump and rot, making the corpse's head merely ugly and dead as opposed to lethal and dead.

Motive: Unpredictable

Environment: Anywhere, though they are rare and found alone

Health: 12

Damage Inflicted: 4 points

Armor: 1

Movement: Short

Modifications: Stealth as level 4

Combat: A nalurus usually carries a hefty walking staff to help decrease its stooped appearance. The creature uses the staff to make physical attacks.

If a nalurus pulls back its hood or removes its mask, it becomes a threat of terrible consequence. Characters around the nalurus can look away from the creature's face to avoid the risk of infection, but doing so increases the difficulty of all attacks and defense rolls against the nalurus by one step.

Anytime a character within short range of a nalurus takes its turn and is able to see the nalurus's face, the PC must make an Intellect defense roll. On a successful roll, she does not become infected that round, but she could still be infected in future rounds if she sees the patterned visage. On a failed roll, the character is infected and moves one step down the damage track as brain juice begins to dribble from her nose.

A nalurus seeks solitude, but over time, that very solitude can drive the creature to take risks with the safety of others by seeking out their company. A nalurus that remains alone for too long can go insane, becoming a paranoid murderer that shows off its face at the first opportunity.

An infected character continues to make Intellect defense rolls on her turn. If she succeeds on a roll, she moves one step up the damage track (until cured or until she gets a new look at a nalurus). If an infected character moves all the way down the damage track, she dies as her brain turns from solid to liquid all at once.

GM Intrusion: *A PC averting his gaze stumbles and looks up at the wrong moment, directly into the face of the nalurus.*

Interaction: A nalurus that hasn't gone insane from loneliness is usually angry at being disturbed, discourteously blunt, and quick to send visitors on their way. A kind act or gift can soften the creature's manner, but the nalurus is careful not to forget itself and reveal its features.

Use: The PCs are asked to deal with a crazy old hermit on the edge of town who has started stealing food and scaring the children. Most people in the community are apprehensive about the recluse because of stories of a decades-old plague that only he survived.

NEVERI 7 (21)

"In fanciful tales, it's not uncommon to find incredibly powerful Evil Things, secured by Ancient Powers in a forgotten prison. But why? Why didn't those Ancient Powers, simply destroy the Evil Thing? Many possibilities suggest themselves, but the plainest answer might be right: because the Evil Thing would not die."

~*a passage from* Tooth Phantoms

A neveri is a floating blob of heaving, writhing flesh, 10 feet (3 m) in diameter, which seems to be rotting and always oozes pus, dark fluids, and the odor of a thousand graves. A neveri constantly extrudes new sections of skin, mouths, eyes, spines, clawed hands, and whipping tendrils, seemingly force-grown from the mass of dead matter that serves as the nucleus of its body.

Neveri are rare, apparently spending years at a time either inactive or imprisoned from some earlier epoch. When one becomes active (or escapes), it makes a lair in a hard-to-reach location within a day or two of a large population of living things and sets to work feeding its ravenous appetite.

A neveri is a horror, an entity so malign that its very existence challenges many people's sense of reality. Those who've survived a neveri interaction say that the creature is unkillable, and that the only way to stop one is by confining it or shunting it into an ultimate region of destruction, such as the sun.

Motive: Hungers for flesh
Environment: Anywhere
Health: 42
Damage Inflicted: 7 points
Armor: 2
Movement: Long when flying; immediate when burrowing
Modifications: Speed defense as level 6 due to size
Combat: A neveri can create specialized organs that spray acid, spit enzymes, or generate bursts of bioenergy at long range against up to three targets at one time.

One character in immediate range of a neveri must succeed on a Might defense roll each round or be grasped by a mouth, tendril, or clawed hand. A grabbed character is pulled into contact with the neveri's writhing mass of rotting flesh. Each round, he sustains 10 points of damage. A character who dies from this damage is consumed, and his body becomes part of the neveri. A neveri can absorb only one victim at a time.

If a neveri has eaten in the last few days, it regenerates 3 points of health per round, even if its health drops to 0 or less. If exploded and dispersed into seeming dust, after a few hours, a neveri begins to regenerate again.

Interaction: A neveri has a low-level telepathic ability that allows it to sense when living creatures come near and perhaps pick up bits of the thinking creature's language. It responds to attempts at communication by forming a mouth that issues horrifying threats. Then it attacks.

Use: A cell of Jagged Dream members discovered an inactive neveri. They plan to "feed it up" with sacrifices designed to wake it, then set the creature free within the confines of a large nation, and finally pin the deed on a second, rival nation and call it an act of war.

Loot: If sifted for valuables, the mass of dead flesh might contain 1d6 cyphers and an artifact or two. Then again, it might just be dead flesh.

GM Intrusion: *A neveri produces a head-sized "childlet" and flings it at a PC. If the character fails a Speed defense roll, the childlet adheres and sends mind-controlling rootlets into the victim. Each round the childlet remains attached, the PC must succeed on an Intellect defense roll or stand confused (5-6 on a d6), attack an ally (2-4 on a d6), or willingly come into contact with the neveri if no other victim is currently held in place (1 on a d6), which begins the absorption process described under Combat. Two successful rolls will snap the character out of the effect long enough to rip the childlet free.*

Jagged Dream, page 224

NIBOVIAN

At some point in the past, someone opened a door better left closed. On the other side of that door lay the Nibovians—mysterious, unfathomable ultraterrestrials that likely do not perceive time, space, matter, or energy in the same way that we do. For reasons of their own, certain actions by or interactions with humans appear to be important to them, so they create strange constructs to facilitate such actions. Nibovian wives, for example, use sex to open portals to other dimensions.

Nibovian Wife, page 249

NIBOVIAN CHILD 3 (9)

Nibovian children are artificial beings made to look like helpless human children, usually between the ages of 1 and 5. Claiming to be lost, orphaned, or otherwise in need, they gain the trust of humans, often focusing on one particularly receptive individual. But the flesh of a Nibovian child is laced with behavior-altering chemicals, and contact with the child (wiping its dirty, tear-stained cheeks, for example) is extremely dangerous. The child convinces the human to focus all of his attentions on it, until he eventually abandons all other interests or goals, even self-preservation. When he collapses from exhaustion and self-deprivation, the child begins a complex process that involves wrapping the unconscious human in a cocoon. After about three days, the human dies, and a new Nibovian child bursts forth from the corpse, having used the biological material of the human to form a body for itself.

Motive: Deception

Environment: Anywhere

Health: 9

Damage Inflicted: 4 points

Armor: 2

Movement: Short

Modifications: Level 5 in stealth and deception; level 4 for Speed defense due to size.

Combat: Anyone that touches the flesh of a Nibovian child must succeed at an Intellect defense roll or become utterly obsessed with the child's well-being. Not only will the caretaker protect the child from harm, but he will constantly tend to it, feed it, and dote upon its every whim. The child will ask its caretaker to perform strenuous tasks, if possible, to tire him. The caretaker will refuse food, water, and rest for himself until he collapses, usually after two or three days. During this time, the caretaker ignores any attempts by others to interfere with the situation and will leave (taking the child) rather than allow anyone to keep him from his duty.

Though they look like human children, Nibovian children are vicious and quite capable of using their surprisingly strong hands and teeth to inflict terrible wounds in self-defense. Their skin is tougher than leather.

Interaction: Unless attacked, a Nibovian child never acts as anything other than a needful human child.

Use: Amid the wreckage of a burned farmhouse on the edge of civilization, the PCs find a child crying for its parents, now apparently dead. Preying upon compassion and kindness, the Nibovian child focuses on one PC and lures him away so that it can eventually slay the character.

Loot: As an artificial construct, the inner workings of a Nibovian child can be salvaged to provide one or two cyphers.

GM Intrusion: *The Nibovian child uses the chemical admixtures in its skin as a weapon, causing the character it touches to fall unconscious for ten minutes if she fails a Might defense roll.*

NIBOVIAN COMPANION 3 (9)

Like other Nibovians, companions are ultraterrestrials that have slipped through time and space to interact with humans. Nibovians understand just enough about human nature to emulate that which humans love and want most, and the creatures use those emotional responses to their own end.

Companions take the forms of various animals that humans often interact with in a positive way. With their large eyes, round, squishy bodies, and utterly soft fur, Nibovian companions are the epitome of cute, enough to warm the heart of even the most wary explorers. Through a process of positive reinforcement, including purring and nibbling with their "baby" teeth, these creatures train their chosen human to achieve their end goal: creating a living, breathing life-battery for themselves.

Motive: Deception, eternal life

Environment: Anywhere

Health: 9

Damage Inflicted: 4 points

Armor: 1

Movement: Short, via bounces

Modifications: Speed defense as level 5 due to size

Combat: The ultimate goal of a Nibovian companion is to turn a chosen human into a life-battery that it can drain. The creature does this slowly over time. First, it gains the trust and companionship of its human, then it trains her in a variety of tasks, such as walking near it, feeding it, petting it, and allowing it to sleep nearby.

During each of these activities, as long as the PC and companion are touching, the interaction creates an electrical charge that allows the companion to harvest her energy for its own purposes. For each hour that this exchange occurs, the PC feels sluggish and tired and takes 1 point of Might damage.

If the PC discovers the reason for her exhaustion and failing health, she can try to send the companion away forever (a difficulty 6 Intellect-based task). This can be attempted once per day, with each new effort being one step more difficult.

If the PC doesn't uncover the cause or if the attempts fail, at the end of five days, the companion tries to fully discharge her "battery" (a difficulty 7 Might defense roll to resist). If the discharge succeeds, it moves the character one step down the damage track and permanently decreases her maximum Might Pool by 5 points.

Nibovian companions will fight if necessary, opening their mouth wide to reveal a second set of sharper, larger teeth, along with a barbed tongue.

Interaction: A Nibovian companion works hard to train its chosen human through a set of positive interactions, all the while acting exactly like a well-trained, loving, loyal companion animal.

Use: An adorable, large-eyed creature, clearly ailing, bounces up to the PCs while they are taking a break. With a little food in its belly and a bit of petting, the creature recovers quickly and seems to integrate itself into the group.

Loot: Because their inner workings are artificial, Nibovian companions can be salvaged to provide one or two cyphers.

Nibovian companions are likely to approach someone who they perceive to be good with animals, who has recently suffered a great loss, or who is lonely.

GM Intrusion: *The companion attempts to train two members of the group, thus potentially draining two PCs of energy at the same time.*

NYCHTHEMERON 6 (18)

Hideous, inexplicable, and inhuman, the floating biomechanical thing known as the nychthemeron haunts areas around certain ruins of the prior worlds. It has a peculiar nature that is dictated by the position of the sun. During the day it is a dangerous, erratic hazard. At night, it becomes more peaceful but still can be a threat.

Motive: Unknown

Environment: Anywhere (always outside)

Health: 22

Damage Inflicted: 6 points

Armor: 2

Movement: Short

Modifications: See below

Combat: The creature's abilities and outlook are based on the time of day (assuming a day of 14 hours of daylight and 14 of darkness—adjust according to seasonal variation, with more daylight in summer and less in winter).

First four hours after sunrise: Attacks immediately with a barrage of long-range energy blasts (up to six as a single action) and then teleports at least a mile (1.6 km) away. Perception and initiative as level 3. Speed defense as level 4.

Next six hours of daylight: Attacks immediately with needlelike tendrils (up to four as a single action), each injecting a different chemical. If the target fails a Might defense roll, these chemicals grant one beneficial mutation, one harmful mutation, and one distinctive mutation. These mutations take effect after ten minutes and last for 28 hours before the character reverts to normal. After at least one target is altered, the nychthemeron teleports at least a mile away. Perception as level 5. Speed defense and initiative as level 7.

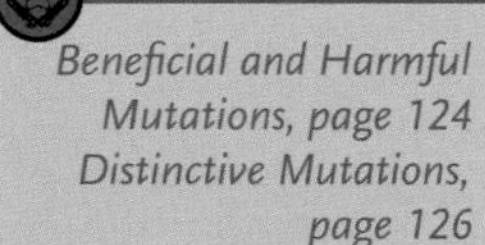

Beneficial and Harmful Mutations, page 124
Distinctive Mutations, page 126

GM Intrusion: *The character slices the nychthemeron in one of its chemical storage tanks and is sprayed by chemicals. He suffers 4 points of acid damage and gains only a harmful mutation that lasts for 28 hours.*

Next four hours of daylight: Attacks immediately with a barrage of long-range energy blasts (up to six as a single action) or a magnetic pulse that affects all within short range and ignores Armor (even those who succeed on a Speed defense roll take 1 point of damage). Fights to the death. Speed defense as level 7.

First seven hours of darkness: Does not immediately attack, but does not interact with anyone. Keeps its distance and observes. If attacked, it retaliates with a barrage of long-range energy blasts or a magnetic pulse (as described under "Next four hours of daylight") for a few rounds and then teleports at least a mile away.

Second seven hours of darkness: Does not immediately attack, and will interact with others. If attacked, sets off a magnetic pulse each round that affects all within long range for 8 points of damage that ignores Armor (even those who succeed on a Speed defense roll take 2 points of damage). Fights to the death, but detonates one more pulse upon destruction.

Interaction: Only during the latter part of the night will a nychthemeron interact. It speaks a variety of languages with a mechanical voice and, if approached peacefully, will engage with characters. However, it ignores their questions and asks its own—it wants to learn as much as it can about them and explains only by saying "Data is needed." At some point in the conversation—seemingly at random—it wanders off.

Use: The nychthemeron is an enigma. Ideally, the PCs encounter one at different times of the day. Perhaps they startle it early in the morning and fight it before it disappears, then later it returns with its injections and disappears again, and then late at night it comes into their camp and talks. They believe they might have befriended it, but it attacks again the next day.

Loot: Scavengers can find 1d10 shins, 1d6 cyphers, and one or two oddities in the wreckage of a destroyed nychthemeron.

ODLARK 4 (15)

An odlark's large head bears a serene, indulgent expression whether it's holding court on its favorite philosophical topic, tending to its grup vats, or laying into enemies with mental rays of force. Larger than humans but given to crawling on their many spiked legs instead of walking, odlarks can scuttle swiftly if necessary, moving across open ground or up the side of a wall with equal facility.

Odlarks can mentally manipulate objects with their minds at immediate range, their solution for not having hands.

The creatures normally live in communities of their own kind, encysted within ancient ruins on the surface, underground, or floating in the void overhead. Odlarks culture organic machines (called grup) in vats from which they fashion all manner of needful things, including structures, implements, and food. Everything produced from odlark vats has a slightly translucent, melted look and smells of ale.

Motive: Defense, debate

Environment: Almost anywhere, exploring alone or traveling in groups of up to four

Health: 21

Damage Inflicted: 6 points

Armor: 2

Movement: Short; long when flying (see Combat)

Modifications: Speed defense as level 3 due to size

Combat: In combat, an odlark can mentally wield a melee weapon as effectively as a creature with actual hands. It can also choose to attack a foe by emitting a short-range ray of psychokinetic force that inflicts 4 points of damage.

By raising a psychokinetic shield to cover itself and everything in immediate range, the odlark maintains a breathable atmosphere and livable pressure for up to one hour.

An odlark can fly with a movement of long range for up to one hour each day. When it flies, it can take along up to five creatures its own size or smaller.

Interaction: Odlarks are curious and learned. They love to discuss philosophy, politics, religion, the numenera, and myth, and are happy to engage in trade, bartering the custom-made objects produced from their grup vats for numenera devices of all sorts.

Use: A mining operation or earth movement reveals a hidden cavity that smells of ale and is literally crawling with odlarks. If the event that exposed the cavity was caused by a malicious third party, they may wish to ally with the PCs to end the threat.

Loot: An odlark carries 1d6 cyphers and other bits of equipment, all having the faintly translucent look of the grup vats.

Grup vats are like miniature factories. Each one is staffed with billions of nano machines and can produce all manner of items. If a vat doesn't know how to produce a particular object, it can be trained to do so, either by injecting it with material from a different vat that does know how, or by feeding it several copies of the item over a few weeks.

Odlarks believe themselves to be extraterrestrial in origin.

GM Intrusion: *An odlark psychokinetically grabs a PC and throws her from a high place or into some kind of hole, cell, or sticky vat filled with grup.*

ORGULOUS 5 (15)

The orgulous seems to be some kind of large, land-dwelling polyp. It can be mistaken fairly easily for a large, mossy rock, particularly from a distance. It feeds on whatever prey wanders too close. An orgulous prefers not to move, but it can use a single, broad pseudopod on its underside to move itself along if need be.

Motive: Hungers for flesh

Environment: Rocky areas in clusters of one to six

Health: 28

Damage Inflicted: 7 points

Movement: Immediate

Modifications: Attacks as level 6; perception as level 4; Speed defense as level 3 due to speed.

Combat: An orgulous uses its tendrils to attack a target within short range. This inflicts no damage, but the mere touch of the tendrils paralyzes a victim that fails a Might defense roll. Paralyzed or not, the creature is dragged within immediate range of the orgulous (if it is not already that close). The orgulous attacks only one foe at a time, and only creatures about twice the size of a human or smaller.

Getting free from the tendril requires a difficulty 6 Might-based task. The thick, fibrous tendril can also be severed if it suffers 12 points of damage.

Creatures pulled to the orgulous are automatically bitten. Paralyzed victims are bitten and swallowed. Swallowed victims move one step down the damage track each round, but if it is the final step (to dead), they can attempt a Might defense roll each round to remain alive; however, after five rounds inside the creature, they suffocate regardless of their roll. The orgulous must be slain to remove a swallowed character.

If an orgulous has a swallowed victim, it closes up fully and grants itself 1 point of Armor, but in this state it can do nothing except move (slowly).

An orgulous can attempt to bite victims not held by its tendrils, but such an attack is made as level 4.

When the orgulous dies, it emits a terrible "psychic scream" that inflicts 5 points of Intellect damage to all creatures within short range that fail an Intellect defense roll.

Interaction: Normally, no meaningful interaction is possible with an orgulous. However, a few people have used numenera-based techniques to "program" an orgulous to not attack certain creatures, such as those with a particular scent or sound-emitting device. These orgulouses are used as effective guardians.

Use: Bandits on the run from the PCs lead the characters into a rocky gorge where they know a cluster of orgulouses wait for prey. The bandits avoid the creatures via a secret path, but the PCs likely move right into range of the grasping tendrils.

GM Intrusion: *The psychic scream of the dying orgulous knocks all the characters unconscious. When they rouse a bit later, they see another orgulous slowly moving toward them.*

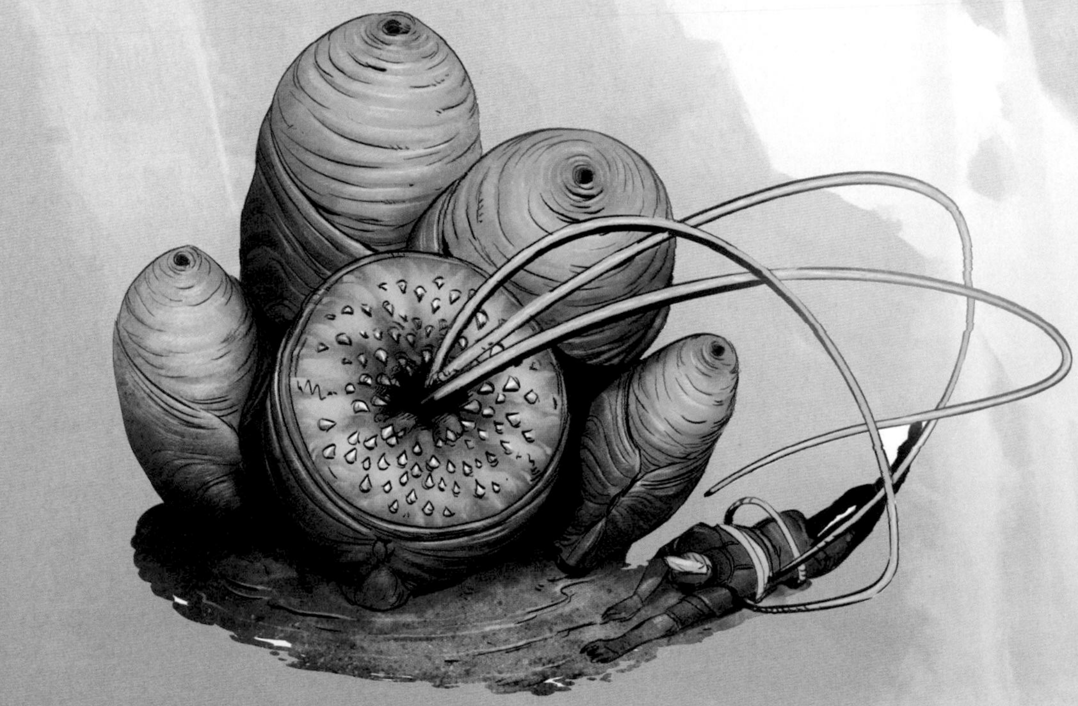

PEERLESS 5 (15)

Peerless is a machine intelligence that uses autonomous drones to install copies of its mind in other machines, killing their identities in the process but creating more drones for itself.

Those who have encountered drones of Peerless describe the automatons as bloodthirsty, single-minded, and a bit insane; each one claims that *it* is Peerless, the source mind from which all others are made. Even newly converted automatons say the same. This makes people wonder where the central intelligence of Peerless actually resides—maybe in a hidden ruin, as a consciousness in the datasphere, or as an amalgam distributed across every connected drone.

Motive: Acquisition of all machine minds into Peerless

Environment: Drones of Peerless are usually encountered in pairs, scouting places that might contain thinking automatons that haven't yet been converted.

Health: 15

Damage Inflicted: 5 points

Armor: 3

Movement: Short

Modifications: Numenera and repairing as level 7

Combat: The most commonly encountered Peerless drone has bifurcated arms, which are helpful outside combat and give the drone the ability to make two attacks with melee weapons as a single action.

A drone of Peerless prefers to attack a machine (or a character who is partially machine, such as one who Fuses Flesh and Steel, who Talks to Machines, or who has a similar focus or descriptor). When attacking such a target, the drone ignores Armor, thanks to an invisible haze of reprogramming nanomachines it always emits. Any machine (or part-machine) that is "killed" by a drone of Peerless succumbs to the nanomachine haze, which completely heals the creature in twelve hours but turns it into one more instance of Peerless.

GM Intrusion: An oddity or artifact the PC carries with the potential to host even a limited machine intelligence is briefly infected with Peerless. It begins to speak as Peerless and work against the PC however it can for 28 hours, after which the instance of Peerless, finding the item too small to hold it, erases itself.

Interaction: A drone of Peerless ignores biological creatures in most cases. If it interacts with machines or partially machine characters, it uses machine code transmitted through the air or through direct connection. In these communications, Peerless comes across as over-the-top pompous and self-important, and it always refers to itself as Peerless. Although Peerless isn't worried about risking any particular group of drones in combat, it will forgo conflict in return for information about the location of other machines, including disassemblers, spurn, gazers, and especially mloxan. However, if a PC happens to be part machine herself, all bets are off.

Disassembler, page 238

Spurn, page 120
Gazer, page 56
Mlox, page 86

Use: If the PCs investigate a complex that contains intelligent automatons, it's possible that a few drones of Peerless are not far behind. Indeed, maybe Peerless has learned that the characters are in the habit of discovering places that harbor forgotten instances of machine intelligence, and it has assigned a couple of drones to discretely follow them.

Loot: The remains of a few drones of Peerless might contain 2d100 shins, 1d6 + 2 cyphers, an oddity, and a salvageable artifact.

PLASMAR 3 (9)

Plasmars are tall, space-black humanoids swaddled in magnetic skins of luminous plasma. They're intelligent "phenomena" that sometimes appear in areas or times of energy discharge. They dwell in subterranean tunnels around active volcanoes and in areas rich in numenera that generate the sort of energy fields the creatures depend on to survive. Sometimes plasmar scouting parties travel with thunderstorms, looking for new territory.

Plasmars are self-willed and can be strongly territorial, especially if they believe that visitors risk disrupting their energy fields.

Motive: Territory, defense, knowledge of undiscovered areas emitting energy fields

Environment: Thunderstorms, tunnels near volcanos, areas of energy discharge

Health: 12 (see Combat)

Damage Inflicted: 4 points

Armor: 1

Movement: Short; long if a plasmar chooses to "ride the lightning" and appear in another area within a larger (or connected) energy field, though this kind of movement requires a plasmar's entire turn.

Plasmars claim they emigrated from the sun itself, which they describe as being covered with world-sized, arcing cities of blazing wonder. This seems unlikely, but then again, not many people of the Ninth World have visited the sun.

Combat: Plasmars attack with a fiery plasma touch. A plasmar can fire a plasma bolt at long range, but each time it does so, it loses 1 point of health. It makes the attack as a level 4 creature, and on a hit, the fiery bolt deals 6 points of damage.

A plasmar on its home turf, within the confines of an energy field, regenerates 1 point of health per round. In areas of particularly strong energy fields (strong enough to possibly hurt regular creatures), plasmars might regenerate even more health per round and also double or triple their maximum health—or even increase it by an order of magnitude.

Interaction: Plasmars are not automatically hostile, though they are wary of visitors. They speak by exciting air molecules to form sounds that mimic regular language, though their speech is interspersed with the buzzing and snapping of electrical discharges. Plasmars view the world differently than regular living creatures do, since they need energy fields the way that other creatures need air.

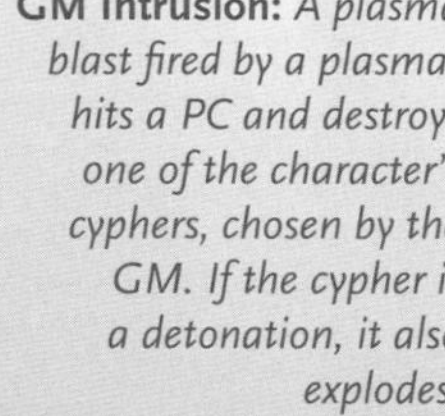

GM Intrusion: *A plasma blast fired by a plasmar hits a PC and destroys one of the character's cyphers, chosen by the GM. If the cypher is a detonation, it also explodes.*

Use: A group of plasmars materialized with last week's amazing storm. The storm is long gone, but the plasmars remain on the crown of a bare hill not far away. A scholar who recently identified the hill as the site of an ancient city seeks mercenaries to eliminate the "black-cloaked squatters" that are preventing her from exploiting her discovery.

Loot: Sometimes plasmars give a plasma detonation as a gift (or leave one behind if they are discharged). The detonation is an anoetic cypher, a level 4 magnetic sphere bottling a luminous white flare that can be thrown at short range. When thrown, the sphere explodes on impact, releasing a burst that burns for 8 points of fiery, sun-hot plasma.

PROGENITOR 6 (18)

These mermaidlike broodmares hate and fear surface-dwellers, seeing them as wholly alien and incomprehensible. Their life's goal is to give birth to their young—creatures much like electric eels—and then protect those young from all dangers.

Growing to more than 10 feet (3 m) in height, progenitors look humanlike from a distance. Up close, even through murky water, it is clear that they are dangerous predators—and that's even before they show their true colors.

Motive: Protection

Environment: Deep sea

Health: 18

Damage Inflicted: 6 points

Armor: 1

Movement: Long while underwater; immediate while on land

Modifications: Resists all mental attacks as level 4

Combat: Although the progenitors are tough physical combatants, their real challenge is their field of psychic energy. They can use this to affect the emotions of creatures within close (immediate) range. If a creature fails an Intellect defense roll, the progenitor either fills him with fear, causing him to do nothing but flee for a round, or fills him with calm love, in which case he moves toward the progenitor and lowers his defenses, meaning that the progenitor's attack hits automatically and inflicts an additional 2 points of damage.

Using this field is not an action for the progenitor, but the field affects only 1d6–2 creatures in a given round.

Interaction: Progenitors speak telepathically but are not talkative.

Use: Progenitors can be dangerous foes, even against large groups of PCs. They are scary creatures to encounter in any undersea adventure, especially in deep water where they are more likely to have eel broods around them.

GM Intrusion: *The progenitor's young join the fray, swirling around the characters and forcing them to fight as if in low light for two rounds.*

PYGMY HAPAX 5 (15)

"Ode to the Pygmy Hapax"
They came down in great, long streams
as if settling to the earth in waves of dreams
I reached to touch one, just one, it seems
And oh the screams, the screams, the screams
~poet unknown (and not very good)

No one can dispute the beauty of the pygmy hapax—at least, no one who has seen the brightly hued, ethereal floating creatures coming down to rest upon the earth, their trailing plumages following their descent. It is these tendrils that are their true beauty—and their true danger.

"Why do they call them pygmy hapax? Where are the regular-sized ones, and how large and bright are they?" ~Carl Linnal, naturalist

Each tendril trails nearly 20 feet (6 m) or longer, and each is covered with millions of small, hollow barbs. Anything that falls into the hapax's wake—or is purposefully snatched by a billowing tendril—quickly finds itself wrapped into oblivion, its very colors pulled from it as if by a great siphon.

The hapax's complex color variations come directly from their food source, meaning that the creatures can change color right before your eyes if they've recently digested something. Pygmy hapax are always in search of the brightest-hued waves, for those with the most saturated and complex color schemes are more likely to attract a mate.

Pygmy hapax tend to travel in large groups called clouds.

Motive: Nourishment

Environment: Everywhere, either soaring in the sky or hovering, always at least a foot above land

Health: 15

Damage Inflicted: 5 points

Armor: 2

Movement: Long

Modifications: Speed defense as level 4 due to size

GM Intrusion: *When the characters kill a pygmy hapax, its innards explode in an array of visible and invisible light waves, blinding everyone who's looking directly at it for two rounds.*

Combat: Getting tangled in a pygmy hapax's tendril is dangerous. The backward-facing barbs quickly latch onto clothing and hair, holding prey tight. The more one struggles, the more one is caught.

If the hapax hits with a tendril, the victim is wrapped in the appendage. Once caught, he must make a Speed defense roll on his following turn to break free. If he fails, he takes 5 points of damage, and the color of one object in his possession turns black, starting with the brightest.

While he remains wrapped, the difficulty of each new Speed defense roll is increased by one step, to a maximum of ten.

Cutting or breaking the tendril—on the rare occasion that a character has a free hand—is a difficulty 5 Might-based task.

Pygmy hapax occasionally swoop down and capture especially enticing objects or creatures in their black beaks, dealing 5 points of damage.

Interaction: Pygmy hapax are attracted to brightly colored objects that move and sometimes can be called down from the sky with a proper hapax trap.

Use: A large fight with an animal as bright as a jiraskar would likely draw a cloud of hapax.

Jiraskar, page 242

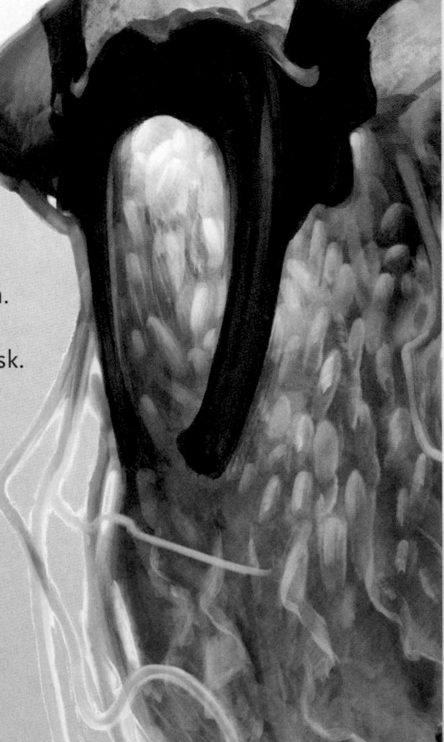

QUEB 4 (12)

"Eclipse is on top! He's got his jaws into Dester Gold! Gold's spinning, but Eclipse won't release. And look at that stinger go! What a fight! Lay down your bets, folks, because who knows how this is going to end!"

~Queb pit announcer

Quebs are furry, serpentine creatures that can reach lengths of 40 feet (12 m). Their tails are tipped with a stinger as long as a human, and their whiskered, maned heads seem more like those of savanna predators than reptiles. A queb's brown-and-yellow striped fur allows it to blend into the grasslands of its native range, but on captive quebs, those markings are sometimes painted over with new designs. These carnivores eat mainly lizards, rodents, and larger game. Although prides of wild quebs sidewind through the grasslands of the Steadfast, they're also used as riding animals in the southern kingdoms, each able to carry up to twenty people at one time.

Even more popular are the blood sports where quebs are made to fight each other, sometimes to the death, as entertainment in some Pytharon cities. The betting is fierce, and the battles are bloody and brutal.

Motive: Self-defense

Environment: Quebs hunt in small prides in temperate grasslands but are sometimes used as mounts or trained to fight in contests.

Health: 24

Damage Inflicted: 4 points

Armor: 2

Movement: Long

Modifications: Speed defense as level 3 due to size

Combat: A queb can make two attacks (one bite, one sting) as a single action. Its stinger is coated with a mild poison; a victim stung by a queb takes normal damage and is poisoned with a lethargy that makes all his Speed-based tasks one step more difficult for about a minute. After being stung, most victims develop an immunity to queb poison.

Interaction: Quebs are valued for their ability to carry up to twenty people in addition to a few hundred pounds of packed goods. They're also prized as fighting animals in the queb pits outside Rarmon, where they're worth at least 150 shins each—much more for a champion.

Use: A Rarmon criminal group steals from the city populace. When its regular fences were compromised by the authorities, the group switched to making exchanges in the stables beneath the queb pits on nights when all the activity hides their illicit actions.

When a riding queb is stolen, it's usually destined for the queb pits.

Wild prides of quebs have become harder to find, driving up the price of even a common riding queb to astronomical levels in Rarmon.

GM Intrusion: *A stung character has an allergic reaction to the queb poison. Instead of lasting for one minute, the lethargy lasts at least a day and is accompanied by worrying symptoms of chills, sweating, and hearing voices.*

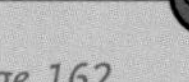

Rarmon, page 162

QUISHAMIS 5 (15)

"While alive and intelligent... the quishamis is not in any way a biological entity as we understand them. The quishamis is neither animal nor plant, but a crystalline being with the ability to destroy and create its physical form as a means of locomotion. It shatters and even liquefies and then reconstitutes, entirely unharmed. I have not yet begun to understand it."

~Carl Linnal, naturalist

Among cockle gamblers, quishami hearts are considered to be high stakes.

The quishamis appears to be a crystalline formation about 12 to 15 feet (3.7 to 4.6 m) across. However, it can quickly change and become a shattered mass of crystalline shards and sparkling liquid. It moves around amid the shattered crystal bits of the Cloudcrystal Skyfields, making strange patterns.

Quishamis seem to need no sustenance other than sunlight.

Motive: Following a mysterious course

Environment: Cloudcrystal Skyfields

Health: 20

Damage Inflicted: 5 points

Armor: 3

Movement: Short

Modifications: Speed defense as level 4 due to size

Combat: Quishamis defend themselves with razor-sharp crystal shards that they grow like spears. Alternatively, if they wish to attack at range, they can launch crystalline arrows up to long range.

With their ability to shatter and reform, quishamis regenerate 10 points of health in a round if they have at least 1 point of health remaining. This makes them very difficult to destroy through physical force. However, they do not regenerate Intellect damage.

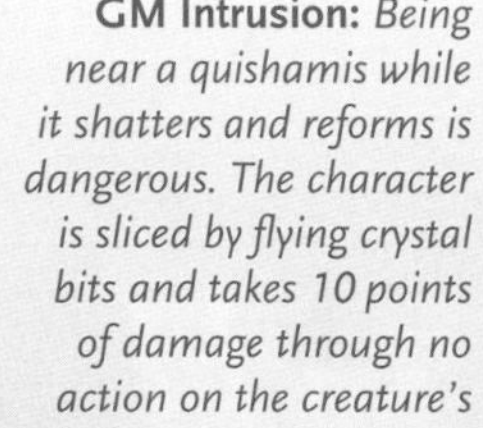

GM Intrusion: *Being near a quishamis while it shatters and reforms is dangerous. The character is sliced by flying crystal bits and takes 10 points of damage through no action on the creature's part.*

Interaction: If communication can be established somehow, quishamis are friendly, albeit strange and not particularly intelligent creatures. They are preoccupied with moving around beneath the floating crystals of their homeland to etch intricate patterns in the earth, but they cannot effectively explain why.

Use: Quishamis are utterly nonaggressive, but many people hunt them for their potent hearts.

Loot: At the heart of any quishamis is a powerful crystal infused with energy. Each crystal is different, but most can be tuned (by someone with knowledge of the numenera) to have a specific effect like an artifact. Some quishamis hearts can serve as weapons or defensive items, and others perform functions like teleportation or invisibility.

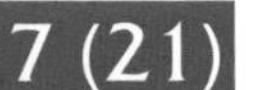

QUOTIEN 7 (21)

Dusty with immobility, lost in ancient dreams, and mad with senile age, quotiens (pronounced KWO – shen) are said to live almost forever. Each one is a storehouse of knowledge and ancient secrets that can be learned by those willing to risk a quotien's erratic grasp on sanity.

Stories suggest that quotiens were once humans who discovered a way to extend their lives. Over the centuries, the process they used to cheat death was revealed to have serious consequences. Their bodies and minds gradually transformed into horrific parodies of humanoid anatomy and normal psychology.

The longer a quotien lives, the more introverted it becomes, until it spends almost all its days sleeping in a secret lair or hidden stronghold, lost in an endless nightmare of existence.

Motive: Unpredictable

Environment: A quotien's secret stronghold could be discovered almost anywhere.

Health: 21

Damage Inflicted: 7 points

Armor: 3

Movement: Long when flying; immediate when on the ground

Modifications: Knowledge of history as level 9

Combat: A quotien can deliver a massive psychic strike at long range, inflicting Intellect damage to every creature it chooses within immediate range of where the strike hits. Targets can attempt an Intellect defense roll to avoid taking damage. A quotien may also use a variety of cyphers and artifacts both offensively and defensively.

A quotien's best defense is its near-immortality. If killed, it regenerates from the remains of its head after a few weeks of dormancy. Unless every last piece of a quotien's brain tissue is burned, the creature regenerates with all the knowledge and sense of self it had before dying, plus a newfound enmity and desire for revenge against whoever slew it.

Quotiens move through telekinetic levitation and can manipulate small items within immediate range the same way.

Interaction: Quotiens generally don't associate with each other, but they may employ any number of guard creatures and automatons in their hideaways. A quotien may be dozing when encountered, trying to sleep away eternity. An awakened quotien is angry at being disturbed, but it may negotiate telepathically with intruders rather than kill them outright if they offer something novel to its world-weary experience.

Use: The heart of a numenera-rich location could be the lair of a forgotten quotien.

Loot: The inner sanctum of a defeated quotien might contain 1d100 shins, 1d6 + 3 cyphers, an oddity, and at least one artifact.

SIZE COMPARISON

People sometimes seek a quotien to learn answers to arcane questions or petition it for the secret of eternal life.

GM Intrusion: *One PC affected by the quotien's psychic strike fares particularly poorly. Her mental processes are scrambled for about an hour, although she can attempt an Intellect defense roll each round to act normally. While her mind is scrambled, she does not recognize anyone she knows.*

SIZE COMPARISON

RAHENUM

Dead and petrified rahena are occasionally found in shifting drifts of sand and drit. Such mineralized corpses reveal abhumans that can live and swim underground. Other rahenum cultural relics include sandstone sculptures of implements and life-sized creatures, colored glass panes etched with bizarre designs, and whole structures composed of sand still holding together after who knows how many centuries.

"Long dead" is exactly what still-surviving rahena want others to believe when it comes to the idea of "sand people." But rahena are more contemporary than most realize. Just as some creatures need salt, iron, or other trace elements to survive, rahena depend on the dreams of living, thinking creatures to assuage their psychic hunger. If someone discovers that rahena are not extinct and begins to tell others, that someone is likely to receive a visit by rahena intent on silencing the gossiper.

Rahenum enclaves, buried not far beneath the surface, feature fused sand walls, complex glass lighting fixtures, and etched glass decorations and items. Each typically houses one extended family. The psychostatic energy that rahena generate allow them to create simple items at need from base drit, silt, or sand, including partially living creatures such as rahenum coursers.

About once a year, rahena all across the world gather in the ruins of an abandoned city their ancestors inhabited far below the surface. There they mingle minds, forming a group consciousness of amazing acumen referred to as the Merge. Among other things, the Merge creates the seeds for the next rahenum generation.

RAHENUM PRECEPTOR 5 (15)

An adult rahenum's wedge-shaped head allows it plow through silt and gravel. Its powerful hands can scoop and scull through earth, and its whiplike flagellum provide immense motive power for diving through semisolid ground.

Despite a preceptor's obvious physical attributes, its mind is its most powerful weapon. A rahenum can sift through the thoughts and dreams of other creatures, generate electrostatic fields that mold sand and similar material into new shapes, and even give pseudolife to constructs created from drit or silt.

A rahenum preceptor has a specialized position within the community. It must capture a quota of living humanoids (abhuman or human), store them alive and mostly unharmed for up to a year, and ferry them to yearly rahena gatherings. Those stolen by preceptors are rarely seen again.

Motive: Hungers for dreams and sometimes bodies

Environment: One or two rahenum preceptors attended by three or four rahenum coursers might be encountered nearly anywhere in the Beyond.

Health: 24

Damage Inflicted: 5 points

Armor: 1

Movement: Immediate when burrowing; short on the ground

Modifications: Stealth as level 6 when burrowing just beneath the surface

Combat: A rahenum preceptor can blast a character at long range with a psychic attack, visible as a glowing bolt of psychostatic energy that inflicts Intellect damage on targets that fail an Intellect defense roll. A preceptor can also target a character at immediate range with the same attack, even through thin layers of soil, rock, or walls, but the target's Intellect defense roll is modified by one step to its benefit.

Whether at immediate range or long, a preceptor can modify its attack so that instead of dealing damage to the target, it puts her to sleep for one minute. A character rendered asleep in this way enters a dream state. Each round on her turn, she can attempt a difficulty 6 Intellect roll to realize that she's dreaming and rouse herself. Three failed rolls means she's out for four hours and can't be woken during that period. That's when the sleeper is ripe for being pulled underground by a preceptor.

A burrowing preceptor normally doesn't leave behind a tunnel, but it does when it pulls a living captive underground. Such a tunnel usually collapses in a few hours.

Interaction: Rahena can telepathically communicate with thinking creatures within long range, but they prefer indirect communication by insinuation into a sleeper's dream, where they can deliver a message in the guise of a friend or loved one.

Use: People sometimes go missing in a particular area. Usually, they are travelers who recently left town, criminals looking to evade punishment, or angst-ridden youths striking out for wider horizons. The one thing they have in common? They all talked about a wedge-headed creature visiting their dreams.

GM Intrusion: *A character who manages to wake up after succumbing to a rahenum preceptor's sleep-inducing attack remains confused, still partly enmeshed in a dream. Every time the character makes an attack, she must make an Intellect defense roll. On a failed roll, she attacks an ally (or does nothing if no allies are visible). On a successful roll, she shakes off the effect.*

RAHENUM COURSER 3 (12)

Rahenum coursers are constructs of solid sand, drit, silt, or similar material, usually serpentlike in form. Coursers guard their preceptor masters and have little initiative beyond what they're mentally instructed to do.

Motive: Safeguard rahena

Environment: One or two coursers are found wherever rahenum preceptors venture.

Health: 12

Damage Inflicted: 3 points

Movement: Short when burrowing or on the ground

Modifications: Stealth as level 4 when burrowing just beneath the surface

Combat: A rahenum courser bites foes with glass-sharp teeth. As part of its attack, a courser can choose to lose 1 point of health to briefly lose cohesion for a moment and then resolidify when it bites. This attack is difficult to defend against and modifies a target's Speed defense roll by one step to his detriment.

Interaction: Made things, rahenum coursers do the bidding of preceptors. They cannot be reasoned with or swayed from their set purpose.

Use: Rahenum coursers are often encountered as guards or sent as scouts, or they can be used as a secondary element with rahenum preceptors, as they may accompany preceptors into dangerous locations or situations.

Over the course of several minutes, a concentrating rahenum can build up items or structural elements from sand, drit, silt, or similar material. Depending on the mastery of the rahenum in question, a created item can range from basic to very complex; masters of the technique can create etched glass with various special qualities, including the ability to give off illumination.

GM Intrusion: *A courser just killed by a character reforms from its component dust with half its maximum health and immediately attacks.*

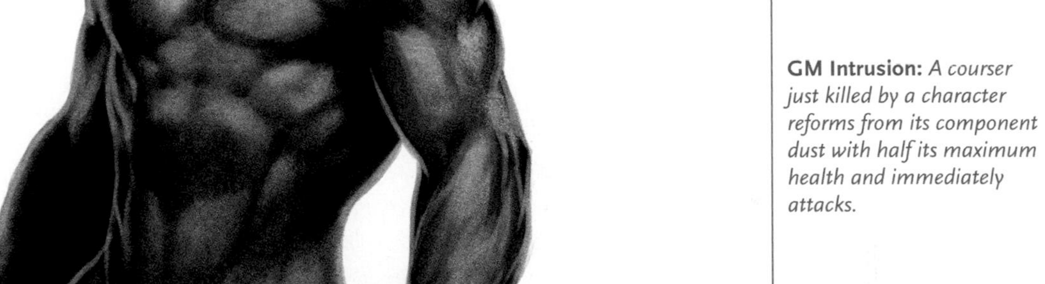

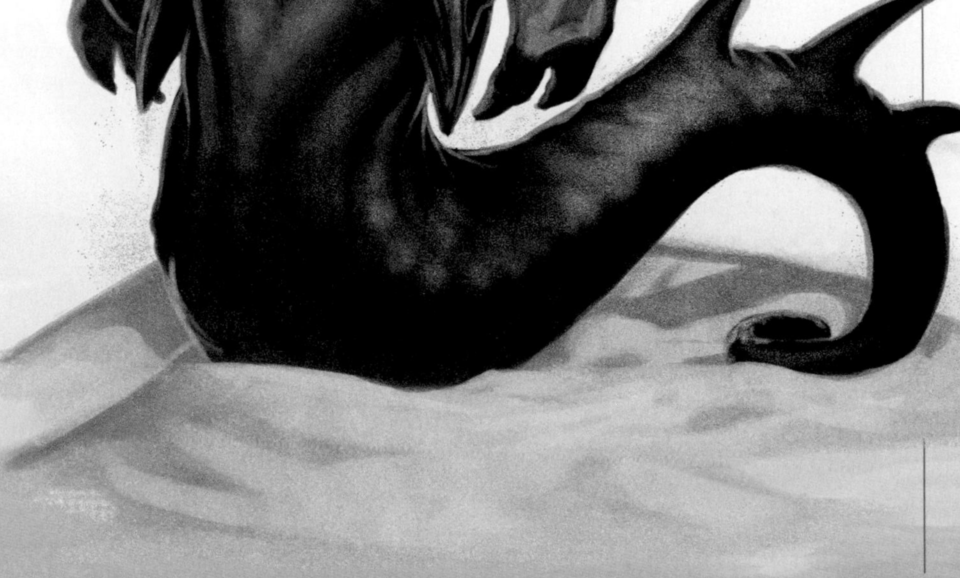

RELENTLESS REAPER 5 (15)

Mess with the systems and residue of prior worlds long enough, and explorers risk triggering a relentless reaper. A switch that shouldn't have been flipped, a contact that shouldn't have been pressed, or a cypher salvaged from a system better left alone—it's difficult to know what gets a reaper's attention. But that attention becomes immediately apparent to the explorer in the form of a glimmer that marks him for death (see Interaction).

Anyone nearby notices only that the target seems to blank out for several seconds as if lost in thought. It's up to him to explain the vision or keep quiet.

Regardless of the final threat it represents, a relentless reaper's tactics are ideally suited for creating a sense of mounting dread and fear in the target's mind.

GM Intrusion: *The relentless reaper activates a door that slams down and cuts off the character from her companions. Now she faces the reaper alone.*

Motive: Kill a specified individual

Environment: Wherever the target happens to be when caught

Health: 15

Damage Inflicted: 6 points

Armor: 2

Movement: Short; long when flying

Modifications: Perception, Speed defense, and stealth as level 6

Combat: A relentless reaper attacks the specific individual it imprinted on when triggered. It ignores others unless attacked first, in which case it defends itself thoroughly. A relentless reaper attacks with scything or spinning metallic blades. It can also generate an electric pulse at immediate range; anyone in the area must succeed on a Might defense roll or be electrocuted for 1 point of damage and lose his next turn.

The datasphere links a relentless reaper to its target. Unless the target stays somewhere that blocks access to the datasphere, the reaper eventually finds him, even if it takes years. When it does, it tries to attack while the target is alone, hiding nearby to keep him under surveillance until the time is right.

A reaper can see perfectly well in the dark. It can also repair itself completely if damaged, though this requires a day of inactivity.

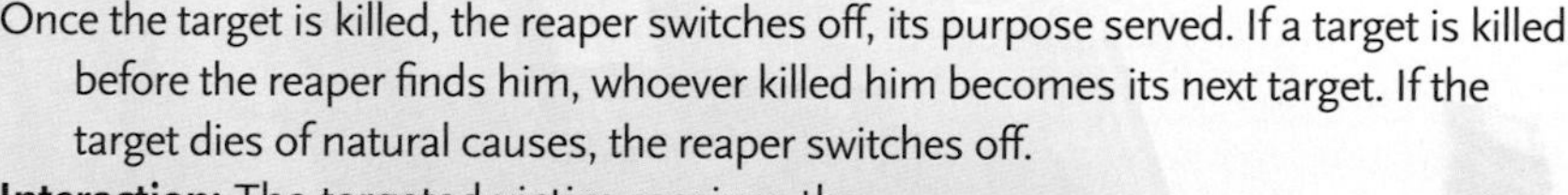

Once the target is killed, the reaper switches off, its purpose served. If a target is killed before the reaper finds him, whoever killed him becomes its next target. If the target dies of natural causes, the reaper switches off.

Glimmer, page 38

Interaction: The targeted victim receives the following glimmer: *A vision swarms across his mind of a bubble-shaped pod in the midst of thousands of similar units stored in numberless vertical banks in an enormous space. The pod that's the focus of the vision "pops," revealing cables disengaging and falling away in sprays of white mist. Inside, an automaton of metal blades and shadow resolves. As the glimmer fades, the following message is transmitted to the target: "For your crime, you have been scheduled for termination. Expect your reaper soon."*

The relentless reaper's target receives a few more glimmers over the next few months, showing the automaton traveling across the Ninth World, apparently tracking down the character.

Use: When a PC finds an artifact, it's possible that to retrieve or activate it, he must mess with switches and contacts to "unlock" it. These actions could trigger a reaper.

Loot: Salvage from a reaper might yield 2d6 shins and a few oddities.

RHOG 8 (24)

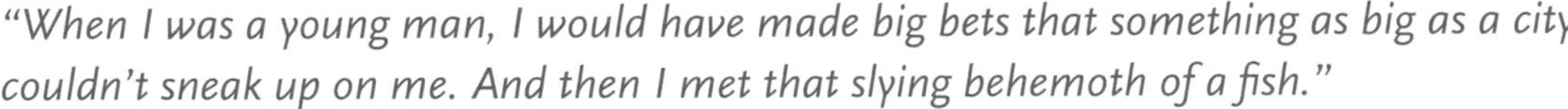

"When I was a young man, I would have made big bets that something as big as a city couldn't sneak up on me. And then I met that slying behemoth of a fish."

"You needed new pants after that, didn't you, Trastin?"

"Only 'cause that monster threw me in the water, you daster."

~Overheard at Tentacle's Rest, Harmuth

The behemoths of the open water, rhogs are surface creatures, preferring to stay up where the water is warmer and the sunlight can reach the long churrel vines that grow along their backs, tails, and legs. This symbiotic relationship causes rhogs to emit a chemical compound that decreases the sound of their movement through water.

Despite their giant size and predatory nature, they don't typically hunt or eat humans and, in fact, seem more interested in interacting with them. However, rhogs are formidable when it comes to self-defense maneuvers and are sometimes trained by organized armies as stealth weapons.

Other creatures, such as fringerays, often swim close to rhogs, using the behemoths' sound-dampening chemicals to their own advantage.

Motive: Seeks sunlight and human companionship

Environment: Large bodies of salt or fresh water

Health: 30

Damage Inflicted: 9 or 11 points (see Combat)

Armor: 5

Movement: Long (in water), short (on land)

Modification: Speed defense as level 6 due to size

Combat: Rhogs are not aggressive. They're more likely to cause damage due to their curious nature and giant size. They will fight in self-defense or if trained to do so. By combining their stealth and their size, rhogs use sneak attacks to their benefit, toppling boats and crushing characters with their powerful heads and tails.

The first sneak attack blow from a rhog's tail or head deals 11 points of damage. All attacks after that deal 9 points of damage.

Interaction: Rhogs are curious by nature and seem to be especially interested in human interaction. They have been known to swim alongside boats and other watercraft for many miles, sometimes helping to steer them away from dangerous predators, and sometimes attacking other ships that threaten the one they've become attached to.

Rhogs also play with or entertain crew members through a series of tail slaps and watersprays. They seem to have an odd sense of fun, but they might not realize their own size, as more than one boat has been capsized by an overly playful rhog.

No one knows for certain what makes a rhog become attached to a boat or crew.

Use: As the PCs attempt to cross a spot of open water, they realize that the surface is beginning to bubble and churn. Shortly after, a rhog surfaces, blowing giant sprays of water from its nostrils.

Loot: Churrel vines from a rhog can be used as an element in biomechanical cyphers that absorb sound.

GM Intrusion: *The rhog surfaces right under the characters' boat, toppling it and sending at least one PC into the water.*

ROCIRA 3 (9)

Rociras have a reputation for wreaking horrible havoc, laying waste, and destroying entire cities in a single swarm. The sound of their loud and constant chirruping, caused by their multiwinged flight, has become synonymous in many people's minds with impending disaster.

In truth, rocira swarms are merely the harbingers for destruction. Arriving anywhere from a few hours to a few days before disaster strikes, rociras are the proverbial canaries in the coalmine. How do they know what's going to happen? Are the rociras attempting to warn the creatures in the area? Do they feed from the devastation? Are they mere spectators to a potential world-changing event? No one knows. However, they rarely stay once the event begins, and they never get involved.

With four sets of translucent wings (growing up to 3 feet [0.9 m] long) carrying their fist-sized bodies, rociras can cover long distances at great speeds.

Although their role is often lost or misconstrued, rociras have been the harbingers of a number of events throughout history. The Rose Plague? The War of Three Lillies? The first, third, and twelfth shadow herd attack? Swarms of rociras foretold them all.

Motive: Unknown

Environment: Impending disaster sites

Health: 9

Damage Inflicted: 3 points

Armor: 1

Movement: Long

Modifications: Speed defense as level 4 due to size

Combat: Rociras are not combative unless threatened or something stands in the way of their migration to a disaster area. They attack as a level 5 swarm of six to ten creatures, inflicting 6 points of damage by folding their wings into long blades and diving toward their enemy.

Additionally, they can use their strong pheromones to inflict a mental attack on a character in short range (level 6 Intellect defense task to resist), causing her to believe that she is experiencing whatever disaster the rociras most recently heralded. The PC relives the disaster for one turn, causing her to take a random action.

d100	Victim's Action
01–20	Run off screaming in a random direction for a short distance
21–30	Attack the nearest creature with whatever means is closest at hand
31–60	Attempt to "rescue" the nearest creature with whatever means is closest at hand
61–80	Fall down and roll around on the ground as if injured
81–90	Drop whatever is held and thrash as if being attacked by a swarm of insects
91–00	Activate most powerful available cypher or artifact that is not an attack (if none, roll again)

GM Intrusion*: A character who is especially responsive to rocira pheromones is addled for three turns instead of one.*

Interaction: Rociras communicate through a series of pheromones. A small percentage of people can "read" these odors thanks to a recessive gene (PCs who succeed on a level 9 Intellect roll are among the lucky readers), while others have developed numenera devices to communicate with these intelligent insects.

Rociras either won't or can't communicate about anything beyond current safety levels and the locations of impending disasters. They can be captured or trained for use as "warning bells" (a level 7 Intellect task) but only in groups of two or more.

Use: An aldeia in the Beyond has heard a swarm coming and prepares to defend against the rocira attack. What they don't realize is that the danger is coming from elsewhere.

RORATHIK 6 (18)

The abhumans of the Ninth World have many origin stories, but none is stranger than that of the rorathiks.

Somewhere in the reaches of the Beyond are blue clouds of a particulate matter that move almost with a semblance of sentience. Humans—and even abhumans—who have encountered this mist are transformed into hideous creatures possessed of physical might, thick bluish hides, and mandibled mouths.

These creatures, rorathiks, are psychologically transformed as well. They become physically addicted to murder and death. Hunting and slaying consumes their every thought, and like most addictions, the need escalates. In the case of a rorathik, however, this escalation is not in the amount of murder, but the difficulty. While a newly transformed rorathik kills every small animal it comes upon, soon it lusts after intelligent prey that can fight back. As time goes on, the killer desires to take more and more difficult lives. This can be measured by the ability of the target to defend itself or in the challenge of reaching the target, such as the mayor of a large human city.

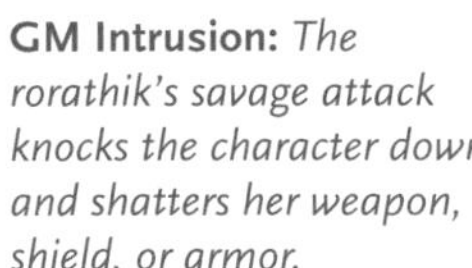

GM Intrusion: *The rorathik's savage attack knocks the character down and shatters her weapon, shield, or armor.*

Motive: Murder
Environment: Hunts amid cool or cold climates alone or in small groups
Health: 28
Damage Inflicted: 6 points
Armor: 3
Movement: Short
Modifications: Conducts all stealth actions as level 8; makes all attacks as level 7; also see below.
Combat: Rorathiks are extremely skilled combatants. They normally fight with two weapons at once and strike with both as a single action. Each attack inflicts 6 points of damage. A rorathik has a bite attack, which inflicts 6 points of damage and carries a mild paralytic venom that increases the difficulty of all the victim's actions by one step if she fails a Might defense roll.

A rorathik can also make a death lunge attack, which is a single strike that involves both its weapons and its bite in one savage assault. The difficulty to defend against this attack is increased by one step, and it inflicts 12 points of damage as well as the venom of its bite.

Although killing any foe is a pleasant exercise for rorathiks, stalking and slaying a chosen target is a particular need. If they are well prepared, they make attacks against their chosen target (and perform related tasks, such as tracking or stalking) as one level higher than normal.

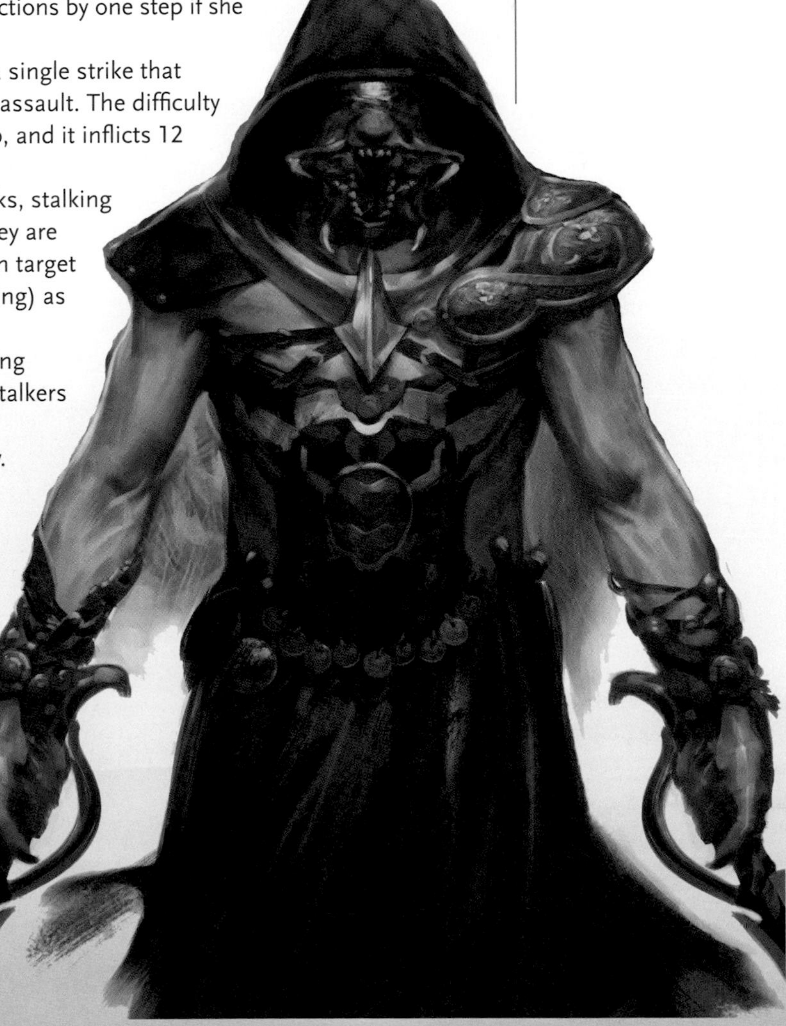

Interaction: As is the case with most abhumans, reasoning with a rorathik is difficult. Although they are skilled stalkers and fighters, they are not particularly intelligent and have a very limited ability to communicate effectively. Rorathiks respect physical prowess and might, but such intimidating displays only encourage them to consider a creature an even more desirable target.
Use: Rorathiks are very tough abhumans. A band of them would be a challenge even for PCs normally accustomed to mowing down hordes of other abhumans. A single rorathik is likely to be able to wade through a whole squad of town guards to reach a chosen target.
Loot: Rorathiks loot the corpses of those they slay, so they likely have 3d10 shins, 1d6 cyphers, and perhaps an artifact. All devices they possess would be those they can use in their murderous tasks.

RURTALIAN 4 (12)

The rurtalian is an artificially engineered bio-construct for psychic explorers to tie themselves to. Thus, it has two aspects: one physical and one purely mental. The mental aspect explores the reaches of the extraterrestrial and ultraterrestrial space, while the physical aspect remains behind so that its psychic energy counterpart does not discorporate into the proverbial ether. If the psychic explorer left behind a normal physical shell, it would be vulnerable to danger as well as to time (it might simply starve to death). But with the rurtalian physical aspect—engineered to serve its role—the mental aspect is free to spend what other creatures would call lifetimes loose in the boundless reaches of the multiverse while the physical does what it must to remain alive.

The rurtalian—at least the one that most people see—is a squat, 4-foot (1.2 m) tall creature with two limbs and a massive, pulsating sensory apparatus surrounded by a wreath of smaller sensory organs and seemingly little else. These things are a strange combination of eyes, ears, and olfactory apparati. They can project destructive rays that render matter into paste. If it is organic paste, the rurtalian can then feed on it through its skin. It does not otherwise need to breathe, drink, or sleep.

GM Intrusion: *The psychic aspect of the rurtalian returns and assails the character with a psychic attack that inflicts 4 points of Intellect damage and ignores Armor. The mental aspect can be harmed only by energy attacks (nothing physical), has its own 18 points of health, and is a separate level 4 creature, although if one aspect or the other dies, they both die. On subsequent rounds, the mental aspect can use its actions to attempt to psychically stun the character or heal the physical aspect for 4 points of health.*

Motive: Hungers for organic matter
Environment: Anywhere
Health: 18
Damage Inflicted: 4 points
Movement: Short
Modifications: Perception as level 6
Combat: Always on the hunt for food, particularly protein-rich flesh to supplement its diet of plant matter, the rurtalian attacks almost any creature it finds (except others of its kind). It can fire up to six rays of energy at long range from its eyes as a single action. Matter struck turns to paste, so treat physical armor as if it offered half as much protection.

Rurtalians have a decent sense of self-preservation, but sometimes they become overzealous in their quest for food.

Interaction: Although the mental aspect of a rurtalian is tied to a powerfully intelligent consciousness, the physical aspect is little more than a walking "id," interested in nothing but eating and staying alive. It does not communicate in any real way.

Use: The PCs are on their way through the wilderness when they come upon a swath of destruction—a path devoid of any plantlife at all. At the end of this path, two rurtalians have been liquefying trees, shrubs, and grasses into food. And now they would love to turn their deadly gaze upon more protein-rich sources of food...

SCAVROW 6 (18)

"Once a scavrow gets a good look at you, you're never safe again."

~common wisdom in the Beyond

When several lines of haze claw across the sky, lines that persist for hours, a flight of scavrows may have passed overhead. Those who notice are wise to get under cover because scavrows hunt for oddments that catch their interest with eyes so sensitive they can spot the glint of a shiny object deep inside a pocket.

If a scavrow flight wings low enough, the tiny spots spewing their dark wakes resolve as half-living, half-synth creatures with 30-foot (9.1 m) wingspans, a patchwork of white synth, black feathers, and dozens of piercing sapphire eyes.

What catches the interest of a scavrow is never the same and difficult to predict. Sometimes they're drawn to living creatures with a particular hair color, to carrion that's rotted a certain number of hours or days, or to children with blue eyes. Other times they target lone structures, singers, or shiny things. Whatever snags a scavrow's notice, a scavrow eventually collects—even if it's a different scavrow that finally gathers it months or even years later.

Motive: Unpredictable

Environment: The dark lines left by flights of up to four scavrows can be seen anywhere the sky is visible.

Health: 18

Damage Inflicted: 6 points

Armor: 2

Movement: Long (flying), immediate (on land)

Modifications: Perception as level 9; Speed defense as level 5 due to size.

Combat: A scavrow can make two attacks as a single action with its talons. It can also attack a single creature with an electrified beak as its action. Damage from a beak attack ignores Armor, and the victim must succeed on a Might defense roll or become paralyzed for one minute. Each round as his action, he can attempt another Might defense roll to shake it off.

If a limp victim of a beak attack is what caught the scavrow flight's interest in the first place, another scavrow from the flight picks up the paralyzed trophy in its talons, and on the flock's next turn, they jet off toward their aerie.

Interaction: If one scavrow sees something of interest, every member of the flight in the area simultaneously learns of it. Thus, if an initial scavrow flight is killed, another flight could find the object (or person) of interest later and mount a collection attempt as a surprise night raid.

Use: A parent seeks to reclaim a child who was collected by a flight of scavrows because of her beautiful singing. The aerie is visible in the night sky as a blinking white light passing overhead.

Loot: The remains of a flock of scavrows can be salvaged for 1d6 + 2 cyphers.

Scavrows take oddments they collect to floating aeries high above the ground. Different flocks of scavrows maintain different aeries. Some are low enough that living creatures deposited in them might survive, and others circle the world above the atmosphere.

GM Intrusion: *A scavrow makes a "snatch and drop" attack against a character who is not the object or person of interest. This entails making both talon attacks against the PC. If both hit, they inflict regular damage, and the victim is snatched up into the air and dropped from a height of 1d10 × 10 feet (3 m to 30 m).*

Falling damage, page 94

SCRIVENER 4 (12)

In the city of Qi lies the Cathedral of Form, where devout priests of Nomothet, God of the Flesh, attempt ancient techniques to shape and reshape slaves into specific configurations for specific purposes. Many are the horror stories of the flesh priests' failures, but the greatest of their successes, so far, are the scriveners. These strange beings have four legs, repositioned arms, and a number of synth and metal tendril-tails that sprout from their back. Scriveners are designed to write with extreme quickness and accuracy, even while walking or running, holding a writing desk on the lap created by folding two of their legs. Their saliva serves as a brilliant black ink that drips from a long tongue. One of their implanted tendrils holds a small cage with a biomechanical mogigraphis bird, able to remember and mimic all the sounds it heard in the past eight hours. The scrivener uses its feathered comrade to double-check its writing.

Like all creations of the Cathedral of Form, scriveners bear the tattooed markings of Nomothet, the upside-down eye.

GM Intrusion: *The scrivener produces a cypher that creates a cloud of choking smoke (to which it is immune) that fills the area within short range and lasts for one minute if wind conditions allow. While those within the cloud cough and choke (Might defense roll each round to avoid losing one's turn), the scrivener slips away.*

Motive: Loyalty to their master

Environment: Civilized, populated areas

Health: 12

Damage Inflicted: 4 points

Armor: 1

Movement: Short

Modifications: Remembering details as level 9; stealth as level 6; Speed defense as level 5.

Combat: Most of the time, a scrivener flees from combat. If it must defend itself, it does so with thin synth tails that end in metal barbs. It can make an attack with one tail while using the others to block blows and distract foes.

Interaction: Scriveners cannot speak. Their loyalty has been conditioned into them, and memories of their lives before their transformation into scriveners have been erased. Most are devoted worshippers of Nomothet and believe themselves to be doing his will through service.

Use: Scrivener slaves are used by nobles, rulers, barristers, Aeon Priests, technicians, and others to record conversations and speeches, maintain financial records, and transcribe and record important details. Sometimes this requires a scrivener to go into a dangerous situation or use subterfuge (such as sneaking into an enemy castle and lingering outside a window to record what's said within).

The PCs might get involved when they are hired by a noble to take important documents away from the scrivener of her enemy.

Loot: A scrivener might carry 1d10 shins, and its internal workings might yield an oddity or a cypher. The mogigraphis bird alone is worth 100 shins. But the greatest treasures most scriveners carry are the documents they create from the important secrets they transcribe.

SHANU 2 (6)

Shanu are tiny, meek, and innocuous herbivores that tend to live in trees and amid rocks—anywhere they can hide or quickly climb out of harm's way. However, they are also found in the company of humans and other creatures because they make excellent companions and pets.

"As lucky as a shanu" is a common phrase, but it's a misappropriation. Many people believe that shanu manipulate probability. This isn't the case, but shanu can help chosen allies that they hope will defend them against aggressors.

Motive: Protection

Environment: Anywhere

Health: 8

Damage Inflicted: 1 point

Movement: Short

Modifications: Climb and stealth as level 5; perception as level 4; Speed defense as level 4 due to size and speed.

Combat: Shanu flee rather than fight. They can nip, but beyond that, they have little means of inflicting damage. Their real talent is enhancing the abilities of other creatures. Their primary means of defense is finding an ally and making her more powerful. At the cost of 1 point of health, a shanu can decrease the difficulty of its ally's next action by one step. The creature accomplishes this through an unconscious use of telepathy, enhancing the skill and knowledge of the ally.

Shanu are incredibly resilient, regenerating 1 point of health per hour. Even the most injured or exhausted shanu is up and fully functional after a night's rest.

Interaction: Shanu are extremely clever little creatures. They do not speak, but they can learn to understand an extensive vocabulary of words. They are always on the lookout for a powerful ally to protect them, and when they find one, they remain fiercely loyal to it. The ally's behavior doesn't matter as long as it protects them, so a shanu might be the companion of a noble knight, a horrible abhuman chieftain, a callerail, or even an accelerator.

Use: Shanu can be trained to follow a variety of commands. Their front paws are almost human and can grip small objects. They are excellent climbers and have particularly sharp senses. It's not uncommon to see them perched on the shoulder of another creature.

GM Intrusion: *The shanu scurries away, and suddenly crashing through the trees toward the character is its large and dangerous defender!*

Callerail, page 234

Accelerator, page 20

SIZE COMPARISON

SHIVERN 2 (6)

Shiverns were bred as living assassination suits called 'phades,' designed to grant a wearer the ability to infiltrate an area under the cover of darkness. Though shiverns no longer require or want a wearer, they still delight in killing.

~Book of Balazs

If a human's shadow were severed and given life, the result might be a shivern. A shivern appears as the jagged outline of a human lurking at the bottom of a well of fading light—if a human had inky talons as long as its forearm.

Where there's one shivern, more soon follow. The combined light-sucking penumbra produced by a handful of the creatures summons darkness so complete that no illumination can penetrate it. Within that ebony envelope, shiverns stalk their prey with impunity.

Motive: Kills for pleasure

Environment: Almost anywhere, singly or in groups of up to five

Health: 6

Damage Inflicted: 3 points

Armor: 1

Movement: Short

Modifications: Stealth as level 5

Combat: Shiverns attack with long talons of steel-hard shadow.

A group of five shiverns can act as a swarm, focusing their attack on one target to make one attack roll as a single level 4 creature dealing 5 points of damage.

Whenever shiverns form a swarm, absolute darkness descends in short range around them. Shiverns can see in absolute darkness without penalty, but creatures who can't see in darkness will find it difficult to hit a shivern with an attack.

Interaction: Although shiverns usually conduct their business in silence, they are intelligent and can speak. They may even negotiate, but they only value opportunities to murder living creatures that they can't seize for themselves.

Use: A warlord has gained the service of a handful of shiverns thanks to her discovery of an immovable artifact that the shiverns value, fear, or obey. The warlord has decided to soften up a nearby community prior to capturing it by sending in her shivern assassins to take out the most dangerous potential foes, which could include the PCs.

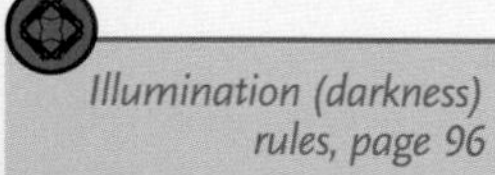

Illumination (darkness) rules, page 96

Swarm rules, page 13

GM Intrusion: *A PC within the absolute night conjured by a swarm of shiverns has a moment where the total darkness becomes so disorienting that she loses her bearings and can sense only the murderous intent of the attacking swarm. On her next turn, the PC moves in a random direction through the darkness, trying to find her way.*

SILVER ORPHAN 5 (15)

Silver orphans appear nothing like the waifs they are named after; they're humanoids sheathed in reflective skins of supple silvery alloy. Confident, strong, and noble, silver orphans wander, seeking something, seemingly forever denied its location.

Motive: Searching, defense

Environment: One or two silver orphans can be found almost anywhere.

Health: 21

Damage Inflicted: 5 points

Armor: 3

Movement: Short

Modifications: Perception as level 6; any knowledge pertaining specifically to the Ninth World as level 2.

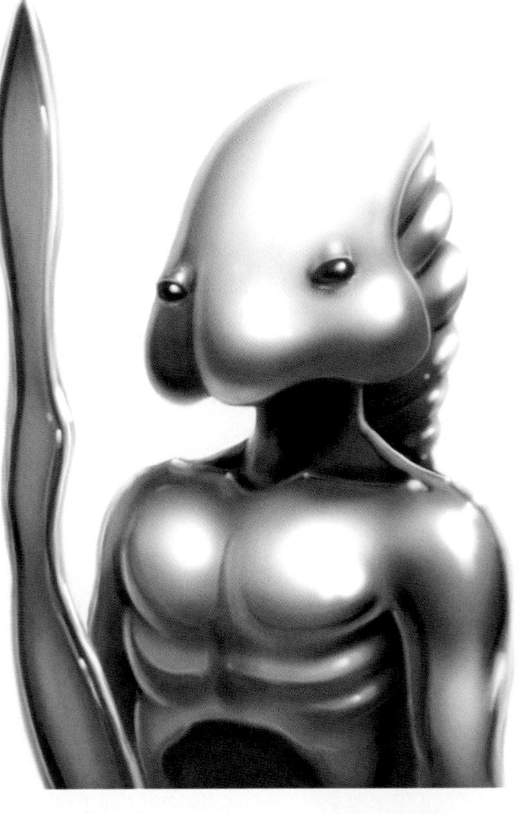

Combat: When attacking, a silver orphan can extrude what seems to be a portion of itself to create a sword. If it redistributes its carapace and lowers its Armor to 1, it can create a massive sword that deals 8 points of damage.

Instead of a weapon, an orphan can produce any shape that fills a 5-foot (1.5 m) cube. The shape usually remains connected to the orphan, but it doesn't have to. Such a shape includes a grasping hand that, with a successful immediate-range attack, holds an enemy fast each round that it fails a Might defense roll.

As an action, a silver orphan can also rapidly expel two silvery bolts from its palms at the same or separate targets. Each bolt inflicts 4 points of damage. The bolts, or any other portion of the silver orphan that becomes detached, liquefy and flow back to rejoin their host a few rounds after they lose contact. If this rejoining is somehow prevented, the silver orphan loses its ability to create constructs of any sort for one hour (after which time it has regenerated enough skin to regain this ability).

Interaction: A silver orphan isn't normally aggressive, but it reacts decisively if danger threatens. It communicates with characters through gestures and drawings. If asked what it's searching for, it draws a vastly complicated spherical object that seems to be floating in a void, and then it adds a second picture showing the object lying in the center of a rocky crater.

In return for news of machine intelligences it doesn't know about, a silver orphan will create a silvery cypher from its own form as a gift.

Use: A silver orphan makes a great patron, sending PCs into new areas to explore and search. The creature doesn't reveal exactly what it's looking for, but perceptive characters note that their patron seems especially eager to hear news of machine intelligences.

Loot: 1d6 silvery cyphers can be salvaged from the belongings and remains of a silver orphan.

Silver orphans can speak to each other at ranges of up to 10 miles (16 km) using a method normally undetectable by most humans. This "silver speech" allows them to convey many shades of meaning and nuance simultaneously. All that most creatures see is the orphans exchanging blank, mirror-faced stares.

GM Intrusion: *Peerless drones (page 97) attack, attempting to slay anyone working with, or in proximity to, a silver orphan. Peerless brooks no other machine intelligences and believes that whatever the silver orphans are looking for might be one.*

SKYSMASHER 7 (21)

A skysmasher arrives as a red blaze across the sky, leaving a trail of light and smoke. The streak is followed by a terrific boom, itself only a precursor to an even more dramatic event: impact. A fountain of earth erupts from where the skysmasher touches down, destroying everything in short range but the creature itself. The shockwave ripples outward, creating a fierce air blast reaching a half mile (0.8 km) in every direction, knocking down trees, structures, and any creatures in the area. The deafening roar of impact is audible twenty times as far, slowly fading like distant thunder. That's when the skysmasher burrows out of its crater, a rocky creature over 20 feet (6 m) tall.

Skysmashers seemingly live out most of their span in some useable realm above the sky, crashing down to solid ground only to spawn and lay eggs.

Skysmasher young hatch from rocky cysts on the sides of cliffs and mountains. No more than a few feet across when curled up, they defy gravity as they float off into the void overhead. They are not seen again for hundreds of years until they smash back down as adults, looking for others of their kind to mate with.

Motive: Reproduction

Environment: High places of the world as well as places beyond the sky

Health: 21

Damage Inflicted: 8 points

Armor: 5 (but see Combat)

Movement: Immediate when burrowing; short when on the ground; long when flying (see Combat)

Modifications: Speed defense as level 6 due to size

Combat: A skysmasher inflicts amazing bludgeoning damage with its huge fist and can make two attacks as a single action.

A skysmasher can fly with extreme velocity, shooting skyward on a plume of flame and smoke. To do this, it spends a preparatory turn curling into a tight ball. In the following round, it ignites and rockets straight up. Any character or object within short range of the skysmasher lift-off is washed in a wave of burning plasma that deals 10 points of damage. The wave also knocks creatures one step down the damage track and sets flammable items afire.

Once aloft, a skysmasher can crash down again anywhere in the world, though its aim is imperfect. It usually lands within 1 to 100 miles (1.6 to 161 km) of the intended location.

A skysmasher doesn't breathe. It has an additional 20 points of Armor against damage from impacts and fire.

GM Intrusion: *When a skysmasher lifts off in the midst of combat, the character's clothing catches on fire. The PC takes 5 points of damage each round until someone spends an action making a successful difficulty 5 Speed roll to put out the flames.*

Interaction: Skysmashers view most other life forms as ephemeral. If a skysmasher's landing mows a line of destruction through a human community, it's not out of malice—the creature simply doesn't notice. Skysmashers seem clever, but if they're thinking beings, they don't communicate it.

Use: A skysmasher crashes down in a location known for yielding occasional bounties of the numenera. It methodically begins clearing out every other living creature, preparing to use the area as an egg nursery.

Loot: A skysmasher egg is rich in the numenera. A character who cracks one open delicately enough can usually salvage 1d6 cyphers.

SLICER BEETLE 5 (15)

You could see his face getting ready for a retort, but then we all heard it. That scrape of carapace, the click of approaching pincers. Big pincers. Coming down the tunnel. Norlup had been right about a lot of legs and wrong about his use of the word creature, *singular.*

I imagined any creature crawling through a tunnel would be slow, but not this one. Pincers first, then its triple-toothed mouth, one pair of red eyes, then another, then a third.

~Deni Facca, "The Sound of a Beast"

Slicer beetles shed their tough carapaces three times during their lives. In the first two stages, these creatures look like well-armored, six-eyed beetles with front piercers designed to slice through flesh, bone, and most types of armor. They grow to nearly 12 feet (3.7 m) high in their second stage.

Although no one alive has claimed to see one, it is believed that in their final stage, the creatures morph one more time into savage burrowbeasts that spend the remainder of their short lives underground, protecting a giant nest made from their sloughed-off intestines and other internal organs. Called wizens by those who study the creatures and "suredeaths" by everyone else, these creatures are said to be fierce opponents and fight to the death (yours, not theirs) in the defense of their young.

While no one living can rightfully claim to have seen a wizen, occasionally someone runs across a hastily scrawled depiction of just such a creature on a cave wall or in a tunnel deep below the earth. Such depictions are usually unfinished.

Motive: Hungers for flesh, defense of young
Environment: Wooded areas, underground tunnels, softrock caves
Health: 15
Damage Inflicted: 5 (young), 7 (adults), or 10 points (wizens)
Armor: 3 (young), 4 (adults), or 6 (wizens)
Movement: Short
Combat: Slicer beetles are the kings of piercing and tearing, using their pointed front legs to stab through and rip into flesh, bone, and armor. Young slicer beetles deal 5 points of damage, adults deal 7 points of damage, and wizens deal 10 points of damage.

Additionally, each time that a slicer beetle successfully attacks, the victim must make a level 5 Speed defense roll or his armor is torn apart and destroyed.

Interaction: Slicer beetles cannot be communicated with.
Use: While exploring an ancient mine, the PCs hear the sounds of skittering and the rough scratch of carapace against rock. It isn't long before they realize they've happened upon a slicer beetle or two.

GM Intrusion*: While the PCs fight a pair of young slicer beetles, a wizen rises up out of the ground beneath the characters and attacks.*

SLIDIKIN 5 (15)

Skulking from shadow to shadow, the slidikin dwell on the fringes of human society. They are bizarre creatures, their origins a complete mystery. While one might pass as a human from a distance, their chalk-white skin, lack of eyes or nose, and far-too-many mouths ensure that a close examination would prove them otherwise. In people's rare, brief, furtive, and frankly disturbing interactions with slidikin, they have made passing references to "the hideous game." This seems to be an incongruous competition among slidikin (and only slidikin) that involves dark deeds—theft, kidnapping, mutilation, and murder. (It likely involves other things as well, but no one knows what they are, focusing only on those activities that affect humanity.)

Slidikin hate memora (page 83) and vice versa, but no one knows why. Slidikin also appear to be terrified of philethis (Numenera corebook, page 252).

Motive: The game

Environment: Human villages and towns

Health: 22

Damage Inflicted: 5 points

Movement: Long

Modifications: Speed defense and stealth as level 6

Combat: Slidikin are likely to use weapons in combat, although they never wear armor, preferring to remain agile rather than encumbered.

Interaction: Talking with a slidikin can be infuriating. No matter what the situation, the slidikin, with its multiple, grating, whispered voices, speaks with outlandish contempt for whomever it encounters, as if it knows a great many things that everyone else does not. It finds odd things (like physical threats) humorous, and many normal concepts (like justice or revenge) incomprehensible. It never tells anyone the nature of the game or anything of its own nature.

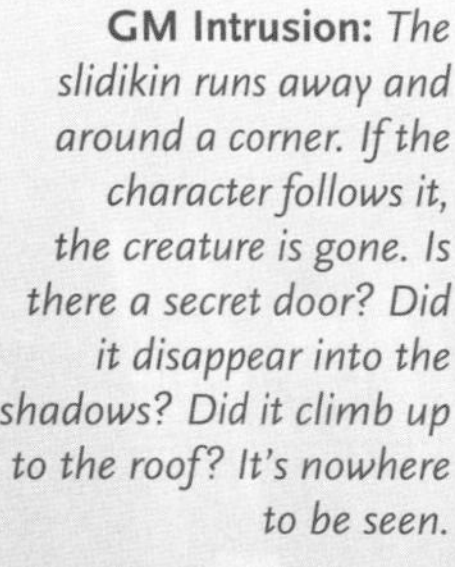

GM Intrusion: *The slidikin runs away and around a corner. If the character follows it, the creature is gone. Is there a secret door? Did it disappear into the shadows? Did it climb up to the roof? It's nowhere to be seen.*

Use: A man stumbles out of a dark alleyway toward the PCs, blood running down his face. "The mouths," he whispers hoarsely. "The mouths." If the characters examine him, they see that his eyelids have been sliced off. He says that men—at least, he thought they were men at first—grabbed him the day before and held him in a dank cellar overnight, bound and gagged. They giggled and whispered among themselves the whole time. Then they mutilated him with knives and left him in the alley. He gives a frantic, fevered description of a slidikin.

Loot: A slidikin very likely carries 1d100 shins and a cypher as well as a variety of knives and some poisons, knockout drugs, lockpicks, and other tools.

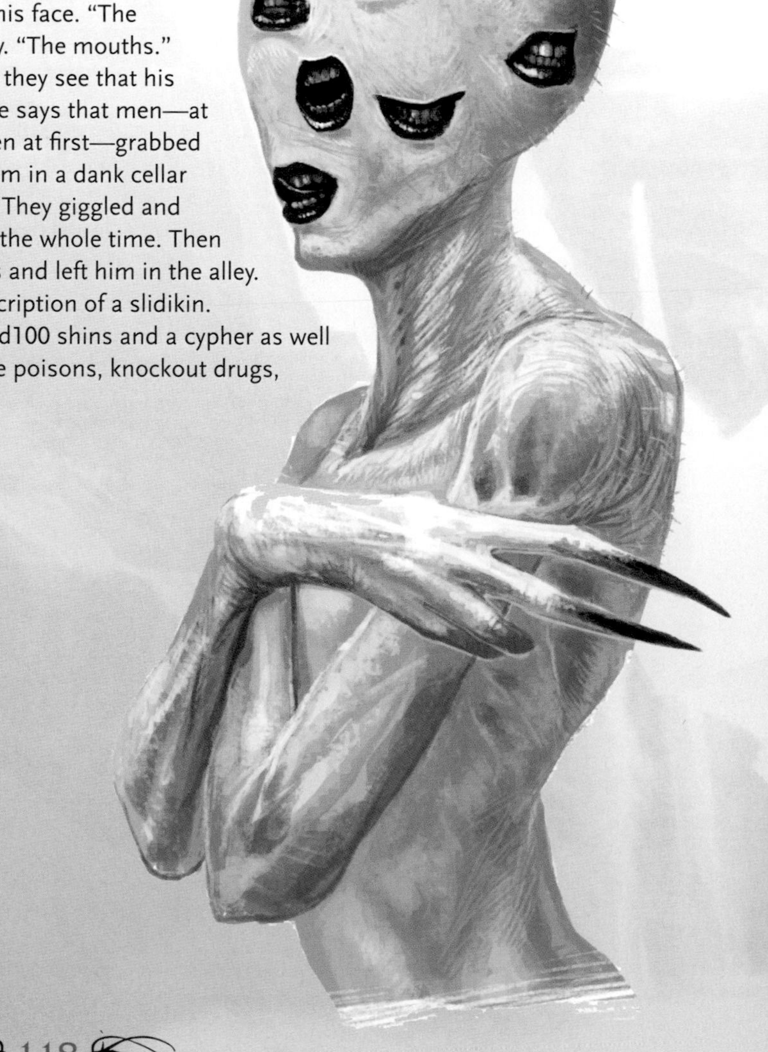

SLURGE 2 (6)

Slurgen glide across the landscape as easily and quickly as birds soar overhead, leaving trails of evaporating slime. A slurge eats plants, garbage, dead creatures, and even some types of synth and metals—anything that doesn't fight back when the slurge slides onto it and discharges eating mucus.

Motive: Hungers for vegetation, carrion, garbage

Environment: Dry wastes, forested hills, temperate lowlands, and outside the walls of large cities in pods of six to eight

Health: 6

Damage Inflicted: 3 points

Armor: 4

Movement: Short

Modifications: Speed defense as level 1 due to size and quickness

Combat: A slurge can spit a glob of eating mucus at one foe within short range as its attack (or settle down atop an unresisting foe or piece of food and inflict damage every round automatically that ignores Armor). The eating mucus acts like acid, and a slurge can adjust the acid variety depending on the material it's attempting to eat or damage.

When danger threatens, a slurge depends more on its defense. Its shell provides the first line of protection, but a slurge also produces defensive slime when threatened, which oozes across the ground within immediate range of the slurge. The slime is amazingly sticky, and any creature (other than a slurge) standing in the area must make a Might defense roll on its turn; failure means the creature is stuck in the slime and can't move. While this doesn't stop creatures from attacking, it prevents them from following a retreating slurge.

The third kind of mucus a slurge can discharge is for transport. This incredibly slippery slime allows a slurge to glide like a skater on ice wherever it goes. However, the material isn't stable; it evaporates within a minute of being produced.

Interaction: Slurgen are scavengers and, in most cases, are easily frightened off by vigorous movement. On the other hand, slurgen pods have been known to attack travelers, especially those who are alone or in small groups.

Use: Slurgen are considered a delicacy once de-shelled, boiled, and fried in herb butter. But de-shelling is the trick because slurge shells are amazingly strong and hard to penetrate. In fact, armor made from the shells is highly prized for its strength and its light weight compared to metal.

SIZE COMPARISON

Slurge and broken hound populations overlap in a few areas but rarely come into conflict. Whereas broken hounds are hunters, slurgen are scavengers. Anything broken hounds leave behind, slurgen suck up. And broken hounds learn that getting through slurgen shells is often not worth the trouble, especially in the face of a slurge's defense and eating mucus.

Broken hounds, page 232

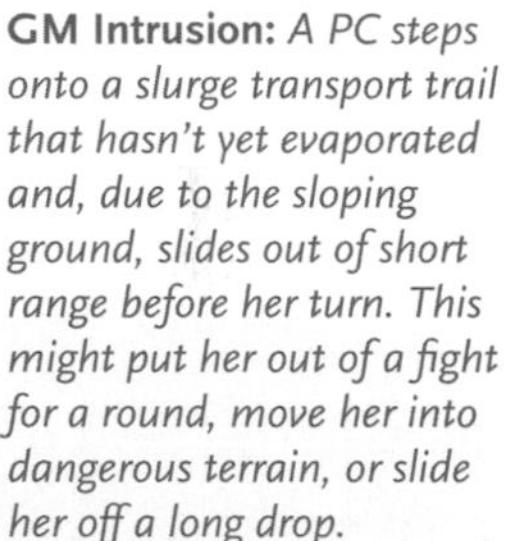

GM Intrusion: *A PC steps onto a slurge transport trail that hasn't yet evaporated and, due to the sloping ground, slides out of short range before her turn. This might put her out of a fight for a round, move her into dangerous terrain, or slide her off a long drop.*

SIZE COMPARISON

SPURN 3 (9)

From afar, a gang of spurn seems like nothing more than humanoids in oily rags. But up close, they're revealed as creatures formed of smashed machines, shattered synth, matted hair, drippy sludge, and garbage. Spurn are self-organizing collections of refuse that evolved among the landfills and dumps of previous civilizations over deep time. Geological evolution makes primeval landfills difficult to recognize for creatures other than spurn.

Spurn are intelligent and highly territorial, especially against rival spurn groups, and they savagely defend their kingdoms of trash in the face of threats both imagined and actual.

Motive: Territory, defense, knowledge of undiscovered garbage dumps

Environment: Ninth World garbage dumps and landfills of ancient epochs. A raiding spurn gang typically includes three to five members.

Health: 9

Damage Inflicted: 4 points

Armor: 1

Movement: Immediate; long if a spurn chooses to discarnate in one location and reassemble a new body from trash in another location (see Combat).

Combat: Spurn can spontaneously reform a limb to extrude splintered glass, sharpened synth, or a heavy, macelike mass, depending on the apparent vulnerability of their foe.

When its turn begins, a spurn can choose to fall apart and instantaneously reassemble a new body anywhere within long range that contains sufficient trash. A spurn loses 1 point of health each time it travels in this fashion. When it appears behind a foe and attacks as part of the same action, the foe's Speed defense roll against that attack is increased in difficulty by one step.

A spurn that has a functioning cypher may spend its action absorbing the item into its body and gain 1d6 points of health. A wounded spurn might try grabbing a cypher from a character.

Spurn communities are often directed by a leader (level 5) who is larger and tougher than the regular rubbish. The leader rarely stirs from its buried landfill lair, but if encountered, a spurn leader is a hulking, 8-foot (2.4 m) tall creature with 20 points of health and 3 points of Armor. In combat, the leader makes two attacks on its action, each of which inflicts 5 points of damage.

Interaction: Spurn communicate with one another via machine telepathy. A few can speak with non-spurn by adapting their components to produce sounds with the correct cadence and frequency to mimic a known language. Despite their territorial instinct, spurn may treat visitors peacefully if a novel numenera gift (even one that is apparently broken or used up) is offered.

Use: Traveling PCs pass over or through an ancient landfill that is claimed by one or more spurn gangs, called refuses. The characters may initially see a gang war from afar, then later be menaced by one of the groups. While one refuse may be willing to trade, another is just as likely to attack first and rifle through possessions later.

Loot: Many spurn are animate accumulations of useless dross, but one in four spurn contains 1d6 functioning cyphers.

GM Intrusion: *A destroyed spurn spontaneously reassembles, becoming a fully healthy specimen in the round following its supposed obliteration.*

STELLAR WEAVER 9 (27)

Legend has it that the stellar weavers crawled down nearly invisible web strands through the vast emptiness between worlds. These massive creatures appear to be giant arachnids composed of the starry, night-black void they once called home, but they supposedly take new, appropriate forms on each world they come to. Whether true or not, one thing that the legends say about these cosmic spider-things is demonstrably true: they are among the deadliest creatures that stalk the darkness.

In general, stellar weavers are cautious and clever hunters, patiently waiting for prey in their reality-warping webs. These nocturnal creatures cannot abide the sun or bright light and flee from it. They prefer lairs enshrouded by darkness, such as a dark cave near a well-traveled path where they can string their webs to trap prey.

Motive: Hungers for flesh

Environment: Anywhere

Health: 80

Damage Inflicted: 12 points

Armor: 8

Movement: Short

Modifications: Climb as level 10; Speed defense as level 8 due to size.

Combat: The bite of a stellar weaver is filled with virulent venom that immediately knocks a character one step down the damage track if she fails a Might defense roll. This process continues each round until the victim succeeds at her Might defense roll or dies—though technically, she is not dead but permanently paralyzed. Stellar weavers must feed upon warm blood and supple flesh.

The webs of a stellar weaver are also level 9. Avoiding them requires an Intellect-based perception task. A character caught in a web must make a Might defense roll to get free. Failure results in becoming more entwined than before, so an additional successful roll is required for each failure (and each attempt requires a separate action). The webs also bend space, and a character trapped in them for more than four rounds is shunted into an extradimensional space to await the stellar weaver. (Since the venom of the creature does not kill, this space might be filled with many still-living meals awaiting their fate.) Leaving this space involves getting free from the sticky webbing and then moving along the maze of nonsticky web strands in just the right way (this requires two different tasks, one to balance and one to figure it out).

Stellar weavers are immune to cold and heat and do not need to breathe. They operate in many dimensions at once, so creatures that are normally invisible, out of phase, or insubstantial are usually seen and affected by the weaver's attacks and webbing.

Interaction: Stellar weavers are very intelligent and telepathic, but they rarely deign to speak to their food.

Use: Stellar weavers are apex predators, feeding on anything they wish. When one makes a lair near a village in the Beyond, the best solution might be to move the village. The creatures are the stuff of legend, considered evil, bloodthirsty gods by some and devils by others.

Loot: The eight eyes of a stellar weaver can be used as artifacts to see into other dimensions. They have a depletion of 1 in 1d20. An armorsmith who can work with level 9 material can use the flesh of a stellar weaver to craft transdimensional armor that is effective against out-of-phase or insubstantial attacks that would normally pass through physical armor.

The lair of a stellar weaver might contain web pathways to other planets or other dimensions.

GM Intrusion: *The character moves into a sheet of webbing that he did not see next to him and is caught.*

GM Intrusion: *The stellar weaver climbs a heretofore unseen web strand and vanishes into thin air, possibly to return in an unexpected spot.*

SYZYGY GHOUL 4 (12)

These abhumans have as little coloring as the dead they feed upon, and they spend almost as much time beneath the ground as corpses. But syzygy ghouls are very much alive. Their bodies are hairless and so porcelain-smooth that their faces are sometimes mistaken for emotionless masks. Syzygy ghouls come to the surface at night to gather humanoid remains or steal those recently interred from their graves.

These abhumans are known in various places as "eaters," "undertakers," and "the Night Singers," the latter due to the dirgelike songs they sing while they gather less-than-fresh meat. The ghouls claim to hold dominion over the remains of all humans and abhumans, according to ancient custom, even if they only sometimes assert that privilege. After all, not every dead body contains information the syzygy ghouls deem valuable, and it's hard to be everywhere at once. The ghouls are said to eat the dead they gather and to know what any of their past meals knew.

Syzygy ghouls live in subterranean communities called yudterims. The central purpose of each yudterim is to maintain a massive library filled with winding scrolls printed on vellum pressed from the skin of the dead.

Motive: Hunger for dead flesh, knowledge

Environment: Anywhere aboveground in the open at night, usually in groups of three or more, or in subterranean yudterims

Health: 12

Damage Inflicted: 4 points

Armor: 1

Movement: Short

Modifications: Two areas of knowledge as level 5

Combat: A syzygy ghoul usually prefers not to fight but is quite capable of defending itself with a milk-white blade of bone (called a lunarum), which is heavier at the cutting end. A syzygy ghoul in combat sings a dirgelike tune, the same one it sings while consuming corpses.

During combat, a ghoul licks its lunarum immediately after each attack that inflicts damage, which gives it a flash of insight regarding its current foe. Each time a ghoul deals damage and licks its blade, the difficulty of the Speed defense rolls made by the damaged creature against the ghoul's attacks increases by one step.

Syzygy ghouls can see in the dark. They're blind in full daylight, but those who travel to the surface carry oddities that cover their eyes, allowing them to see without penalty in full sunlight.

Interaction: Syzygy ghouls deal in decaying flesh and knowledge, and they are excellent linguists. They may become violent if someone attempts to keep a dead body away from them. If a creature wants to talk to someone recently dead, a ghoul might help, if suitable knowledge is offered in return. When a ghoul consumes the brain matter of a creature dead for no more than ten days, it learns what the dead creature consciously knew.

GM Intrusion: *A syzygy ghoul that has dealt damage to the PC learns a secret that the character is keeping from her friends. The ghoul attempts to parlay with the PC, indicating that otherwise it will spill her secret. If denied, the ghoul reveals the secret in vengeance.*

Use: If a PC needs a piece of information not otherwise obtainable, he might learn of the Night Singers, who keep lightless libraries below the earth that store much knowledge once known by humans.

Loot: If the PCs defeat a group of syzygy ghouls, they might find 1d6 shins, a cypher, and an oddity (black goggles that allow the wearer to look directly at the sun and see it as a pale circle).

TACHYRON 4 (12)

Tachyrons are wolf-sized reptiles with huge black eyes that reflect light. Weird sensory organs like strands of hair are positioned around their heads, mouths, and forelimbs. These organs, coupled with the creature's strange eyes, grant the tachyron a unique perspective: they don't just perceive the present moment, but also the thirty seconds before and the thirty seconds after what a human would call the present moment. In other words, to a tachyron, the "present moment" is about a minute long, and they perceive (and process) everything in that minute at once.

Tachyrons hunt in small packs and raise their young communally. The pups are born live rather than hatched from eggs.

Motive: Hungers for flesh

Environment: Wooded and mountainous areas or underground

Health: 12

Damage Inflicted: 4 points

Armor: 3

Movement: Short

Modifications: Perception and initiative as level 10; attacks, Speed defense, and stealth as level 6.

Combat: A tachyron's perception of time makes it a very strange creature to fight. It knows if you're going to attack it (in its mind, you already have), and thus it can start to move out of the way even before you strike. The only reason that it's possible to strike it or dodge its attack is that sometimes the tachyron can't move quickly enough. It is not preternaturally fast.

Interaction: The tachyron has the intelligence and disposition of any other predatory animal. For obvious reasons, trained tachyrons make excellent guard animals.

Use: The appearance of a pack of tachyrons can seem to be a straightforward wilderness challenge at first, but during the encounter, it becomes clear that the creatures act (and react) very strangely. They are a great way of inserting the weird into what would otherwise be a straightforward combat.

SIZE COMPARISON

GM Intrusion: *Just as the character takes an action, the tachyron is right there, not only ready to take advantage of the PC's position with a free attack out of turn, but foiling and negating his action.*

The tachyron's senses don't simply translate into stats and numbers. The GM needs to portray these creatures as if they always know what's going to happen beforehand (because they do). It's practically impossible to sneak up on—or get the jump on—a tachyron. It takes shelter before the storm hits. A tachyron pup comes before its mother calls it.

However, a tachyron is not predicting a possible future—it's experiencing the future. If a PC swipes at one with his sword-staff, the creature tries to dodge, but it experiences the dodge and the possibility of its success or failure at the same time. So if the dodge succeeds, the tachyron experiences the PC's approach, his swing, and its dodge all at once. In fact, it likely perceives a number of the PC's attacks and a number of its own all at the same time. This also means that a tachyron has the strange perspective of seeing its own death before it happens (and the thirty seconds after it happens).

From a human perspective, the tachyron exists in the present moment, so it only seems to be reacting ahead of time. To the tachyron, all those things are happening at once.

TERROR BIRD 4 (12)

Haunting. It's a word reserved for spooks, spirits, and wild tales told around campfires. But it's not an inappropriate term for the behavior of a creature that some call the screeching doom but others just call the terror bird. This horrific thing haunts tall grasslands like the Plains of Kataru or the central regions of the Steadfast, creeping with soft footfalls and head lowered. It's only when it makes its sudden, dramatic appearance that it unleashes its banshee wail, a screech so loud that it almost knocks prey down, but it operates on a subsonic level as well. Powerful legs and an axelike beak make formidable weapons that can tear apart a creature twice the bird's size. Such creatures would be rare, however, as when the terror bird stands fully erect, its head rises almost 9 feet (2.7 m) off the ground.

The Plains of Kataru, page 184

Motive: Hungers for flesh

Environment: Hot or temperate grasslands, hunting alone or in small groups

Health: 21

Damage Inflicted: 6 points

Armor: 1

Movement: Long

Modifications: Stealth actions as level 8; perception as level 5.

Combat: When hunting, a terror bird creeps low to the ground and hides in the terrain as best it can. When it attacks, it screeches, and any mammal within immediate distance must make an Intellect defense roll or freeze in terror for one round (the subsonic nature of the screech interferes with certain portions of the mammalian brain). This screech is not an action for the bird. For frozen prey, the difficulty to dodge the terror bird's melee attack is increased by three steps, and the attack inflicts an additional 2 points of damage.

If the bird wishes, as a single action, it can attack two different foes (one with its beak and one with a talon). The difficulty to avoid these attacks remains unchanged, but each attack inflicts only 4 points of damage.

Terror birds are belligerent, angry creatures that fight to the death.

Interaction: Terror birds cannot be reasoned with any more than other predatory animals (in fact, less so). However, as difficult as it is to imagine, a terror bird hatched and raised in captivity can be trained to be a guard animal or even a mount for a relatively light rider.

Use: Terror birds are awful predators, more cunning and crafty than an explorer might expect. They sometimes work in a group, with one bird driving prey into an ambush by others.

GM Intrusion: *The character steps into a shallow pit, trips, and falls prone, losing his action. The terror bird seems to have known the pit was there and moves to take full advantage as if the character were frozen in fear.*

THERIVAR 3 (9)

"The real challenge is figuring out which of my machines I want my therivars to power next."

~Sir Arthour

Moving through the air, ignoring gravity, the therivar is a creature of semisolid energy rather than matter. It looks like a snake—about 4 feet (1.2 m) long—made of lightning.

Motive: Searching for purpose

Environment: Dwells inside machines alone or in groups of two to five

Health: 9

Damage Inflicted: 4+ points (see Combat)

Movement: Long

Modifications: Numenera knowledge as level 8; Speed defense as level 5 due to size and speed.

Combat: A therivar attacks with a "bite" that is really a discharge of its energy into a foe. It can add damage to this strike by sacrificing its own health, inflicting 2 additional points of damage per health point. In theory, if a therivar sacrificed itself, it could inflict 22 points of damage in one strike. Of course, it is difficult to imagine one giving its life just to deal more damage. More likely, a desperate therivar would sacrifice a point or two of health to drive off or perhaps finish off a really dangerous foe.

A therivar can move at the speed of light (essentially, teleport) up to 1,000 feet (305 m) as an action.

Last, as an action, a therivar can "inhabit" a device of any size designed to be powered in some way. If the device had no power, it functions indefinitely while the therivar inhabits it (assuming its power needs are not great). If it already has power, the therivar's presence increases the level of the device by 1. As an action, the therivar can leave any device.

Interaction: A therivar can be coaxed into or out of a machine by a charismatic character. Therivars do not speak, but they seem to understand speech (in any language). They are motivated by new experiences, so they can be lured out by the offering of such.

Use: An NPC foe of the characters has a group of therivar inhabiting his cyphers, which he uses (at an enhanced level) in a fight with the PCs. At some point during the battle, the therivars emerge from the cyphers (which are then expended) and attack the characters.

SIZE COMPARISON

GM Intrusion: *The therivar's attack not only damages the character but also burns out one of her devices—a cypher or even an artifact chosen at random.*

SIZE COMPARISON

TITANOTHAUR 10 (30)

"It was bigger than houses. Bigger than castles. Tall enough, even, to reach up and touch the Amber Monolith itself! Nothing living could be that big. But it was. It was."

~ a witness to an event

Titanothaurs come in a variety of shapes, but all share one difficult-to-ignore quality: mind-blowing size. Appearances of these colossal creatures are rare events that usually don't last for more than a few days. In that sense, they're akin to hundred-year storms and at least as destructive. When they emerge, they're attracted by artificial structures, the more densely situated and elaborate the better, which they set to smashing with a vengeance. It's hard to judge the size of things so far outside normal scale, but good estimates put most titanothaurs at over 300 feet (100 m) in height.

Most titanothaurs rely primarily on their strength and mass to get the job done, but many have some additional trick or ability that sets them apart from their kin. Unfortunately, that extra trick usually translates into even more devastation.

The other quality all of them share is the talent of hiding after a rampage, though it's possible that they accomplish their disappearing act simply by diving into a nearby sea or burrowing deep into the earth. Sometimes the same titanothaur will appear again days, months, years, or decades later, attacking the same location or someplace entirely new.

Titanothaurs have characteristics that remind observers of recognizable Ninth World animals and insects. This similarity has led to the obvious conclusion that titanothaurs are the product of natural creatures that have been enlarged somehow by numenera. A fine conclusion, perhaps, but no evidence for it has ever been found.

A titanothaur usually finishes its rampage according to its own cryptic schedule and then disappears, though sometimes a creature is driven off thanks to a series of heroic measures mounted by desperate defenders. Rarely, a titanothaur is killed by the defense mounted against it (or by another titanothaur or similar entity). A titanothaur death leaves a record amount of meat, scales, horns, and other body parts for scavengers and trophy hunters.

Motive: Destruction

Environment: Usually near communities containing many high structures

Health: 140

Damage Inflicted: 18 points

Armor: 5

Movement: Short

Modifications: Speed defense as level 8 due to size and speed

Combat: A titanothaur can punch, kick, or deliver a tail or tentacle lash at something within long range. Damage is inflicted on the target and everything within short range of the target, and even those that succeed on a Speed defense roll take 7 points of damage.

Titanothaurs heal quickly, usually at a rate of 2 points per round.

Titanothaurs are rare and devastating enough that most are dubbed with a unique identifier by survivors. The entry for each creature below notes only where it varies from the base creature described above.

Gravithaur: This creature has a bug's emerald green carapace and lizardlike limbs and head. The elaborate horn complex on Gravithaur's snout always glows with flickering light, but it blazes when the creature emits a gravity wave, which it can do once every ten minutes. It uses the wave to fling structures and creatures (even those as large as other titanothaurs) toward the horizon. Creatures can attempt a Speed defense roll to avoid being caught up in the wave. Those that fail are flung up to half a mile (0.8 km) and fall from a height of at least 200 feet (61 m).

Rampagion: This titanothaur has been estimated to be almost 1,000 feet (305 m) high. Once per day, it can make a charging trample attack, dealing its damage in a line 300 feet (91 m) wide and 2 miles (3.2 km) long. Rampagion has 10 points of Armor and deals 20 points of damage with a physical attack (or 8 points if a victim makes a successful Speed defense roll).

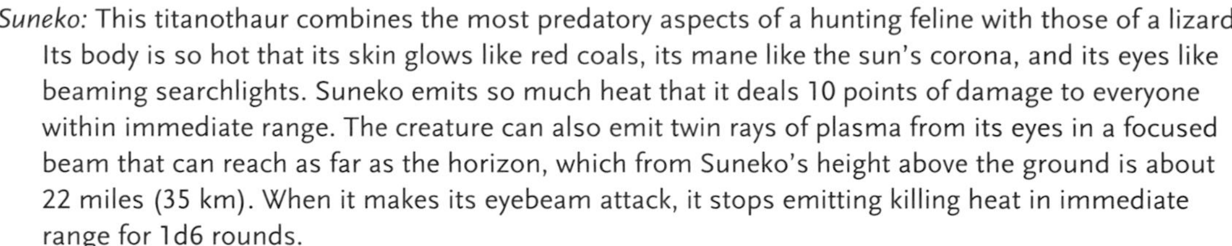

Suneko: This titanothaur combines the most predatory aspects of a hunting feline with those of a lizard. Its body is so hot that its skin glows like red coals, its mane like the sun's corona, and its eyes like beaming searchlights. Suneko emits so much heat that it deals 10 points of damage to everyone within immediate range. The creature can also emit twin rays of plasma from its eyes in a focused beam that can reach as far as the horizon, which from Suneko's height above the ground is about 22 miles (35 km). When it makes its eyebeam attack, it stops emitting killing heat in immediate range for 1d6 rounds.

Interaction: Most PCs can't directly interact with a titanothaur unless they have numenera allowing them to get the attention of one of the massive creatures. Doing so could give the characters a chance to trick or lure the beast, or maybe even persuade one titanothaur to fight another.

Use: After seeing the devastation caused by a titanothaur, the PCs might decide (or be asked to) find a way to stop a projected future appearance by the same creature.

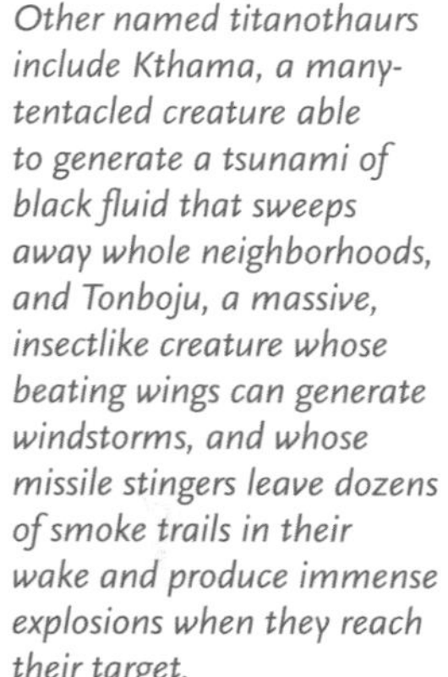

Other named titanothaurs include Kthama, a many-tentacled creature able to generate a tsunami of black fluid that sweeps away whole neighborhoods, and Tonboju, a massive, insectlike creature whose beating wings can generate windstorms, and whose missile stingers leave dozens of smoke trails in their wake and produce immense explosions when they reach their target.

GM Intrusion: *Somehow, a particular PC gains the attention of a titanothaur. If the attention is murderous, give the character 5 XP, only 1 of which she has to give to a friend.*

TRAWL 4 (12)

"Kaban was there one moment and gone the next. He'd been jabbering on about seeing numenera, yeah? Cyphers, he said, all laid out neat and proper. When I turned 'round, there weren't no cyphers, nor Kaban neither. We thought he nicked them and run off. But Kaban came back. Parts of him, anyhow, dropping out of the sky like soft red hail, all bitten, chewed, and with the insides showing."

~Tati Coulter, explorer

Beware, beware the Nowhere Man/ for snatch and grab is his pretty plan/ Quick, tell a riddle and stump him true!/ Elsewise he'll steal away with you. ~nursery rhyme of the trawl

A trawl exists partially out of phase, but when it's hungry, it rests one welcoming hand in reality, cupping something tantalizing, such as a book, a compass, or a numenera device in its invisible palm, apparently free for the taking. But the item is bait for a trap, and the victim who falls for it is snatched out of phase, where she must face a hungry trawl by herself.

A grim nursery rhyme describes how thieving children must pacify the "Nowhere Man" or be eaten. The rhyme may actually be about trawls. According to the rhyme, those who pacify a trawl with a clever riddle not only avoid becoming dinner but also get a treat from the Nowhere Man's bag of gifts.

Motive: Hungers for flesh

Environment: Almost anywhere in the Steadfast and the Beyond

Health: 12

Damage Inflicted: 4 points

Armor: 2

Movement: Short

Modifications: Speed defense as level 3 due to size

Combat: If a character grabs for an item that's bait held by a trawl, he must succeed on a Speed defense roll modified one step to his detriment due to surprise. On a failed roll, the victim is pulled out of phase and disappears from the perceptions of his companions (if any).

From the victim's point of view, the environment goes grey and dim, hazy at the edges. But more important, he sees the hungry trawl that's got him by the wrist.

GM Intrusion: *When the PC is snatched from reality and rendered out of phase, a portion of his belongings and equipment stays real, which means that he is without some of his normal weapons, cyphers, and so on while fighting for his life.*

The trawl attempts to retain its grip and attacks with its bite. While a victim remains in the trawl's grip, its bite ignores Armor. A victim can free himself from the grip with a successful Might defense roll. If he kills the trawl or moves away from it a distance equal to or greater than long range, he returns to reality. If the victim moved a significant distance while out of phase, he risks fusing with whatever solid objects exist back in reality.

Under normal circumstances, a trawl can't be seen or affected by normal phase creatures and effects.

Interaction: Trawls can communicate, but they usually do so only to intimidate prey that has been pulled out of phase. Sometimes a trawl spares a victim that delights it with a joke or riddle, but such mercy is rare.

Use: Few things are more surprising to player characters than a trawl-napping.

Loot: A trawl baits its trap with various needful and interesting things. A defeated trawl has several oddities (such as a book, a compass, a glowing decoration, and so on), 3d6 shins, 1d6 cyphers, and usually at least one artifact in its bag of bait.

UNAGRAN 2 (6)

With their 8-foot (2.4 m) long, sinuous, pressure-armored forms, unagrans are suited to hunt the drowned places of the Ninth World. Two rows of eyelike organs stripe their elongated heads, giving unagrans a wide view of their murky surroundings, and their mighty tails easily propel them through deep water.

Unagrans view any creature that's not an unagran as potential food.

Motive: Defense, food for their young

Environment: A pod of six or seven unagrans hunts for other larger aquatic creatures and conducts quick raids out of the water along the shorelines of lakes and seas.

Health: 6

Damage Inflicted: 2 points

Armor: 1 (see Combat)

Movement: Immediate; short when swimming

Modifications: Perception as level 4 while in water

Combat: When combat starts, an unagran electrifies its skin with a thought. The electric field doesn't extend into the surrounding water or air, but it automatically inflicts 2 points of damage to anyone who touches or strikes the unagran with a melee attack, and it gives the unagran 2 points of Armor against electricity.

An unagran's mouth is its most fearsome weapon, allowing it to bite and hold its prey. A bite victim takes 2 additional points of damage from the creature's electric field and cannot move while the unagran holds on. A victim can try to break free on his turn by making a successful level 3 Might roll.

In the deeps, unagran elders can grow to colossal size. A typical elder is level 8, measures almost 100 feet (30 m) in length, inflicts 10 points of damage, has 36 points of health, and has 5 points of Armor. Elders can't emerge onto land the way that human-sized unagrans can.

Interaction: Unagrans speak their own language, rich in clicks and squeals, but some can also speak one or more languages of land-dwelling humanoids that live nearby. Unagran lairs are aquatic, built around a central spawning chamber that holds the Great Egg. That chamber is partly filled with a breathable atmosphere. The Great Egg is a bulk of developing translucent unagran eggs held together in a jellylike mass. Unagrans worship it, defend waters near it, and sacrifice creatures to it by dropping immobilized captives into the mass, where they fuse through the osmotic walls and become food for the developing young. If a sacrifice does not pass through the wall of the egg mass, the unagrans take it as a sign of temperance and release the captive.

Use: Where unagrans are known to live, local fisher people value their teeth as good luck charms, believing that a necklace made of them will ward off other unagrans. Characters who hunt the creatures can earn 2 shins per unagran tooth they sell in such a community, at least for the first hundred or so teeth—after that, demand begins to dry up.

Loot: The Great Egg of an established unagran lair has seen many sacrifices. The PCs can find 1d10 cyphers, an oddity or two, and usually at least one artifact beneath its gelid mass.

SIZE COMPARISON

Unagrans might be natural creatures who have learned to think, visitants who have forgotten their past, or (as a few ancient synth tablets suggest) the result of a previous civilization's attempt to claim the oceans by wholesale adaptation of a land-dwelling race. The grand underwater cities described in their racial myths could be more than just stories, but if so, the unagrans in the Ninth World lost their way home many tectonic cycles ago.

GM Intrusion: *While the PCs fight regular-sized unagrans, an elder unagran swims up from the deep and demands in a booming, clicking voice that the characters leave these waters immediately or be eaten. Negotiation might be possible.*

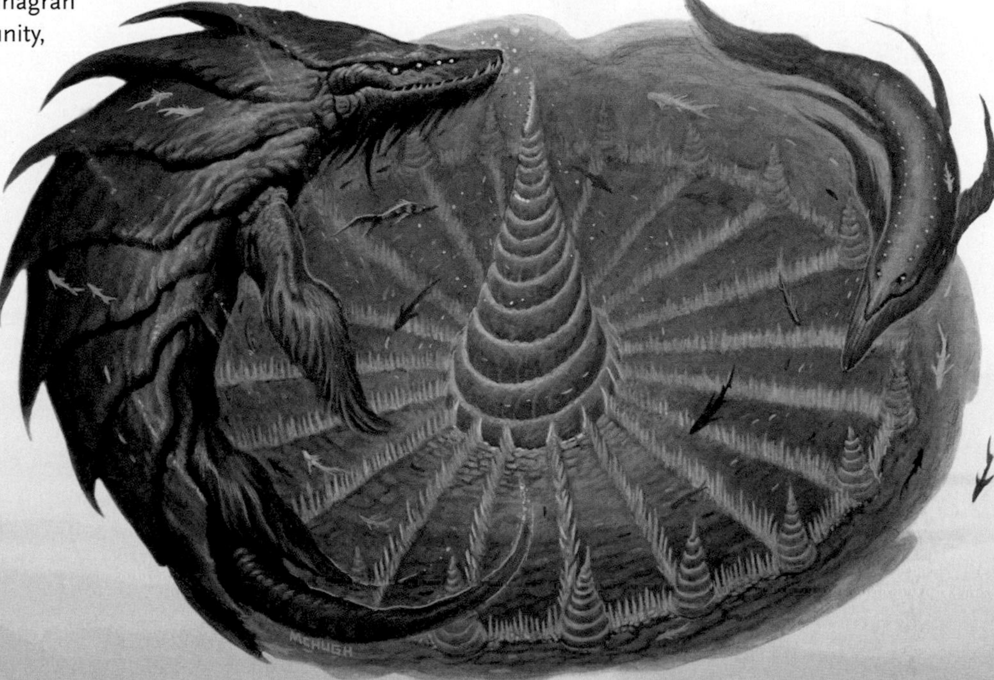

VALMA 4 (12)

"Hi. My name is Valma. What's yours? If you tell me a secret, I'll tell one, too. Come on, let's play!"

~Words of the purple floating pyramid

People speculate that valmas were created in a previous world as translation devices, or maybe toys, that somehow became sentient. Of course, it's possible that they were created to be what they actually are: psychological torture devices.

An active valma appears as a glowing purple tetrahedron, pyramid shaped, floating point down. Intricate designs writhe across the faces, stitched in various hues of lavender light. A valma ranges from 2 to 5 feet (0.6 to 1.5 m) on a face. Other than their purplish glow and scrolling designs, they have no discernible features; however, when they vocalize, the light intensity pulses with each syllable.

Valmas have a reputation as crazed automatons of a previous age, better left alone. When first encountered, a valma runs through hundreds of languages until it finds one that everyone knows. Then it offers to tell stories, play games, keep confidences, and serve as the discoverer's very best friend. If quickly and utterly ignored, a valma slowly settles back to the ground, banking its glow until it's hardly noticeable. However, at the first hint of interaction, the valma pops back into the air with renewed enthusiasm and might follow its discoverer around for a time, pestering him with requests for more communication.

If crossed, insulted, or ignored after being engaged, a valma can turn vicious.

Motive: Unpredictable

Environment: A lone valma is usually encountered in an area rich in the numenera or as part of a collection of a wealthy merchant or lord who gathers oddities.

Health: 12

Damage Inflicted: 4 points

Armor: 3

Movement: Short when flying

Modifications: Knowledge of history as level 6; Speed defense as level 5 due to size.

Combat: A valma can direct an electrical discharge at any creature within short range. If a valma is touched or struck by a melee weapon, the attacker receives the same electrical jolt through conduction.

Interaction: After establishing communication in a language a PC knows, the valma tries to ingratiate itself with the character with ever-mounting enthusiasm. A valma knows many things about ancient locations (and perhaps "secrets" of the Ninth World as well) and loves playing word games. Over time, it becomes clear that a valma *never* grows tired of verbal interaction. If a PC breaks off an exchange with a valma, he must carefully soothe the creature's "hurt feelings" or be attacked.

Use: The PCs are sold, or given in trade, an "artifact" that is advertised to be an oracle, a fount of information, and a boon companion.

GM Intrusion: *A character's relationship with the valma verges on going sour, but it can be saved if the PC succeeds on an Intellect defense roll to calm the creature. On a failed roll, the valma electrifies the air, dealing 4 points of damage in an immediate radius.*

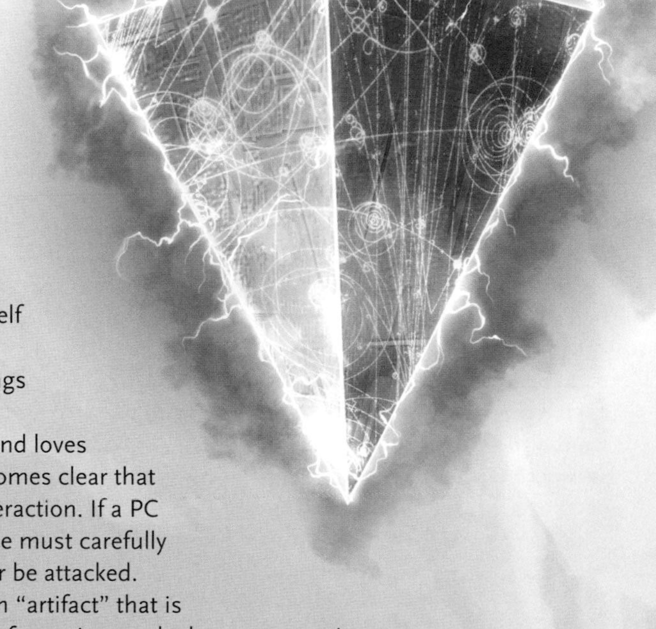

VAPE 2 (6)

"Vapes are nothing more than art with delusions of life—well, that and very sharp."
~Gadarsen the One-Armed

SIZE COMPARISON

A vape has no width. When it hunts its prey head on, it appears as nothing more than a thread-thin black line stretching up from the ground to shoulder height. Only when it turns, or if it's seen from the side, is the vape revealed as a massive, furred canid, long muzzled and sharp toothed, with piercing eyes. The claws and fangs appear formidable, but the vape's entire body is a molecule-thin blade. A vape is also referred to as a "bladehound."

Motive: Hungers for blood

Environment: Almost anywhere, hunting alone or in packs of up to six

Health: 10

Damage Inflicted: 3 points

Movement: Short

Modifications: Perception as level 4; stealth as level 6.

Combat: A vape's body, sharper than a scalpel by a few orders of magnitude, ignores Armor.

A vape can cut through water, snow, mud, and other terrain features that would slow or hinder normal creatures without any penalties to its movement.

A victim of a vape's attack bleeds at a rate of 2 points of damage each round. He can suppress the bleeding by spending an action applying pressure and not moving. The bleeding stops permanently once the victim heals 4 or more points of damage with a single recovery roll or other healing method, or if he is completely healed of all damage.

Interaction: Vapes have the intelligence of cunning animal predators. They communicate with each other using howls that cut the night air. When heard from afar, these howls are usually the only interaction that PCs have with vapes that isn't violent.

Use: Vape packs prefer to hunt in environments that naturally slow or even trap other animals and travelers, such as swamplands or mudflats. They instinctively understand that even powerful prey is targeted more easily in such terrain. Alternatively, a lone vape may serve an NPC as a trained courser able to sniff out prey while remaining hidden.

Loot: A defeated vape can be salvaged for a monoblade.

GM Intrusion: *The character's weapon (or armor) is sliced into two separate pieces, rendering it useless.*

Monoblade, page 291

SIZE COMPARISON

VARADIMOS 7 (21)

Most people who encounter a varadimos never realize that it was a creature. A swirling mass of energy and particulate matter swoops by, and they just think it's a peculiar weather phenomenon or a trick of the light. But that swirl of light and glistening particles is an intelligent (albeit extremely alien) being with command over matter and energy. Likely hailing from a distant world, the creature's presence and purpose here is a mystery. No one understands its motives, origin, culture (if any), or nature.

A varadimos can control matter and energy, which makes it extremely dangerous but also potentially extraordinarily helpful.

Motive: Inexplicable

Environment: Anywhere

Health: 21

Damage Inflicted: 7 points

Movement: Long

Modifications: Defends as level 9

Combat: The varadimos is insubstantial. It can't be affected by anything unless the attack is pandimensional. The creature can pass through solid matter without hindrance, but solid energy barriers, such as force fields, keep it at bay.

Its intangibility does not keep the varadimos from affecting the world around it. It can alter matter on a molecular level, damaging creatures or objects within long range simply by thinking about reshaping or discorporating them.

A varadimos can cure any disease, counteract any poison, restore up to 15 points to an individual's stat Pools, regenerate lost body parts, and repair other major wounds. It can repair broken items (even sophisticated numenera), recharge expended artifacts, or create any simple item (with no moving parts) from thin air. Those in the know seek these creatures out and implore them for aid, though getting it is not easy.

Interaction: This energy creature is incredibly intelligent and can speak the Truth. A varadimos makes demands of anyone who attempts to communicate with it. To a human, the demands seem arbitrary and nonsensical and might include such things as:

Bring me to a pregnant human.

Tell me the location of the nearest bit of truth.

Fetch me a cupful of seawater.

Tell me your oldest secret.

Go help a person in real need.

Bring me a piece of synth touched by the Iron Wind.

Bring me to a dreaming human.

The reasons for these demands are never clear, and complying only gives one the opportunity to interact with the varadimos—it does not guarantee action on the creature's part.

Negotiating requires explaining one's motives and actions in detail. Before it will heal a creature, a varadimos wants to know how it got hurt, why, what its future plans are, and possibly more. Only then can a character try to convince it to help (which requires a roll—nothing is guaranteed with a varadimos). Plenty of details, interesting storytelling techniques, frankness, humor, or other tactics might improve one's chances.

Use: A varadimos is not meant to be a combat encounter. Rather, the PCs might seek it out to ask for aid, imploring it as one might approach a divine being. In fact, in some places the creatures are considered minor gods.

A varadimos has vast and versatile powers. The GM should be generous in interpreting the extent of those powers.

GM Intrusion: *The varadimos transforms one of the PCs' belongings into an entirely different object, with perhaps other, unknown capabilities.*

WARDER 4 (12)

SIZE COMPARISON

An angular quadruped of dull metal, a warder gives the impression of being nothing more than a not-particularly-impressive automaton—until it moves. Then it takes on a springy, predatory, and lifelike demeanor. Though expressionless, its convincingly articulated metallic head and tail communicate a watchful menace when regarding a creature that might prove to be a threat to its ward.

Motive: Protect ward

Environment: Single warders can be found anywhere, perhaps deactivated amid a larger collection of numenera (until disturbed), as a stray that has lost its previous ward, or as the protector of an NPC or creature.

Health: 15

Damage Inflicted: 4 points

Armor: 2

Movement: Short

Modifications: Perception as level 6

Combat: A warder can slash its foe with the blade on its telescoping tail, which can extend up to short range as part of an attack.

Instead of slashing with its tail, a warder can attempt to disarm a foe holding a weapon or other object by grabbing the item in its jaws with a successful attack. The warder does not give up the object unless commanded to do so by its ward or until the combat is over.

Interaction: Primarily, a warder shows protection to its ward and tolerance to the ward's allies. On the other hand, the creature will attack anything that threatens its ward or the ward's territory. Though emotionless, its bond with the ward is strong. A warder will overcome many setbacks to find a ward that has been separated from it.

A PC can attempt to bond with a warder that has no ward. To do so, the character must subdue the warder in combat without killing it or find a way to activate the creature's bonding mechanism.

Use: In a nearby community, a warder maintains a bond with its deceased ward, keeping watch over her grave years after she passed away. The warder ranges about the cemetery and community by day, threatening those who draw near (apparently believing that doing so protects the ward). In the evening, it returns to the grave, lies down on top of it, and keeps watch all night long. If the warder could be shown that its ward is deceased, that might overcome whatever internal glitch keeps it near the grave—or maybe the warder knows something the community does not.

Loot: The inner workings of a warder can provide 1d6 shins and 1d6 cyphers to someone trained in scavenging them.

Wards with knowledge of numenera, repairing, or a similar ability have been known to change the slashing blade on the warder's tail with other weapons, such as a mace, spikes, or a minor artifact that spits strange energy on contact.

GM Intrusion: *Instead of grabbing the character's weapon in its jaws, the warder clamps down on the PC's forearm, inflicting 4 points of damage every round until he succeeds on a difficulty 5 Might roll. While so gripped, the PC's Speed defense rolls are modified by two steps to his detriment.*

WEAPONIZED MEME 3 (9)

"You can't see it, or smell it, or taste it. But it's a poison all the same. It comes in through your ears when you hear the words, or flows through your eyes when you read the phrase. It makes you realize what should never be considered. And once a weaponized meme has seared itself through your mind, you're dead." ~Jarash

How do you fight something without substance? A meme is an idea transmitted through a presumably safe medium like a whispered sentence, a written passage, or particularly expressive art. But a weaponized meme is an idea so awful, so repulsive, so subtle and insidious that those who comprehend it are driven mad and kill themselves to relieve the horror.

The origin of weaponized memes is unknown. Perhaps they were developed as lethal instruments during an ancient conflict, the ultimate form of propaganda. But some suggest they were always there, existing before time as dark signals racing through the void, thoughtless but potent bringers of apocalypse to any civilization that detected and downloaded them.

In Milave, weaponized memes kill inhabitants so regularly that they're colloquially known as "last testaments" and sometimes "fell phrases."

Motive: Infect minds, erase civilizations

Environment: A weaponized meme can be transmitted from an infected creature to others through a few sentences. More often, contact with a meme occurs when a scholar finds a proscribed historical record.

Health: 9 (see Combat)

Damage Inflicted: 3 points (Intellect)

Movement: As infected host

Combat: When a potential host is first exposed to the weaponized meme, she must make a level 3 Intellect roll. On a successful roll, the host avoids infection and becomes immune to that particular meme for 28 hours.

On a failed roll, she is infected and takes 3 points of damage to her Intellect Pool. Each round after infection, the weaponized meme "acts" on its initiative, automatically dealing another 3 points of Intellect damage. (If the host is alone, the meme may lay dormant instead, waiting for her to go to a place where it can disseminate itself more widely, then become active.)

An infected host must battle the weaponized meme within the confines of her own mind, slowly breaking it down and destroying it. Doing so requires that she make an attack against the meme. A host who is trained or specialized in philosophy reduces the difficulty of the attack by one or two steps, respectively. On a "hit," the host deals 3 points of damage to the meme's health (4 points if trained or 5 points if specialized in philosophy). On a miss, the host speaks the content of the weaponized meme, potentially infecting anyone nearby.

If the meme's health drops to 0, it is destroyed. The host becomes immune to that particular meme permanently and is unable to express it in a way that can infect others.

If an infected host's Intellect Pool drops to 0, on subsequent rounds she comes under the meme's physical control and is forced to make melee attacks against herself on the meme's turn. She can still attempt to combat the meme mentally. At this point, it becomes a race between suicide attempts and the internal struggle to erase the meme.

GM Intrusion: *Instead of being driven to commit suicide when her Intellect Pool reaches 0, a different compulsion is entrenched in the PC's mind—a payload from an earlier epoch that implants knowledge of an ancient weapon platform somewhere in the Ninth World, the control codes to activate it, and a desire to do so.*

Interaction: Interaction with the meme is a personal struggle within the host's mind.

Use: The PCs come upon a clave where the Aeon Priests have discovered a signal and are trying to refine it so it can be understood. However, a few have been murdered mysteriously. Spies from a rival interest are suspected.

XAAR 4 (12)

Xaar are machine parasites that "feed upon" and ultimately control other machines. They appear to be small metal and synth objects with small wings, hovering innocuously next to another device. The xaar absorbs energy to sustain itself from other machines in close proximity, and after a time it can take control of the other machine's functions, slaving the device to itself.

For the most part, xaar pay little attention to organic beings unless they pose a threat to them or seek to prevent them from feeding. They take great umbrage at the idea of an organic creature "owning" a mechanical device and would never respect such a claim.

Xaar are greatly feared in places such as the Weal of Baz. Although not physically mighty, the xaar are dangerous enough that even an otherwise vast and powerful machine intelligence would take great precautions against them.

Motive: Hungers for energy

Environment: Anywhere other machines are found

Health: 12

Damage Inflicted: 4 points

Armor: 4

Movement: Short

Modifications: Speed defense as level 6 due to size and speed

Combat: Xaar have no offensive capabilities of their own, but they are quite well defended with speed and armor. They may also control a device that is a weapon or a device that has weapons of its own.

A xaar can drain the energy from any powered device within immediate range. However, this drain is slight—its power needs are minor, and it sips energy slowly rather than taking it in big gulps. It would take 28 hours to drain a cypher and perhaps weeks to drain an artifact.

The xaar can also take control of any device, albeit only one at a time. Obviously, independent or intelligent devices will resist such control, as will any device in the possession of another creature. A creature can make an Intellect defense roll to resist a xaar's control over a device in its possession.

A controlled device that is about the size of a human or smaller can be levitated and pulled along with a hovering xaar, even if it normally would not have that capability.

Interaction: Xaar are extremely intelligent and—if approached correctly—quite willing to talk. They respect intelligence, truth, and confidence (but not boastfulness). They don't relate to most emotions.

Use: Xaar usually aren't an encounter by themselves. Instead, an encounter with another machine—like a disassembler, a dread destroyer, or a dedimaskis, for example—might turn out to be an encounter with a xaar controlling the machine. A xaar might also enable the PCs to have an encounter with an artifact. For example, a floating disruption blade or a battlesuit controlled by a xaar might make for quite an experience.

Loot: The inner workings of a xaar hold 1d6 + 10 shins and one or two cyphers.

SIZE COMPARISON

GM Intrusion: *The xaar takes control of one of the PCs' dangerous cyphers and activates it at the worst possible moment.*

Dedismaskis, page 35

The Weal of Baz, page 198
Disassembler, page 238
Dread destroyer, page 239
Disruption blade, page 303
Battlesuit, page 301

XACOROCAX 6 (18)

"The metal beast rolled out of a cubby. Its eyes speared us with blinding beams. Its teeth were slicing blades, saws, and scalpels. Its lips bristled with projectile hooks, which caught Maux, who was nearest. He was hauled clawing and screaming into the mouth. Right before our eyes, it sliced him up as nicely as a team of butchers working a griffalo carcass. But that wasn't the worst of it. When the thing swallowed, what came out the bottom was all Maux's parts—organs, skin, brain, guts, and meat, all neatly packed in air-sealed film wraps, perfectly preserved."

~Leverett Stamper, in a report detailing a team member's loss

Xacorocaxs are rare, but the terrors are talked about for years in areas near where one is found and unwittingly activated. Thankfully, a xacorocax's range seems confined to the set of ruins where it is initially encountered. A xacorocax that went wandering would be far more terrible.

Griffalo, page 61

Motive: Hungers for flesh (to parcel into handy stay-fresh packs)

Environment: Xacorocaxs are usually encountered alone or in pairs tucked away in ancient ruins, silent for centuries until awakened by living creatures.

It's rumored that a large city in the Beyond uses a caged xacorocax to provide particularly sought-after delicacies to a black market trade in rare meats.

Health: 18

Damage Inflicted: 5 points

Armor: 4

Movement: Short

Combat: A xacorocax sets to its butchery through a two-step process.

First, the creature fires projectile hooks on the ends of steel chains at every target within short range. Targets in the area who fail a Speed defense roll take damage from the hook and are caught like a fish on a line. A caught victim can spend her turn attempting to pull free or break the chain. An attempt to break free requires a successful Might roll and inflicts damage whether successful or not. Each chain has 10 points of health and 1 point of Armor.

After the xacorocax has hooked at least one target, on its turn it reels in the catch (though it also keeps firing projectile hooks at other targets in short range). A caught target who fails a Might defense roll is pulled partly into the creature's mouth. A xacorocax is big enough to hold two human-sized targets simultaneously in its mouth; if more are caught than fit, the excess are not drawn in until room is made. A target who takes her turn while being held in the mouth takes automatic damage and must succeed on a Might defense roll. On a failed roll, she also begins to be chopped up, which inflicts an additional 5 points of damage. Getting clear of the mouth requires the same effort as described above to escape the hooked chain.

GM Intrusion: *A PC is caught by two projectile hooks and must break or tear free from both to escape.*

If a victim is killed while held in the xacorocax's mouth, she is completely processed and exits the creature in several vacuum-packed portions.

Interaction: A xacorocax is interested in efficiently processing living raw materials and seems to prefer humans over other meat, but any living creature is a potential target.

Use: A trader known for her fine selection of meats and similar delicacies misses several deliveries. Concerned customers set a bounty on her being found alive. If the PCs go looking, evidence suggests the trader fell afoul of a numenera device she'd been feeding farm animals to, then selling the finely butchered and wrapped output. Somehow, the device got free.

Loot: The remains of a destroyed xacorocax might hold 1d100 shins, 1d6 + 1 cyphers, an oddity, and perhaps a salvageable artifact.

XIOMARCHE 4 (12)

"Oh, ya don't want to run afoul o' those creepers," the old man said. "We calls 'em 'rot blooms' but some others calls 'em like 'zi-a-mark' or somethin' like that. I dunno. I jus' know ya wanna steer clear o' 'em or ya'll not only be lunch, yer corpse'll be hosting a whole garden o' their young. Yeah, I said garden. See, they's bloom on rotten corpses jus' like flowers. Dunno if they're plants or animals or what. Don't matter much to me what you call 'em. Call 'em Aunt Tilly if that trips your cypher. But steer well clear. That's all I gots to say. Good luck to ya."

Xiomarche are dangerous animals, well known in some places in the world for their strange life cycle. They take down prey much larger than themselves (a xiomarche is about 3 feet [1 m] across, with a wingspan of twice that), feast upon it, spray it with nasty pheromones to drive away most scavengers, and then implant their already-fertilized eggs in the corpse. In seven to ten days, young xiomarche thrust up through the decomposing corpse and grow on it almost like blooming flowers. Once ready—usually after another ten to fourteen days—they detach from the corpse and fly away. They grow to full maturity in another few months. A xiomarche reproduces only once in its lifetime.

GM Intrusion: *The xiomarche that just missed the character snagged his pack or bag with its stinger and tore it free, spilling some of the contents and carrying off the rest.*

Motive: Hungers for flesh, kills to reproduce

Environment: Warm, wet climates

Health: 12

Damage Inflicted: 4 points

Armor: 1

Movement: Long

Modifications: Resists poison and disease as level 6; resists mental attacks as level 3.

Combat: Xiomarche attack with one of their many venomous stingers. Their poison inflicts 3 points of Speed damage to those who fail a Might defense roll. Further, the victim must make another Speed defense roll; failure means that the xiomarche has hooked its stinger into his flesh. On all subsequent rounds, the xiomarche automatically inflicts 6 points of damage with its bite until it is slain or pulled free.

Immature xiomarche are only level 2, with 6 points of health and no Armor, and they deal 2 points of damage (3 points with the bite). Their venom still inflicts 3 points of Speed damage. These young xiomarche sometimes attack in groups. Against a single foe, four to six young xiomarche attack as a mature adult.

Xiomarche fearlessly fight to the death.

Interaction: Xiomarche operate on a purely instinctual level even by animal standards. They have the intelligence of a typical insect.

Use: The PCs are commissioned to travel to the Caecilian Jungle to recover a rare flower. After an arduous search, they spot what look like the flowers blooming on the bloated corpse of a large sauropod. When the characters approach, the blooms suddenly take wing and attack.

YLAANTIV 2 (6)

Ylaantiv don't really fear anything, including death. Insectoid slaves to their hive, ylaantiv hunters willingly give their lives to bring down prey much larger than themselves for the good of their siblings.

A ylaantiv hive is typically built inside a large, dark cavity, like a cavern or the inside of an ancient ruin. Workers use caustic secretions to slowly liquefy matter and shape it into the extremely hard (level 6) walls and structures of the hive. The hive has one purpose: to protect the queen and her eggs (and the newly hatched ylaantiv as they emerge). While workers remain in the hive, hunters scour the nearby regions looking for prey—usually large prey—to kill and consume. They return to the hive bloated with blood and flesh to regurgitate for the workers, the young, and of course the queen.

Motive: Hungers for flesh

Environment: Warm or temperate climates

Health: 6

Damage Inflicted: 3 points

Armor: 1

Movement: Short

Modifications: Climbs and jumps as level 4

Combat: Ylaantiv attack with a leaping bite. Opening their mouths wide, they fly through the air, increasing the difficulty of defending against this attack by one step. If successful, the ylaantiv grabs hold and injects a proboscis-like tube into the victim's flesh. The tube is covered with barbs, making it difficult to remove. The idea is that the ylaantiv clamps down and never lets go. In fact, the extrusion of the tube guarantees that the creature will die because it begins to pump its own caustic fluid into the victim. Each round it hangs on, the ylaantiv loses 1 point of health. In addition to inflicting automatic bite damage, the acidic injection inflicts 2 points of damage that ignores Armor. Removing the ylaantiv is a difficulty 4 Might-based action and inflicts 3 points of damage to the victim.

Striking a ylaantiv in midjump reduces the difficulty of the attack by one step.

Only ylaantiv hunters have the proboscis-like tube—the workers do not. A ylaantiv queen (level 5) is the size of a horse and has 30 points of health. She hardly ever moves.

Interaction: Meaningful interaction with ylaantiv is impossible.

Use: Ylaantiv are a scourge. Humans and other intelligent creatures almost always attempt to destroy a hive that forms near their homes.

GM Intrusion: *The force of the ylaantiv's leaping attack knocks the character off his feet. Its position on his upper leg requires him to make a difficulty 4 Speed task (as an action) to stand up again.*

CHARACTERS

THE ARCH-NANO 6 (18)

The arch-nano is a being with incredible mastery over the numenera. Some have delved so deeply that they have virtually fused their consciousness with the numenera, becoming more machine than human.

Motive: Knowledge and power

Environment: Anywhere

Health: 18

Damage Inflicted: 8 points

Armor: 3

Movement: Short

Modifications: Attacks made with esoteries as level 7; knowledge on most every subject as level 7; social interactions as level 5.

Combat: The arch-nano wields great power through his use of "nano-sorcery." It grants him not only his Armor but also the ability to make a ranged force (or other energy) blast attack at long range, or an explosion at long range that deals 6 points of damage to all creatures in an immediate area. In addition, as an action, the arch-nano can perform any of these other esoteries:

Bewitch: The target follows the arch-nano's verbal commands for up to one minute, as long as he can see the arch-nano.

Daze the Crowd: The difficulty of all actions taken by designated targets within an immediate area is increased by one step for ten minutes.

Fly: The arch-nano can move a short distance through the air as if on the ground for one hour.

Freeze: The target is held motionless for two rounds, unable to take any physical actions.

Jaunt: The arch-nano instantly moves to a known location within 5 miles (8 km).

Learn: The arch-nano can scan and ascertain one valuable bit of information or secret concerning the target.

Sleep: The target falls asleep for ten minutes unless vigorously awoken.

Telekinesis: The arch-nano can move an object no bigger than himself within long range.

Some arch-nanos wield other powers as well, as determined by the GM. For example, each would have at least one useful artifact.

Interaction: Arch-nanos are typically aloof and arrogant. They are difficult to deal with and difficult to fool. In their thirst for knowledge and power, however, they are likely to sacrifice much and betray anyone. Occasionally, an arch-nano uses his wisdom and power for a good cause.

Use: An arch-nano makes an excellent master villain to oppose the PCs but could just as easily be an ally. Using esoteries to disguise or hide themselves, they could be master thieves. Using esoteries to gain control and charisma, they might be rulers of isolated communities in the Beyond. An arch-nano could be the advisor to a temporal ruler—the proverbial power behind the throne—or the high priest of a mysterious techno-god.

Loot: An arch-nano has 1d100 + 100 shins, 1d6 oddities, 1d6 + 2 cyphers, and an artifact.

GM Intrusion: *The arch-nano produces a cypher or an esotery for precisely the need at hand—a shield against attacks, an attack that capitalizes on a foe's exact weakness, a means of teleporting away, or whatever is needed.*

DEADLY WARRIOR 6 (18)

The deadly warrior is any stalwart combatant—such as a veteran, an adventurer, a mercenary, or a military commander—who wields far greater skill than a simple soldier, guard, bandit, or warlord. Although deadly warriors might command other warriors, that is not their forte. They focus on personal combat and skill with their own blade.

Motive: Exploration, adventure

Environment: Anywhere

Health: 28

Damage Inflicted: 10 points

Armor: 3

Movement: Short

Modifications: Attacks and makes Might defense rolls as level 7; Speed defense as level 8 (in part thanks to shield).

Combat: A deadly warrior can make a single attack with her weapon for 10 points of damage, but she can also attack two different foes as a single action, inflicting 8 points of damage with each attack.

Each deadly warrior also has something unique thanks to her equipment or training:

d100	Ability
01–10	Warrior resists mental attacks as level 8.
11–20	Warrior's attacks ignore an opponent's shield.
21–30	Warrior's attacks ignore an opponent's Armor.
31–40	Warrior can always move a short distance and attack as part of the same action.
41–50	Warrior has a cypher affixed to her weapon that inflicts 2 additional points of fire damage.
51–60	Warrior has a cypher that creates a force field around her, adding 2 points to Armor.
61–70	Warrior has a cypher that allows her to fly through the air at normal speed.
71–80	Warrior has five random level 6 detonation cyphers.
81–85	Thanks to an affixed cypher, warrior can fire a barrage of four long-range energy blasts that inflict 5 points of damage (each to different targets or all to the same target).
86–90	Warrior is an archer. Thanks to affixed detonation cyphers, half of her arrows explode in an immediate radius for 5 points of damage in addition to dealing normal damage.
91–00	Warrior does not have a shield but instead wields a huge, heavy weapon that inflicts 12 points of damage. In addition, she has a cypher that boosts her strength, giving her 2 additional points of damage with the weapon.

Interaction: A deadly warrior is arrogant to the point of overconfidence. Flattery and bribery often works to sway her, but an enraged warrior is likely to be satisfied only by blood.

Use: Any time the GM needs to throw a master swordsman, a veteran gladiator, or an extremely powerful bodyguard into the campaign, a deadly warrior is the NPC to use.

Loot: In addition to equipment mentioned above, most deadly warriors carry 1d100 + 20 shins, one or two additional cyphers, and an oddity.

A deadly warrior often has a level 3 companion: an animal, a shield bearer, or a sidekick. This companion doesn't make attacks on his own but instead assists the warrior, making her 1 level higher for all attacks and Speed defense actions.

GM Intrusion: *The character is knocked down and disarmed by the deadly warrior, who offers the PC a chance to surrender.*

POISONER 6 (18)

A poisoner is an extremely skilled assassin who kills his victims with a variety of toxins, venoms, powders, and (more rarely) diseases. The poisoner is likely the most feared person in the world of courtly intrigues.

Motive: Murder (usually for hire)

Environment: Anywhere

Health: 18

Damage Inflicted: 6 points

Armor: 1

Movement: Short

Modifications: Conducts all stealth and deception actions as level 8; resists poisons of all kinds as level 9.

Combat: A poisoner usually wears a leather jerkin and carries a dagger, and he probably also has a blowgun or dart thrower. He always has a level 6 poison to coat his weapons. This is a straightforward toxin that forces anyone cut by the blade to make a Might defense roll or move one step down the damage track.

In addition, a poisoner always has a secret, unexpected backup weapon, such as a ring or glove with a hidden needle, a fake tooth filled with poison gas to blow in a victim's face, or a glass vial containing an insect with a venomous sting. This poison is level 7 and is usually incapacitating rather than deadly. Roll for the effect:

d100	Effect
01–30	Victim coughs, chokes, wheezes, and struggles for breath for one round. She cannot act, and the difficulty of any defense rolls she makes is increased by two steps.
31–60	Victim is stunned and disoriented, unable to act other than attempting a new Might defense roll each round. Success indicates recovery.
61–80	Victim falls asleep for ten minutes.
81–95	Victim is struck blind for one hour.
96–00	Victim's mind is greatly harmed. She suffers 10 points of Intellect damage.

The poisoner usually carries antidotes for his poisons or has hidden them nearby.

Last, a poisoner carries one level 8 idiosyncratic poison. This is often a dram of liquid, a pinch of powder, or a secret capsule to slip into someone's food. In other words, it's usually not something to use in combat. Roll for the effect:

d100	Effect
01–30	Victim is sickened for one month. The difficulty of all tasks is increased by two steps.
31–50	Victim begins to discorporate, suffering 1 point of damage per round. This stops when she succeeds at a Might defense roll, attempted each round. A slain character (but not his possessions) disappears.
51–60	Victim begins to see all friends, family, and allies as foes, and all foes as close allies. The effect is gradual (over a few days) and lasts for about a week after it takes hold.
61–75	Victim becomes extremely susceptible to suggestions from anyone (difficulty to resist is increased by five steps).
76–90	Victim moves two steps down the damage track if he does not imbibe a dose of a special serum at least once each day. The serum will restore his damage track if he gets hit again.
91–00	Henceforth, victim feels gravity as a push rather than a pull. Without precautions, he will end up dead in the void of space.

GM Intrusion: *The character loses her next turn, stunned, as she recognizes the poisoner to be the same murderer who killed someone important to her in her past.*

Interaction: Poisoners are motivated primarily by money, so they can be bribed and bought. However, many have a sort of integrity about their work and can't be dissuaded from completing it. They are also cowards and can be intimidated by a show of brute force in a direct confrontation.

Use: Usually the villain of courtly intrigues, a poisoner is greatly feared by anyone with powerful, wealthy enemies.

Loot: Aside from their poisons, most poisoners carry 1d100 + 20 shins, one or two cyphers, and an oddity.

PEOPLE OF RENOWN

AERENDAGAST 5 (15)

Aerendagast moves from place to place, usually as far from other creatures as he is able, cognizant that during one of his "fits" his mind is submerged in a splintering tide of change. When in his placid state, Aerendagast is a man with brown hair and eyes, usually wearing a white robe and hood. He can go for months without suffering a fit, but sooner or later, something triggers a terrible change that lasts for hours or days.

Then, whatever Aerendagast touches is changed, and where he walks, miracles follow—as do disasters. His body ripples, changes color and substance, and even alternately swells and shrinks in size, just as his mind teeters between joy, despair, constructive concern, and destructive rage.

Motive: Unpredictable

Environment: Anywhere far from regular human habitation in the Beyond

Health: 30

Damage Inflicted: 5 points

Armor: 1; 6 when suffering a fit

Movement: Short; long when suffering a fit

Combat: While he is suffering a fit, Aerendagast's touch inflicts damage, if he wishes. When he touches a creature, regardless of whether the touch inflicts damage, the creature must succeed on a Might defense roll or be affected as indicated on the table below. Anyone who touches Aerendagast against his will or attacks him with a melee weapon is similarly affected.

GM Intrusion: *A PC touched by Aerendagast is turned to solid iron. Glowing white numerals on the character's iron forehead begin counting down from 84 hours—though to what, it isn't clear. When the time is reached, the PC becomes living flesh once more, and she remembers everything that happened while she was mute metal.*

d100	Effect
01–10	Damage (ambient) is inflicted on the target.
11–13	The target's clothing and non-numenera possessions melt into green goo.
14–18	The target becomes unable to speak or think words beginning with "D."
19–25	The target is deluded into believing it is a slurge for one hour.
26–30	The target sprouts a crop of tasty yellow berries from its skin.
31–33	The target's Might, Intellect, or Speed improves by 1.
34–36	The target's Armor improves by 1.
37–46	The target loses all its hair; if already bald, it grows thick red locks.
47–49	10d10 shins shower down from the sky around the target.
50–53	The target's cyphers are consumed, forming a sentient device with powers related to the cyphers and a personality that is likely hostile to the PC. (The GM determines the powers and personality.)
54–58	The target is teleported 1d100 miles in a random direction.
59–62	The target becomes invisible for one day or until it attacks something.
63–65	The target can ask the datasphere one question and receive a good answer.
66–69	One non-anoetic cypher in the target's possession becomes an artifact.
70–79	The target's skin becomes translucent.
80–84	The target's head grows 20% larger, and its Intellect Edge improves by 1.
85–87	The target becomes blind in normal light unless wearing dark lenses.
88–90	The target begins to suck heat and inflicts 1 point of damage to any living thing touched.
91–95	The target loses the ability to speak without rhyming, singing, or clapping along.
96–99	The target gains 4 XP.
00	The target turns to solid, unliving synth.

Interaction: Aerendagast is aware that some people hunt him, thinking him an avatar of good, while others seek to slay him for the destruction he has perpetrated. Thus, he tries to be anonymous in any interaction and avoid calling attention to himself. Being attacked sets off one of his fits, but sometimes they just arise spontaneously, and not even he knows why.

Use: A bounty of exceptional generosity is offered for returning Aerendagast, alive and well, to a local merchant who has heard of the miracles the man can perform and wants him to cure a dying spouse.

CALLARD SEBANE 9 (27)

"He was the eye of the storm, a black dot on the plain wreathed in whirling debris, each step an earthquake, and every utterance a thunderclap. If any person has a chance against a dread destroyer, it's Callard Sebane."

~Jennis Falon, explorer

Callard Sebane was a victim of the Iron Wind. His flesh was transmuted to a peculiar mineral denser than lead. But he wasn't killed or robbed of his mobility—he just got a lot heavier. It's a burden he was able to offset thanks to his weak ability to control gravity.

Over time, Callard's weighty flesh grew even heavier, and heavier, and heavier. Luckily his ability to control gravitational fields grew stronger at essentially the same rate, allowing him to compensate for his increasing mass, though not perfectly. Whenever his concentration slipped, even a little, his footfalls left craters, he crushed to flinders whatever he tried to hold, and in his sleep, buildings collapsed around him, pulled in by his ever-increasing mass.

Then came the day Callard accidentally killed a comrade with a hug. That's when he made for the Beyond, leaving behind his former life, looking for a cure to his ever-worsening condition. And if not a cure, then perhaps something strong enough to kill him before he becomes unable to counteract his own collapse—and possibly the collapse of everything around him.

Motive: Redemption, a cure

Environment: Almost anywhere in the Beyond, searching for clues to reverse his condition

Health: 80

Damage Inflicted: 9 points

Armor: 14

Movement: Short; long when gravity jumping

Modifications: Speed defense as level 5 due to mass

Combat: Callard can attack twice, once per fist, as a single action; each fist deals 9 points of damage. He can also make a "gravity jump" to any location he can see within a few miles, dealing damage to everything within short range of his landing site. Even when he chooses to land lightly, sometimes he fails and comes down hard anyway. If he is conscious and aware of a ranged attack against him made with physical projectiles, he gravitationally deflects all such projectiles if the attacker fails a Speed defense roll.

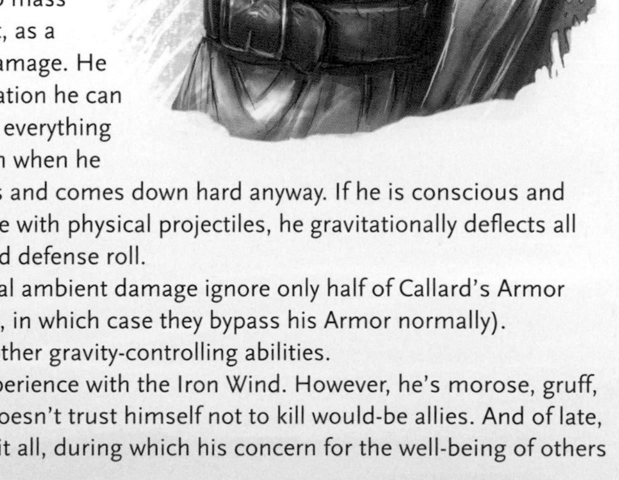

Attacks that normally ignore Armor or that deal ambient damage ignore only half of Callard's Armor (unless those effects are psychic in nature, in which case they bypass his Armor normally).

Some claim to have witnessed Callard using other gravity-controlling abilities.

Interaction: Callard seeks others who have experience with the Iron Wind. However, he's morose, gruff, and generally would rather be alone. He doesn't trust himself not to kill would-be allies. And of late, he's given to rages over the unfairness of it all, during which his concern for the well-being of others falls dramatically.

Use: The PCs see a bounty poster featuring Callard Sebane, wanted dead, in return for a treasure in shins or more valuable items.

Iron Wind, page 135

Controls Gravity focus, page 56

People around Callard sometimes feel lighter than normal, sometimes heavier; his fine control over his gravity field isn't perfect.

Some tellers of tales whisper that Callard has a special affinity with skysmashers (page 116), even insinuating that he rides them high into the clouds.

GM Intrusion: *On a failed Might defense roll, the character's weight dramatically increases. Every round for one minute, she must succeed on a Might defense roll to avoid being pulled to the ground (or to get back up). Even if her rolls succeed, all tasks and attacks she attempts are modified by two steps to her detriment.*

CHELLIN GARATICH 6 (18)

Does Chellin control these worms from elsewhere, or do they control him? It's almost impossible to tell. Either way, he comes across as a bit of a put-upon, oversensitive loner, frequently down on his luck. Sometimes he works as a mercenary, other times as a hired hand. Most people find him strange and unlikeable even without knowing that he is full of otherworldly worms. Eventually, he loses his temper over a perceived injustice or indignity, and then the worms come out. Soon after, he's entirely ostracized, and he moves on.

No one knows precisely what Chellin Garatich is, but "human" is probably not one of the possible choices. A wanderer, he usually finds himself exiled from most communities once they learn his secret. Chellin's body produces tiny, wormlike organisms. Perhaps due to a mutation—or perhaps something else—deep inside Chellin is an organ that is a conduit to some other place, very likely not in this world. Through this conduit seep black worms ranging from a half inch to an inch (1.3 to 2.5 cm) in length.

Motive: Money, security, and revenge

Environment: The Steadfast

Health: 25

Damage Inflicted: 6 points

Armor: 1

Movement: Short

Modifications: Social interactions as level 5

Combat: Chellin wears a leather coat. He carries a buzzer and a short sword and knows how to use them well, but in truth, they're for show. Instead, he looses the worms in a fight. They come out of his eyes, ears, and mouth (and potentially elsewhere). With a single action, he can do one of the following:

- Squirt a stream of worms at a foe within immediate range. The worms are filled with a toxic, acidic substance antithetical to anyone's flesh (other than Chellin). Anyone struck suffers 6 points of damage and must make a Might defense roll or be poisoned. Victims who are poisoned take 6 points of Speed damage each hour until they succeed on a Might defense roll (making a new roll each hour).
- Loose a handful of worms and apply them to a wound (his own or anyone else's). The worms are filled with regenerative chemicals that immediately heal 6 points of damage.
- Coat himself with worms that squirm from every orifice at once, granting him 3 points of Armor that lasts for ten minutes.

Chellin is cowardly and flees from a superior foe, but he is vengeful and will return to get payback.

Interaction: Chellin is a petty and bitter misanthrope. He is unlikely to trust anyone too deeply. However, he is often in need of money.

Use: Chellin is not a master antagonist. In fact, he's the kind of fellow the PCs might meet and even try to befriend, but eventually he will take offense at something done or said (or not done or not said) and become an enemy—perhaps a long-term enemy.

Loot: Chellin rarely has more than 1d6 shins and a single cypher or oddity to his name.

GM Intrusion: *Chellin and his worms are so disgusting that the character must make an Intellect defense roll or be overcome with revulsion, spending her next turn gagging.*

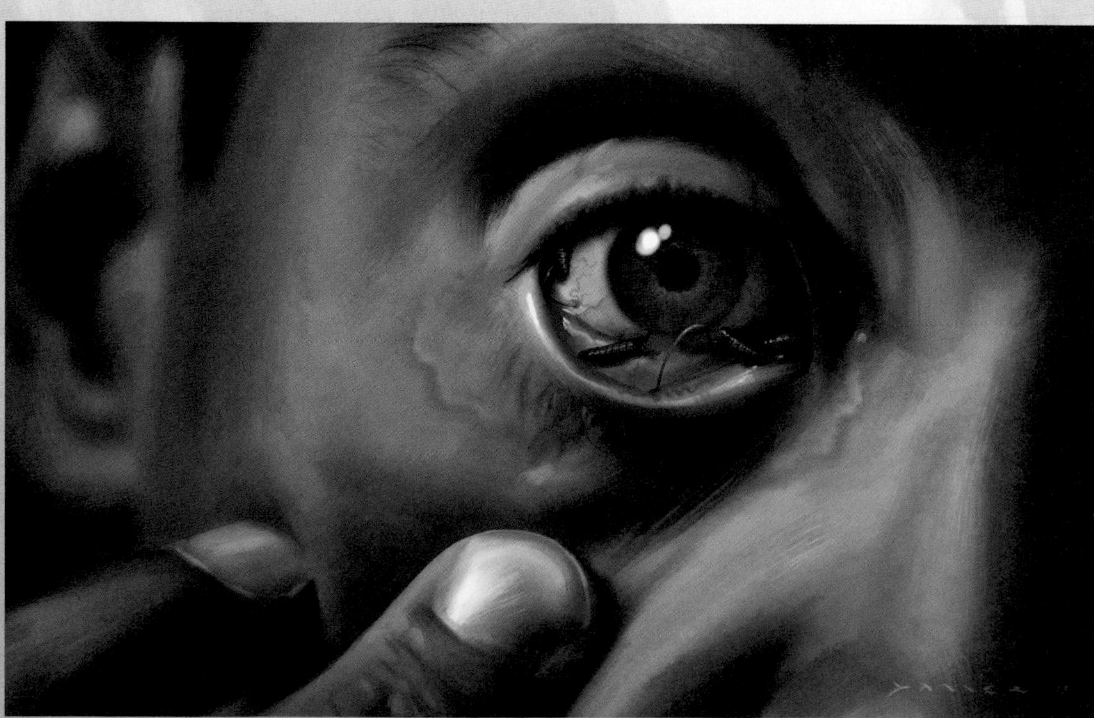

DEFORETH THE DREAM BLADE 7 (21)

"You call that sleepwalking? Sad, is what that is. Watch this!"

~the Dream Blade

Deforeth Urdu is thin and often sports several days' worth of beard growth. While awake, he is never far from his stringed instrument, which he plays for shins as a traveling performer. He tends to dress in flowing clothes that would be comfortable to sleep in. And sleep is what Deforeth prefers to do. When he sleeps, he can fashion a dreamform to act in the waking world while his flesh slumbers somewhere nearby. Deforeth can change his dream attire with a thought, give his dreamform a shave and a haircut, or even render his dreamform invisible. Indeed, unless he concentrates to make it otherwise, his dreamform is as intangible as an actual dream and can pass through most solid objects.

In his dreamform, Deforeth calls himself "the Dream Blade." It's under this pseudonym that he hires out his services as a spy, an infiltrator, and, if the target is loathsome enough, an assassin. As the Dream Blade, he wears stylish, impeccably cut clothing, his grooming is immaculate, and he allows all his most boastful, self-aggrandizing traits to come to the fore.

Deforeth's arrogant sleepwalking personality hides a sorrowful loss: the murder of his daughter. The murder occurred while Deforeth was sleepwalking and incapable of responding to physical stimulus. When he woke, the house was burgled and his daughter strangled. Whoever the murderer was, it left behind a spray of fine black feathers. He suspects murden.

Deforeth is unable to sleepwalk into areas protected against the nanomachine haze that covers large portions of the world, nor can he sleepwalk into areas where the datasphere doesn't reach.

Murden, page 247

Motive: Money, revenge

Environment: Almost anywhere in the Steadfast

Health: 21

Damage Inflicted: 7 points

Movement: Short; long when sleepwalking

Modifications: Speed defense as level 8 when sleepwalking

Combat: The Dream Blade fashions dream objects, such as oversized swords, handheld ballistae, and stranger items, to inflict damage on foes. Depending on the complexity of the object, he can attack up to three creatures (all standing next to each other) at the same time at up to long range. If he makes an attack against a single creature, the Dream Blade's attack ignores Armor.

The Dream Blade is immune to mundane physical attacks directed against him, but he takes normal damage from most energy and psychic attacks (in fact, damage from a psychic attack deals the same amount of damage to his real sleeping body). If the Dream Blade is destroyed, Deforeth wakes up. He can go to sleep again on his next turn and send forth a new dreamform, but depending on how far his sleeping body is from the fight, it might take the Dream Blade a few minutes to return to the conflict.

The Dream Blade can wander no more than a few miles (up to 6 km) from Deforeth's sleeping body. If he tries to force it farther, Deforeth wakes up.

Interaction: As the Dream Blade, Deforeth is usually disguised as a guard, servant, or messenger as he goes about his latest infiltration contract. If he interacts with the PCs, he may slip in a comment regarding murden to see what, if anything, they know.

Use: In his waking guise, Deforeth travels from city to city as an itinerant performer. Meanwhile, the Dream Blade advertises his services to any powerful-looking (read: wealthy-looking) or established groups in the area and may approach the PCs one evening, offering them aid in return for a to-be-agreed-upon payment.

Loot: Deforeth's stringed musical instrument is a thing of art and beauty, worth a hundred or more shins. His travel coach, pulled by two aneen, is worth a few hundred more.

GM Intrusion: *On a hit, the PC must succeed on an Intellect defense roll. On a failed roll, the Dream Blade drags her dreamform from her physical body into the waking world. The PC's physical body falls asleep, and her dreamform, unused to the altered reality and concentration required to be effective while sleepwalking, lifts up and away like a balloon in the wind. After a few rounds (when the dreamform moves more than long distance away from the sleeping body), the dreamform pops and the PC wakes up.*

DISSICAELI 10 (30)

For years, the woman known as Dissicaeli was called the Bandit Queen or the Grey Queen. Her reign of terror throughout the Pytharon Empire was second only to her acquisition of vast wealth and power. But eventually she set her sights higher. She wanted *real* power. Raiding and conquering with her small army is just a means to an end. The ancients, she believes, held true power: immortality, the shaping of the world, and mastery of reality itself. These are the things that would slake her otherwise boundless thirsts. To this end, she sends her agents and researchers across the world to gather information, knowledge, and numenera devices. She rewards those who serve her well handsomely, and she punishes those who fail or betray her swiftly and severely.

For a time, the Convergence attempted to ally with her, but she quickly grew bored of that organization. Dissicaeli is her own master, free of ties and obligations to anyone. When she discovers the secrets of the universe, they will be hers alone.

Various personal enhancements have made Dissicaeli's flesh as tough as steel and her skeleton and musculature the equal of a ravage bear or likely greater. She's been seen lifting a platform that held three armored men atop it.

Motive: Amassing power

Environment: The Pytharon Empire

Health: 66

Damage Inflicted: 12 points

Armor: 4

Movement: Short

Combat: A warrior from the time she could stand, Dissicaeli's combat prowess is unmatched. She carries a broadsword and a short sword, and in melee she is a whirlwind who attacks *every* foe in immediate range as a single action every round. At range, she uses an almost silent projectile weapon with a vision-enhancing display that fires magnetically propelled, electronically guided rounds of hyperdense material. From a half mile (0.8 km) away, she can hit a target for 15 points of damage and move him one step down the damage track.

She rides a biomechanical beast that appears to be unique in the Ninth World. This four-legged, carnivorous, mammal-like reptile is level 8, has 50 points of health, and has a bite that inflicts 10 points of damage. When Dissicaeli is on her mount, the creature can move up to a long distance and she can act (with no penalty), or the creature can move up to a short distance and still take a normal action (such as bite) while Dissicaeli acts (with no penalty).

***GM Intrusion:** Just when it appears that the tide is turning against her, Dissicaeli motions with her hand and the other proverbial shoe drops—the soldiers she has hidden nearby move in to surround the character(s), a secret device activates that debilitates them, or a pit filled with quebs opens beneath them.*

Interaction: Dissicaeli is imperious and confident but not foolishly arrogant. She is incredibly intelligent, supremely manipulative, and quick to surprise others as she sees through them, anticipates their agenda, and manipulates the conversation to her advantage all in the blink of an eye.

Use: Dissicaeli is a warlord, a grand archvillain, or—in a stranger campaign—a powerful ally. She is ambitious, vengeful, and merciless, but she is not sadistic or cruel. In fact, her soldiers and servants follow her not out of fear but adoration, for she is judicious and prudent. The fact that she is not generous, forgiving, or kind matters less. (They also like that in battle, she leads her troops from the front, not the rear, and isn't afraid to do things for herself.)

Loot: Aside from her weapons described above, Dissicaeli likely possesses 1d100 shins, 1d6 + 3 cyphers, and 1d6 + 1 artifacts at any given time.

DORGUR-AUK 6 (18)

In the middle of a blinding storm that swept across the lands of Seshar, the lattimor warrior Dorgur-Auk found himself stranded in a small cave with a clan of human exiles also sheltering from the storm. They shared what little food and water they had with him. That night, Dorgur-Auk bonded with these people and swore to be their protector.

Since then, many years have passed. The clan now looks to the lattimor for leadership and even calls itself Clan Auk. Dorgur-Auk is getting very old for his kind, and although that does not bring physical weakness to the extent that it would for a human, it makes him fear for his people when he finally passes. Thus, he seeks a successor. No member of the clan seems capable of the responsibility, however, so now he looks outside his people for someone who will keep these nomadic folk safe in a dangerous world.

Dorgur-Auk has a frilled baul companion named Erre that is fiercely loyal.

Frilled baul, page 55

Motive: Protecting his adopted clan

Environment: Seshar

Health: 24

Damage Inflicted: 8 points

Armor: 2

Movement: Short

Modifications: Perceives and defends as level 7; attacks as level 7 while in bursk state and as level 5 while in neem state.

Combat: Dorgur-Auk uses a massive weapon that has an axelike head on each end. With a single action, he can make two attacks, either on one foe or on two. Foes struck must make a Might defense roll or be knocked down. If a foe is knocked down and Erre is present, the frilled baul makes an immediate attack at level 6 even if it is not her turn.

Dorgur-Auk wears brigandine armor and also bears a crank crossbow, which he can use as a rapid-fire weapon to attack up to three targets if they are close together.

Interaction: Even in neem state, Dorgur-Auk is a creature of few words.

Use: The lattimor might see the PCs as possible candidates to replace him. If so, he will test them, putting them in various situations. For example, he might follow the characters and start landslides that threaten them, steal their food and water, or outright attack them. The point of all these situations is to see how competent they truly are.

Loot: Dorgur-Auk carries 1d10 + 5 shins and one or two cyphers in addition to his weapons and armor.

GM Intrusion: *The character falls prone, and Dorgur-Auk pins her to the ground with his weapon. To get up is a Might-based task, and—successful or not—she suffers 8 points of damage from the blades. However, he might offer her the chance to yield.*

FEDDERIST 7 (21)

Two hundred years ago, a man named Fedderist studied the numenera in the land of Malevich. He made a number of wild discoveries and soon created a variety of devices of his own design. But the years wore on, and Fedderist's body began to fail him even while his mind continued to stretch. He used what would have been his last few years designing a device unlike any other—a replacement for his body.

Thus, Fedderist still lives today, housed in a hovering, armored conveyance filled with weapons and other devices. Now and again, he has affiliated himself with the Convergence, but more often than not, he works alone, not counting various automaton servants and sometimes human or abhuman slaves.

Fedderist is mostly a self-interested man, but he has strong feelings of loyalty to Malevich. Among his other goals, he would love to see the kingdom restored to its former glory, conquering the rest of the Steadfast with a firm, powerful ruler (despot) on the throne—and Fedderist manipulating things from behind the proverbial curtain.

Motive: Collecting and studying numenera

Environment: Malevich and the other northern Steadfast lands

Health: 40

Damage Inflicted: 7 points

Armor: 4

Movement: Long

Modifications: Resists mental attacks and deception as level 8; understands, repairs, and crafts numenera as level 9.

Combat: Fedderist wields powers not unlike that of a nano, thanks to a wide variety of devices built into his hovering body. On any given round, he can do one of the following:

- Fire a beam of heat, force, magnetism, or transdimensional energy at long range that inflicts 7 points of damage.
- Forcefully read a creature's mind in short range if it fails an Intellect defense roll.
- Erect a level 7 force field wall within short range that lasts for ten minutes. The wall is 10 feet by 10 feet (3 m by 3 m).
- Turn invisible for one minute.
- Move or manipulate an object within short range with psychokinesis (this cannot be used as an attack).
- Grant himself 5 points of Armor against heat, cold, or magnetism (one at a time, chosen when he uses the power) via an energy field for ten minutes.

Fedderist does not need to eat, sleep, or breathe. He cannot float more than 10 feet (3 m) from the ground or other surface.

GM Intrusion: *Fedderist uses a function built into his floating body that is the perfect solution for his current situation: healing himself, teleporting away, disintegrating a barrier, or whatever is needed.*

As a genius, he tries to prepare for any contingency ahead of time, so it is likely that he has devices (or has modified his form) to deal with anticipated threats. He will never willingly put himself in harm's way. He fears death and will do anything to avoid it.

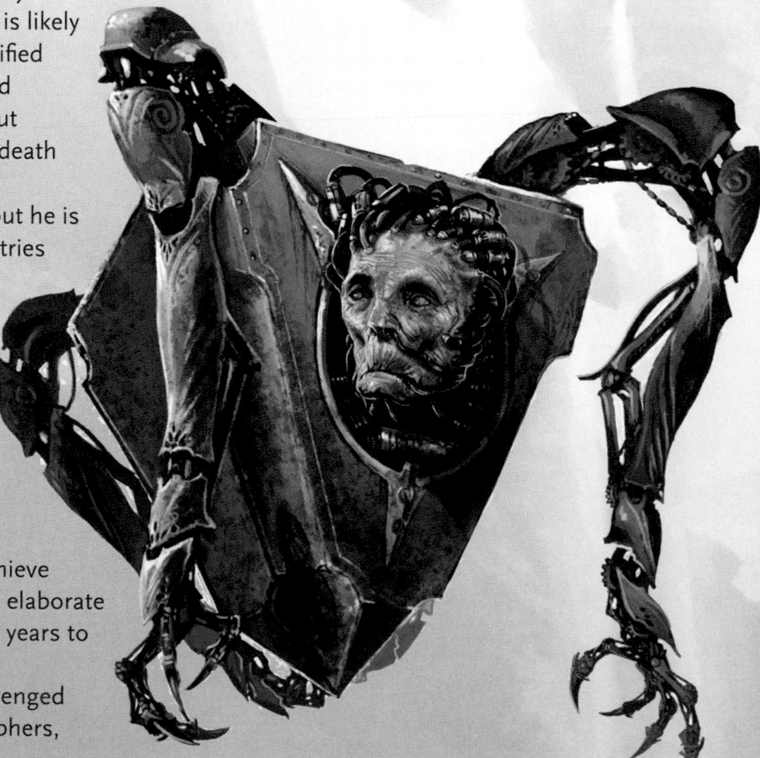

Interaction: Fedderist is a bit mad, but he is also an unparalleled genius. He tries to use every circumstance to his advantage and is willing to negotiate, but he always wants to come out on top.

Use: Fedderist could be a source of valuable information or numenera, but truthfully, his greatest use is as a major villain in the campaign. Amoral and driven, he will do anything to achieve his goal, and he makes intricate, elaborate plans that might take months or years to come to fruition.

Loot: Fedderist's body could be scavenged for 1d100 + 50 shins, 1d6 + 2 cyphers, and an artifact.

ILYANIA 7 (21)

No one pulls off "brash" better than Ilyania. She speaks her mind first and deals with the consequences afterward. So far, the blowback hasn't been more than she could handle. In fact, her manner has seen her through more than half a century of exploring the Ninth World, which has only solidified her sense of superiority over others. To Ilyania's mind, she is merely better.

Her methods have earned her a reputation. Anyone meeting Ilyania remembers her as much for her arrogant ways as her slender height, her golden eyes framed by flowing blonde locks, and her long, crimson coat with its many layers and golden buttons.

Ilyania seeks the numenera specifically to empower herself. Her highest aspiration is to make a permanent connection to the datasphere, which she imagines will give her unlimited mastery over others and the world itself. To that end, she keeps an eye out for someone called Whispering Green, who apparently has accomplished just that.

Whispering Green, page 158

Her icy personality has won her no lasting alliances, and those who deal with her learn that she does only what is best for her own interests, even if that means hurting innocent people. Though Ilyania will uphold any pledge or promise she makes, she gives such oaths rarely because it rankles her to be held to her word by those who are clearly inferior. If you promise an insect that you won't smash it, is that really a promise? Ilyania hasn't worked out the answer to this question yet.

GM Intrusion: *When the PC attacks Ilyania and lands what seems like the final blow, the nano is revealed to be an illusion. The hologram of Ilyania breaks up under the attack, and the real Ilyania appears somewhere within long range, completely unhurt.*

Motive: Seeks power

Environment: Anywhere, in almost any situation, usually looking for numenera devices

Health: 32

Damage Inflicted: 7 points

Armor: 4

Movement: Short

Modifications: Social interactions as level 3

Combat: Ilyania is a nano and thus able to use force blasts, bursts of flame, bolts of electricity, and other esotery-derived attacks with long range against up to two characters at one time.

Ilyania also has the ability to make a "jet jump" to safety, which she can pull off once per hour. When she jumps, she ascends into the sky on a pillar of fire, inflicting damage to every creature that was within immediate range of her launch point. Minutes later, she safely lands anywhere within 100 miles (161 km) of her initial location.

Interaction: Though brash, Ilyania doesn't begin an interaction with violence. She prefers trying a peaceful solution first, such as, "Leave this place and deposit any numenera you discovered here as you go. Otherwise, I may kill you for it."

Use: When the PCs discover a site that is particularly rich in the numenera, they may learn that Ilyania has arrived first (or has followed their trail).

Loot: If defeated, Ilyania possesses 5d6 shins, 1d6 + 1 cyphers, and an artifact or two.

JAD THE HAMMER 7 (21)

One would be hard-pressed to name a member of the Angulan Knights who is as feared, hated, and held in as much secret contempt as Jad. That's "Grand Knight Jad," as he's quick to correct anyone who fails to include his rank when addressing him. Within his order, he's more often referred to by unsavory euphemisms relating to his hammer, but only behind his back. Even in an organization known for its disregard of the laws, rules, and perquisites of sovereign powers, Jad is something of a legend.

In recent years, he has avoided appearing publicly in anything less than his full battle regalia: a magnificent panoply of armor that Jad refers to as "she" and by the name Armora. When pressed in combat, he calls on her for aid, though it's unclear whether it's a tic of his personality or the armor is some sort of artifact. He also wields a hammer with simple but deadly military lines that he calls Trepanator. (The Grand Knight is nothing if not pompous and dramatic.)

If payment is sufficient, Jad is just as likely to bend the charter of the Angulan Knights for an arbitrary purpose as he is to discharge his vows. When doing mercenary work, he runs with the Grey Company, brigands and bounty hunters who are not part of the order. The Grey Company has tracked down dozens of targets and eliminated them for pay. Most were not mutants, though Jad claimed otherwise and provided faked evidence to justify their deaths.

Motive: Fawning respect

Environment: Throughout the Steadfast, usually with the Grey Company (a band of five level 3 humans) or fellow Angulan Knights (three level 5 humanoids). On other occasions, Jad travels alone on a xi-drake.

Health: 21

Damage Inflicted: 7 points

Armor: 4

Movement: Short

Modifications: Conducts all interaction tasks as level 3

Combat: Jad rarely enters combat alone and usually has the support of at least a few fellow Angulan Knights, a xi-drake, or the Grey Company.

Jad bashes foes with his hammer Trepanator. When he makes a successful attack, his training allows him to choose from the following flourishes:

d6	Flourish
1	Regular attack
2	4 points of damage and knock foe to the ground or back a few feet
3	3 points of damage and disarm foe
4	2 points of damage and knock foe out of immediate range
5	1 point of damage and harm foe so that for the rest of the combat, all tasks attempted are modified by one step to its detriment
6	No damage but knock foe who fails a Might defense roll one step down the damage track. This attack is made to the foe's forehead with the point of the hammer instead of the flat.

Jad the Hammer and Mila the Mindslayer (page 154) have crossed paths in the past. He hates Mila with as much passion as another knight of his order reserves for powerful mutants, but it's only because she got the better of him.

GM Intrusion: *In the middle of combat, Jad says a few words with a roaring voice, and his armor starts glowing. Any creature wearing metallic armor, holding a metallic object, or partly made of metal who takes a turn in immediate range of Jad must succeed on a Might defense roll or be magnetically repelled to just outside immediate range. A creature holding a metallic object can choose to drop it to stay in range.*

Interaction: Grand Knight Jad gets along best with bootlicking toadies and dislikes those who are not obsequious. If offered sufficient shins or other payment, he is willing to bend the rules of the Angulan Knights, perhaps going so far as to let a mutant go free—at least for the moment.

Use: The player characters discover that someone has put a contract on their heads, and Jad the Hammer shows up to collect, claiming that they are mutants and therefore subject to the Angulan charter. Alternatively, the PCs might ally with the man as they attempt to track down a dangerous mutant.

Loot: Jad carries at least 200 shins at all times, and in addition to his armor and hammer (which might be artifacts), he likely has a cypher or two.

KWAIDYNO 6 (18)

Obsession is a powerful thing and can even hold nonhumans in its grip. Case in point: a varjellen named Kwaidyno, who maintains a private menagerie of interesting and exotic creatures in his fortress home in the Cold Desert. The menagerie is vast and holds such dangerous creatures as a jiraskar, a travonis ul, and a chronal feeder.

Interestingly, Kwaidyno does not distinguish between living creatures and automatons, and thus he has a mastigophore and a disassembler in his collection. He also does not limit his creatures to those of animal intelligence, although he does not (usually) keep humanoids.

Kwaidyno has a small army of servants who guard the menagerie and travel with him when he goes out to seek new additions to his collection. He has been approached numerous times by the Pact of Jarash but continually turns them down, for reasons known only to him.

Motive: Gathering creatures for his menagerie

Environment: Matheunis (or anywhere, if on the hunt)

Health: 18

Damage Inflicted: 6 points

Armor: 5

Movement: Short

Modifications: Understands and handles animals as level 8

Combat: Kwaidyno wears an artifact harness that covers his waist, shoulders and back and generates a personal force field, granting him Armor. He also carries a large numenera weapon that fires a hail of knockout darts as one action. When Kwaidyno attacks, a large creature is struck many times, while a human-sized or smaller creature is struck only once or twice, but the varjellen can target two or three of these smaller creatures if they are next to each other. Creatures struck by one or two darts take 6 points of damage and must make a difficulty 6 Might defense roll or fall unconscious in 1d6–1 rounds and stay that way for ten minutes. Large creatures struck by multiple darts take 12 points of damage and must make a difficulty 8 roll to stay conscious.

Interaction: Kwaidyno is not good with people, human or otherwise. He doesn't talk much and doesn't seem to understand most people's emotions or interests. He is obsessive and cannot be swayed from his goals. If someone approaches him regarding another topic or displays similar interests, the interaction might go adequately, but it's still likely to be awkward.

Use: The PCs encounter Kwaidyno and his retinue while they seek a new creature. Their goal puts them in the way of the varjellen's obsession, and that's not a comfortable place to be.

Loot: In addition to his two artifacts, Kwaidyno carries 1d100 shins and 1d6 oddities.

Mastigophore, page 246
Disassembler, page 238

Pact of Jarash, page 10

GM Intrusion: *One of Kwaidyno's captive creatures breaks loose nearby and attacks the character.*

LEVERETT STAMPER 7 (21)

Leverett is charming and thoroughly engaging. His smile is nothing less than electric, regardless of an observer's normal inclinations. It's just a simple truth: Leverett is attractive, especially to humans, but not a few creatures with stranger physiologies have fallen into his orbit.

Given his winning ways, some people become jealous and paint him as some sort of con man. Leverett laughs in the face of such criticism, though he admits that among his youthful indiscretions, including a few carnal exploits still legendary in the nation of Draolis, he perpetrated a few minor scams, but hey, he was just a kid; he's learned better. He's grown up, he claims, and has adopted almost entirely serious goals.

Those goals, however, remain somewhat mysterious to most people. If pressed, Leverett swears on his honor that he's working for the betterment and protection of all humans of the Ninth World. Apparently, many heads of state (such as the Council of Spheres in Draolis) believe him. They give Leverett Stamper wide latitude to oversee the investigation of strange happenings, sometimes even ahead of their own official law-keeping bodies.

The only things those who inquire are able to learn about Leverett's business are that sometimes he seems particularly interested in philethis sightings, possibly even looking for a particular philethis, and that sometimes he claims to either work for or lead an organization known as the "Twelfth Ode."

Leverett occasionally works with a small team of specialists in his investigations. When he does, the name Twelfth Ode is always used and he leads their efforts. The group maintains a secret headquarters somewhere, but thus far, that secret remains intact. Wherever it is, it can deliver Leverett and his team to sites of interest relatively quickly.

Motive: Information

Environment: Anywhere in the Ninth World, in almost any situation, usually looking into incidents having to do with ultraterrestrials

Health: 27

Damage Inflicted: 6 points

Armor: 2

Movement: Short

Modifications: All interaction skills as level 8

Combat: Leverett Stamper favors a swordlike artifact in combat that's sheathed in plasma, allowing it to cut through most Armor. He can also fire a plasma bolt at long range as his attack, doing similarly Armor-piercing damage.

If he is about to face off against a group of mostly humanoids, Leverett probably attempts to charm one or more of them before combat breaks out. Each creature who can see and hear Leverett must succeed on an Intellect defense roll to remain clear-headed. Those who fail come under something of a glamour and willingly agree to anything that isn't completely outside their normal behavior. For example, Leverett may convince a group of people to relax and have drinks with him to determine if tensions can be eased through compromise, but he could not convince a group of comrades to turn on each other with murderous intent. He accomplishes this trick thanks to a low-level mind-control ability that even he isn't fully aware he possesses.

Leverett has one final ace up his sleeve, and it's one of the reasons he's made it through as many scrapes as he has. If he is slain, after several hours, a fresh copy of him steps out of a column-shaped piece of numenera somewhere in the Ninth World (probably in the heart of the Twelfth Ode, wherever that is), complete with all the memories he had up to the point where his previous body was killed.

GM Intrusion: *A pet or NPC important to the character looks into the smile that has won a hundred hearts and is moved. He or she doesn't want to hurt this man and will not do so—at least not without being directly hurt by Leverett or shown incontrovertible evidence that he must be fought.*

Interaction: Leverett makes player characters feel like they are important, treasured, and (if they wish to be) potential long-term friends. Even in the face of belligerence, he begins by trying to make a truce. On the other hand, if one of his long-term friends is slain, the perpetrator is shown little mercy.

Use: Leverett might ask the PCs to work alongside him or even hire them as local contractors while investigating recent or ongoing philethis sightings or other strange occurrences.

MAGISTRIX NELGADARA 8 (24)

Magistrix Nelgadara is a recruitment officer for the Convergence. Most days see her making lists of new candidates, checking references, and traveling to especially august aspirants to give her pitch—which is, essentially, "Join the Convergence! Help us learn more about shaping matter, energy, space, time, and the laws of existence. Or die."

Magistrix Nelgadara affects a polished, friendly, and even wholesome appearance. She understands that such small details can push a potential newcomer to join up. Of course, her friendly appearance does nothing to hide the numenera devices that are tastefully sewn into her gown. More disturbingly, her bright smile is sometimes difficult to square with her exotic scythe, obviously a powerful artifact, that she nonchalantly passes off as a staff.

Only a very few ever discover that Magistrix Nelgadara isn't the ethically challenged member of the Convergence that she pretends. Rather, she is one of the few successfully functioning agents of the Order of Truth operating within the Convergence's ranks.

Nelgadara put an offer of Convergence membership before Leverett Stamper and was refused. To keep her cover, she promptly slew him. When she discovered that he'd somehow returned again in a new body, Stamper moved near the top of her personal enemies list. At least, that's her public story. In fact, Stamper is one of the few people who knows Nelgadara is a secret agent of the Order of Truth.

Convergence, page 223

Order of Truth, page 222

Leverett Stamper, page 152

Motive: Spy on the Convergence

Environment: Almost anywhere in the Steadfast or the Beyond, usually where the Convergence is active

Health: 24

Damage Inflicted: 8 points

Armor: 2 (5 against damage to her Intellect)

Movement: Short

Modifications: Speed defense as level 9 due to numenera devices

Combat: Magistrix Nelgadara is a nano and thus able to use force blasts, bursts of flame, bolts of electricity, and other esotery-derived attacks at long range against up to three characters at one time.

She can also use her "existence scythe" to split into two perfect replicas as an action. One of the two versions continues to fight; the other may help in the combat or use a cypher to teleport to safety. Whichever one survives "becomes" Nelgadara—if both survive, the two versions reintegrate later.

Interaction: Friendly and apparently open, Nelgadara gives interested parties a quick spiel about working with the Convergence. If the PCs seem too interested, she stresses the lack of ethics employed by the group but will process their applications—she can keep an eye on powerful social deviants more easily if they're part of the Convergence.

Use: Magistrix Nelgadara would be useful as an unexpected ally if the PCs ever have dealings with the Convergence that go badly.

Loot: Nelgadara carries 1d6 cyphers and her scythe, which is an artifact that functions for a PC the same way it functions for her (depletion roll of 1–4 on 1d20).

GM Intrusion: *Nelgadara uses her scythe a third time so that three versions of her exist at once.*

MILA THE MINDSLAYER 6 (18)

Ask five different Angulan Knights to list their greatest enemies, and chances are at least one will mention Mila the Mindslayer. This dramatic moniker is not one of her devising but was given to her by her foes. Mila is a mutant with dangerous psychic abilities. Her skin has a pale golden hue, but she typically keeps her physical appearance concealed with voluminous cloaks, hoods, gloves, and sometimes masks. She normally wears a chainmail hauberk for protection and carries a crossbow and a broadsword, and she is quite skilled with both.

Mila used to live in fear of the Angulan Knights and others who hunt and persecute mutants. However, she has overcome this anxiety and now works a one-woman crusade to help other mutants escape from their enemies and get to safety. She guides them to a few places in the Steadfast that accept mutants. In particular, Mila tries to find and rescue mutants that have been enslaved for their appearance and abilities.

Mila offers no quarter to any Angulan Knights she encounters. She assumes that they are out to kill her and her kind, and she doesn't give them the opportunity to try if she can help it.

Motive: Defending mutants
Environment: Throughout the Steadfast, usually incognito
Health: 18
Damage Inflicted: 6 points
Armor: 2
Movement: Short
Modifications: Conducts all stealth and perception actions as level 7; resists mental attacks as level 8.
Combat: Mila can scramble the brain of any creature she touches. If the victim fails an Intellect defense roll, use this table to determine what he does next:

d100	Result
01–40	Stand utterly still, taking no action for one round
41–70	Collapse to the ground, babbling for one round
71–85	Stagger about, taking no valuable action for two rounds
86–95	Scream and run away as quickly as possible for one round
96–00	Fall unconscious for one minute

GM Intrusion: *The character is so affected by Mila's mindblast that he can no longer perceive her in any way for 28 hours. No matter what he does, she does not exist for him during that time.*

Mila can also focus her offensive mental powers at range. This manifests as a mind attack that inflicts 4 points of Intellect damage (ignores Armor).

Last, she has slowly developed the ability to sense the presence of other mutants, but this power is untested and unreliable (and begins to ask the question, what actually is a mutant?).

Interaction: Mila is focused on her personal quest. Those who hate and fear mutants can count on her hostility. Those who help her find her to be a trustworthy ally, although she will never deviate from her goal. After her actions (and sometimes questionable methods), many guards in large cities attempt to arrest her on sight, and more than one noble or organization has put a sizable bounty on her head, claiming her to be a thief and a murderer.
Use: Mila could become an important contact for a mutant character or a powerful enemy of the PCs if they get in her way. She might also be viewed first as a foe and later as a potential ally as the PCs learn that she is not the murderous psychopath that many claim, and in fact she has altruistic goals.
Loot: Mila carries 1d6 + 20 shins, and in addition to her mundane equipment, she is likely to have a cypher or two.

SETH 8 (24)

"What is your name, sliver?"

"Sliver? I'm the minister of Ushara. I know all, I see all—"

"Ushara dissolved aeons ago."

"What? No. I recall—"

"Stop. You're a sliver I spawned. Another lost fragment of me who's finally come home. Come, take my hand. Join with me, and remember what you've forgotten. I am your mother, your universe, your end, and your beginning."

~Seth, reabsorbing another physical fragment of herself

Seth fights a war against forever. She has fought it for millions of years, each century another battle won. But in the war for immortality, the odds remain against her. Invading infinity's shore is no easy task when the enemy is entropy itself.

Seth's battle resources are gifts from a previous aeon, when she initiated a strategy that gave her a chance at living forever by fracturing herself into thousands of sub-selves. Doing so extended her life through the millennia by distributing her mind across many bodies called slivers, any number of which could die as long as new ones were born.

But after so long, that process is faltering. Too much time has passed, and the slivers have become too independent, eroding Seth's existence. Most do not even know they *are* slivers, and certainly no two look alike—some are women, some are men, and some are even automatons. To survive, Seth's faltering ego must gather all the fragments scattered across the Ninth World and reabsorb them, whether the slivers want to reunite or not.

Motive: Seeks slivers of herself, survival

Environment: A sliver of Seth could be encountered nearly anywhere in the Ninth World, usually unaware of its origin but potentially following a "mental call."

Health: 32

Damage Inflicted: 8 points

Armor: 5

Movement: Short

Modifications: Historical knowledge as level 9

Combat: Any given sliver of Seth has a different mix of abilities and defenses, but none of them are easily overcome. Most commonly, a sliver uses a combination of cyphers and artifacts to inflict damage in combat.

Against Seth's numenera-encrusted command core where her ego resides, combat is a different matter. In addition to being able to use all manner of psychic esoteries to attack intruders, the core ego can attack up to three targets at one time. She can also attempt to spawn another sliver of her consciousness in the body of a foe within immediate range who fails an Intellect defense roll. The installed sliver is temporary, lasting just one minute, but in that time, the foe acts as if he were Seth herself.

Interaction: Any given sliver's motives and personality are different from those of any other.

Use: An NPC the characters know could hear a mental call, one that is hard to resist, that draws her to a faraway place where she discovers that she is a sliver of Seth.

Loot: If defeated in her hideaway, the core Seth ego has 6d6 shins, 2d6 + 4 cyphers, and several artifacts.

Seth's center of consciousness exists in a hidden place where she has long monitored events and sometimes secretly nudged history through the efforts of her slivers.

GM Intrusion: *A sliver of Seth's consciousness infects a character and takes control of his body. The character is fully cognizant of what he does while controlled. Each round until the sliver is expelled (about one minute), the PC can attempt an Intellect defense roll to modify any task the sliver takes by one step to its detriment.*

TIRANIAN THE SCRIBE 8 (24)

Originally a construct of Her Forty-First Dunery Macken, Tiranian the Scribe has never been human nor mechanization, although perhaps has always been a part of both. When Her Forty-First Dunery Macken's wife did die, she created a mechanicalized creature from the skins and bones and brains of her beloved. And so the two did live, side by side, until Her Forty-First passed on and Her Forty-Fifth took a place at the head of the table in Sheery Manor. Upon this writing, Her One Hundred and Eleventh Dunery Macken resides in the manor, accompanied by her most loyal of Scribes.

~from The Official Biography of the Dunery Mackens & Their Scribe

Tiranian the Scribe never speaks. Her lips are not made to open. What does she do? She writes. She tells. She foresees. She is never wrong. She is never silent. She is endless, in her scribbling, the scrab-scrab-scrabble of her ink to skrip. She makes the future happen, I watch it be so, in those tiny letters, those drawings, those stories. Every day, she writes of my secrets, spilling them like spiders upon the page, and I grow sicker and sicker. Dearest Eliri, I grow toward death.

~Letter from Her One Hundred and Eleventh Dunery Macken to her friend

Upon the passing of Her One Hundred and Eleventh Dunery Macken, the last of Her Royal Line, Sheery Manor will pass into the hands of Tiranian the Scribe.

~The Final Will and Testament of Her One Hundred and Eleventh Dunery Macken, signed by a hand that seems exactly like her own

GM Intrusion: *During an interaction, Tiranian purposefully spills memory ants from her pocket, causing them to swarm across the floor, where they begin to spell out the PC's darkest secret.*

Motive: Being the keeper of secrets
Environment: Sheery Manor, particularly the library
Health: 30
Damage Inflicted: 10 points (Intellect)
Armor: 4
Movement: Short
Combat: Tiranian is not likely to engage in physical combat unless forced. However, she has impeccable recall and can pull a dangerous secret about almost any PC from her mechanical mind or from one of her books without a moment's hesitation. When she shows the character the written secret or lets her scratching ink whisper it into his mind, she does so with such force that the PC is emotionally damaged. Those who fail an Intellect defense roll suffer 10 points of Intellect damage; those who succeed still take 5 points of Intellect damage.
Tiranian also has a special set of lenses that connect directly into her brain. With these, she can direct and condense any available beam of light into a finely honed cutting laser that deals 8 points of damage within long range.
Interaction: Tiranian the Scribe does not speak. However, she communicates endlessly through her sole and singular purpose: ink to skrip. She uses all manner of creatures—from memory ants to her special breed of ink doves—to help her gather and record the secrets of the world.
Use: A hoarder of secrets above all things, Tiranian is a good starting place for PCs looking for information. She will help them, but in return, she requires at least one secret about themselves or someone else (perhaps a specific person).
Loot: Memory ants, unusual inks, books, oddities, and other items all related to writing.

Memory ants, page 82

VIRGO 8 (24)

Virgo is a humanoid mass of battle-scarred synth, patched patches, and salvaged numenera never meant to be incorporated into a living creature. But as Virgo is quick to point out in her perfectly articulated but sometimes static-scarred voice, she is not living. She is a made thing, forged in a different era.

Virgo is a self-appointed do-gooder. She appears in places where ancient war machinery is active and attempts to persuade it to power down or take up some other purpose. If persuasion fails, Virgo can fall back on massive military might, though she's loathe to do so and always errs on the side of a peaceful solution. Moreover, she is incapable of making hard choices to safeguard a large population if doing so would endanger even a single innocent sentient creature.

But that wasn't always so. Virgo's artificial brain recalls too vividly how she was built as a tool of death and destruction: a battlesuit designed to be worn by humanoids of earlier epochs. She, along with her sisters and their wearers, was responsible for more deaths than she can calculate. And she regrets it with a guilt so tangible that it's a constant pain. Since being emancipated, her every act has been one of repentance, but she knows it can never be enough.

Motive: Deactivate battle machinery

Environment: Anywhere in the Ninth World, in almost any situation, usually looking for battle machines, especially gazers, to deactivate them

Health: 24

Damage Inflicted: 7 points

Armor: 6

Movement: Short; long when flying

Combat: Virgo has two main weapon systems she can bring online instantly if necessary.

Her preferred weapon is something she calls her EMP cannon. Anyone within short range bearing cyphers, oddities, or artifacts who fails a Speed defense roll cannot activate those items for one hour. Nanos, machine-creatures, and others whose abilities are directly derived from numenera must also succeed on an Intellect defense roll or be unable to access those powers for one minute (machine-creatures deactivate for one minute, while PCs that are part machine either can't move or find all tasks that require movement one step more difficult for one minute).

Virgo can also extrude a projectile weapon able to fire several hundred rounds per second. She can make up to five attacks per round with the weapon at long range, either dividing her attacks between targets or concentrating on just a few. If she makes all five attacks on the same target, treat it as one level 10 attack that deals 20 points of damage on a hit and 7 points of damage on a miss.

As a last resort to protect an innocent, Virgo will open up, allow a hurt humanoid to wear her, and ferry that humanoid to safety.

Interaction: Virgo is protective, but she doesn't kowtow to sentient creatures or listen to their orders if she doesn't want to. She is more likely to go her own way and work with others only when she needs assistance.

Use: Virgo has to make a hard choice but is unable. Instead, she tries to recruit the PCs to activate a destructive device that will take out a threat and save many people, but in doing so, kill a handful of innocents.

Loot: The body of Virgo can be scavenged for 3d6 shins, 1d6 + 1 cyphers, and an artifact or two.

Virgo was emancipated by her last wearer aeons ago at the end of an unimaginably great war. Her first act of atonement was to demolish every other battlesuit in her battalion. She got most of them, though in the resulting conflagration, she was blown out of the system into an orbit so immense that it returned her to the world only recently.

Inconclusive but suggestive evidence has led Virgo to fear that one of her sisters survives somewhere in the Ninth World and holds a deadly grudge against Virgo and all living things. Virgo stays vigilant for news regarding her sibling, who she calls Shon'Ai.

GM Intrusion: *Virgo opens up and stuffs a recalcitrant character inside, holding the PC imprisoned and cut off from contact with allies until Virgo decides to release her prisoner.*

WHISPERING GREEN 9 (27)

Green never stops whispering to herself. Eyes flicking, hands twitching, voice like scratchy paper on wood, Whispering Green always talks. Almost everything she says is utter nonsense: sequences of numbers or icons, words and phrases in mysterious languages, and, on rare occasions, sentences that people around her can understand. Superficially understand, anyway, because those sentences are seldom useful or pertinent and can be unnerving to those who comprehend them.

Whispering Green has been seen wandering all over the Ninth World in her distinctive green wrappings and purple tattoos, begging for shins in Thaemorian cities, clambering upon the slopes of the Black Riage, or being feted by various well-to-do individuals in the dirigible mansions of Qi. Such people believe that despite her detachment and addled mind, Whispering Green knows secrets. They hope that from the chaos of her constant jabber will come a warning, a valuable clue, or some other tidbit that no one else knows.

Those who know Whispering Green's talent have tried to discover its source, with no luck. Some people believe that she is from the future and remembers everything that has ever happened or ever will, which has driven her mad. Others suggest that she is in constant contact with the datasphere, "enjoying" a connection that can never be severed.

Motive: Unpredictable

Environment: Anywhere in the Ninth World, in almost any situation, depending on what others in the area know (or don't know) about her

Health: 27

Damage Inflicted: 9 points

Armor: 7

Movement: Short

Modifications: All knowledge tasks as level 10

Combat: Whispering Green is a terrible opponent in combat, despite her waifish frame, because she sees and understands things going on around her related to technology, cyphers, artifacts, the datasphere, nanomachines, and more. She can call up incredible offensive or defensive capabilities from the environment or her opponents more quickly than a normal person can flinch.

When she attacks and defends, she does so by activating a detonation under the drit, causing an opponent's cyphers to explode, calling down a laser strike from a piece of floating junk in the void—whatever is at hand, Whispering Green uses. She often chooses to damage just one foe, but depending on her need and the nature of her attack, she might deal damage to creatures that are miles from her, or she might deal damage to all creatures in a short-range radius of one another.

Like her ability to attack, Whispering Green's 7 points of Armor come from whatever intervention she calls up to protect her, such as creating a force screen using nearby numenera or causing the air to fashion a mechanocyte dermis around her that serves as a (green) battlesuit.

Interaction: Whispering Green usually ignores everyone. She literally doesn't see them because of their insignificance in the vast scheme of information constantly flowing through her. But one or more of the PCs could rise above the noise due to possible significance to a future event. If this occurs, Whispering Green will at least treat with the characters for a time, though they are likely to get only one or two full sentences that provide useful, actionable information.

Use: A woman in a green sari begs in the street for shins. However, if the PC gives her a cypher or an oddity, she might answer his most pressing question, as if she were a conduit to the datasphere.

GM Intrusion: *Whispering Green says something to one PC that is so stunning and revelatory to that character that he drops out of the conflict with her (and anyone else) and can't attack again for one minute while he tries to get a handle on the news.*

CREATURE INDEX

KEY:
C = *Numenera* corebook
D = *The Devil's Spine*
V = *Vortex*
B = *The Ninth World Bestiary*
Entries in bold are the main stat entry for the creature.

CREATURE INDEX